Engineering Instrumentation And Control **IV**

Acknowledgements

The author and publishers would like to thank the following organisations and individuals for permission to reproduce photographs or illustrations.

Airflow Developments Ltd (Fig. 6.19(c)); The British Standards Institution, 2 Park St, London W1A 2BS (Fig. 2.6, from BS 1780: 1960); H. C. Bryan (Figs. 8.14, 8.16, 8.17); Bryans Southern Instruments Ltd (Fig. 5.6(b) and (d)); G. Cussons Ltd (Fig. 6.4(b)); Dewraswitch Ltd (Fig. 7.18); Ealing Scientific Ltd (Fig. 6.3a); Fylde Electronics Laboratories Ltd (Fig. 4.11); Kistler Instruments Ltd (Fig. 3.3); Micro Movements Ltd (Fig. 5.6(c), 5.6(d)); Penny and Giles Potentiometers Ltd (Figs. 4.15, 8.2(d), 8.3); Penny and Giles Transducers Ltd (Fig. 8.4); Racal–Dana Instruments Ltd (Fig. 6.4(a)); Smiths Industries (Fig. 6.20(a)); Transport and Road Research Laboratory—Crown Copyright Reserved (Fig. 6.13); Technician Education Council (TEC unit U77/422 syllabus).

The author would like to thank Mrs. Adams for her excellent work in preparing the typescript.

Preface

The introduction of Technician Education Council (TEC) courses, replacing City and Guilds technician courses and Ordinary National and Higher National Certificate and Diploma courses in engineering, has led to a major restructuring. The subject matter of these courses has been reassessed and regrouped into modules of study referred to as *units*. The syllabuses of these units are now written, much more precisely than previous syllabuses, in the form of behavioural objectives, i.e. the syllabus states what the student should know or be able to do in each part of the subject matter.

The importance placed on measurement techniques in the education of mechanical and production engineering technicians, evident in the HNC Engineering syllabuses amongst others, has been recognised by the TEC syllabus drafting bodies. Several of the standard units of study contain sections on measurement, but one unit for the TEC Higher Certificates consists mainly of measurement, with some control work. This is the unit TEC U77/422 Engineering Instrumentation and Control IV. The author's textbook *Engineering Measurements and Instrumentation* covers the measurement content of this unit. However, many students will prefer to use a text written specifically to cover the whole of the unit.

This textbook is intended to provide for technicians a fairly concise course of study for the unit. In the author's opinion, despite the use of behavioural objectives, the syllabus in some parts does not indicate the depth to which study is to be taken. In these sections the work has been taken to a depth where, in the author's judgement, the student of higher than average ability may cope. In some places, a small amount of additional material is included, for completeness.

Also, the syllabus is not always laid out in a sequence suitable for the development of the subject, and in the section on control work, in particular, the order in the text will be found to differ from that of the syllabus. To assist both tutor and student in the selection of material for study, the syllabus is reproduced. Against each objective the chapter and section references are given where the subject matter may be found. It is hoped that in this way, revision for in-course and end-of-course assessments may be facilitated.

The format of *Engineering Measurements and Instrumentation*, incorporating worked examples, tutorial and practical work, and student exercises, has been appreciated by many users of that book, and these features are included in *Engineering Instrumentation and Control* IV. In addition, a section of multiple-choice questions is included, which the author believes will be useful, particularly in revision.

L. F. ADAMS

General Editor's Foreword

Sufficient experience has now been gained in the operation of TEC programmes to appreciate that students prefer to use one text book for a particular unit, rather than to have to search for the necessary information from a variety of textbooks, many of which have been written, quite validly, for courses other than TEC programmes.

The objective in publishing this textbook is to provide a source of reference for students engaged on a TEC programme which includes the unit Engineering Instrumentation and Control IV, the TEC code being U77/422.

The author has a well-earned reputation in the subject. The style of writing is direct and concise. In particular, the sequence of the objectives of the standard unit have generally been followed, except on a minor occasion where, in the opinion of the author (and of the editor), a more logical presentation is possible.

A significant point in the text is the inclusion, at the end of each chapter, of recommendations for tutorial and practical work, which can be used to reinforce not only topics included in the chapter, but also, in later chapters of the book, to link together the items to form a complete structure and not an assembly of individual disconnected items.

It has been said that a technician is someone who solves problems, mainly of a routine nature, by methods which are well known and proved. Since problem solving takes such a prime place in the work of a technician in industry, it can be expected that the educational component of the preparation for technician duties in industry will include a judicious amount of problem solving. Consequently this book includes, at the end of each chapter a substantial number of graded problems for solution by the reader, sufficient for the coursework of even the most diligent student.

M. G. PAGE

Contents

1 MEASUREMENT

1 Measurement systems

1.1 Instruments and measurement systems

Instruments such as micrometers, thermometers, pressure gauges, tachometers, etc. are essential to industry, and familiar to technician engineers. However, present-day trends are towards instrument *systems*. In many cases a system does more than the simple instruments mentioned. For example, a measurement system on a machine tool may simplify the work of the operator by eliminating the need for hand measuring instruments. Alternatively, it may be part of a control system that does not need an operator in constant attendance. Similarly in some plant, measurements of variables such as temperature and pressure may be transmitted to a central control room. On the other hand, even a simple instrument such as a pressure gauge may be regarded as having separate functions such as the sensing of the measured variable, the amplification of the signal, the display of the signal, and so on. We shall study both individual instruments and measurement systems.

1.2 Elements of an instrument system

The functions of the parts of an instrument system may be categorised into three elements.

(a) A *sensing element*, which is acted upon by the variable to be measured, such as length, pressure, temperature, angle, etc., and which gives out some quantity, a *signal*. For example, if pressure (p) is applied to the bellows unit shown in Fig. 1.1, the movement (x) of the free end is the output signal of the sensing element.

(b) A *signal-conditioning element*. The signal from the sensing element is often very small, as in the bellows, and has to be amplified. Hence the movement x of the bellows may be converted to a much larger movement by, for example, a lever system.

(c) An *output element*. The output of a system is required to do

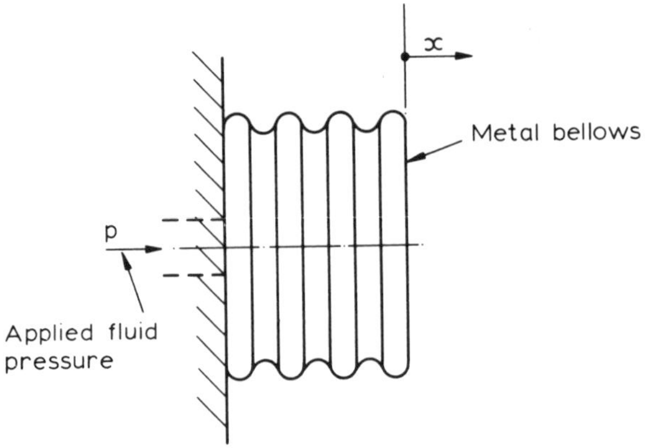

Fig. 1.1 Bellows used as a pressure-sensing element.

something. It may be a visual output, such as the position of a pointer on a scale, the height of liquid in a manometer, or the numerical readout on an electrical instrument. The output may also be recorded on some kind of paper chart, on magnetic tape etc. In some cases, audible alarms may be operated as well as, or instead of, indicated or recorded outputs, to indicate that values have reached unacceptable levels. In some cases, the measurement system may form an integral part of a control system, and the output may not necessarily be displayed.

Fig. 1.2 shows a pressure recorder of a type used in the gas industry, using a bellows as a sensing element, and a 'writing' arm that amplifies

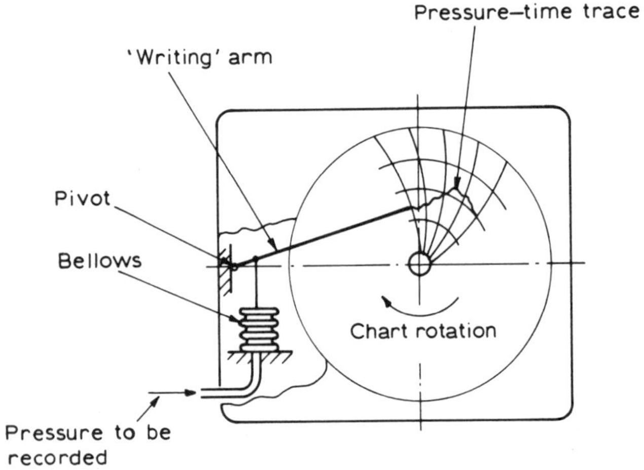

Fig. 1.2 Pressure recorder.

the movement of the bellows, whilst the output is displayed on a circular paper chart driven by a clockwork motor.

1.3 Transfer operators

Whether a system consists of a number of different components, or is contained within one enclosure, it may be represented by a block diagram as shown in Fig. 1.3. The symbol θ is used in general to denote signal, θ_i for input signal, θ_o for output signal. The operation of each element is represented by the *transfer operators*, G_1, G_2 and G_3. The overall effect of the measurement system is given by:

$$\theta_i \times G_1 \times G_2 \times G_3 = \theta_o$$

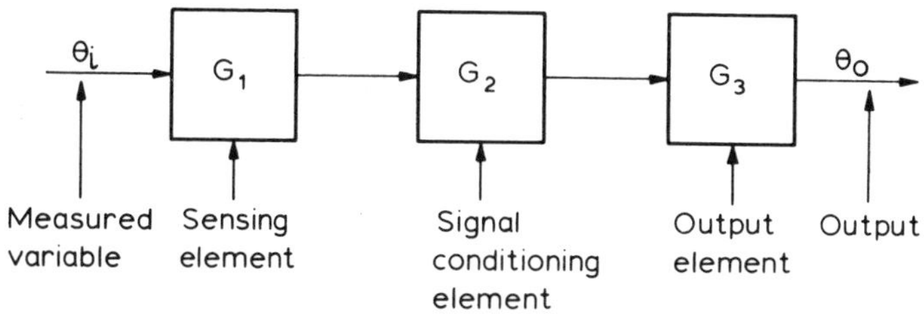

Fig. 1.3 Elements of a measuring system.

1.4 Transducers

A transducer receives a signal of one kind and gives out an output signal of another kind, the output signal being some function of the input signal. For example, the following sensing elements are transducers:

(a) a vapour thermometer, giving an output pressure which is a function of the temperature of the bulb as illustrated in Fig. 1.4(a),

(b) a piezoelectric force transducer, where the output is an electric charge which is proportional to the force applied, as illustrated in Fig. 1.4(b).

(c) an orifice-plate flowmeter, where the pressure difference across the orifice is a function of the rate of flow of fluid through the orifice, as illustrated in Fig. 1.4(c).

Transducers are also used after the sensing element to convert a signal; for example it may be necessary to convert a displacement to an electrical voltage, which may be more suitable for further signal conditioning such as amplification. A voltage-dividing displacement transducer which does this is illustrated in Fig. 1.4(d).

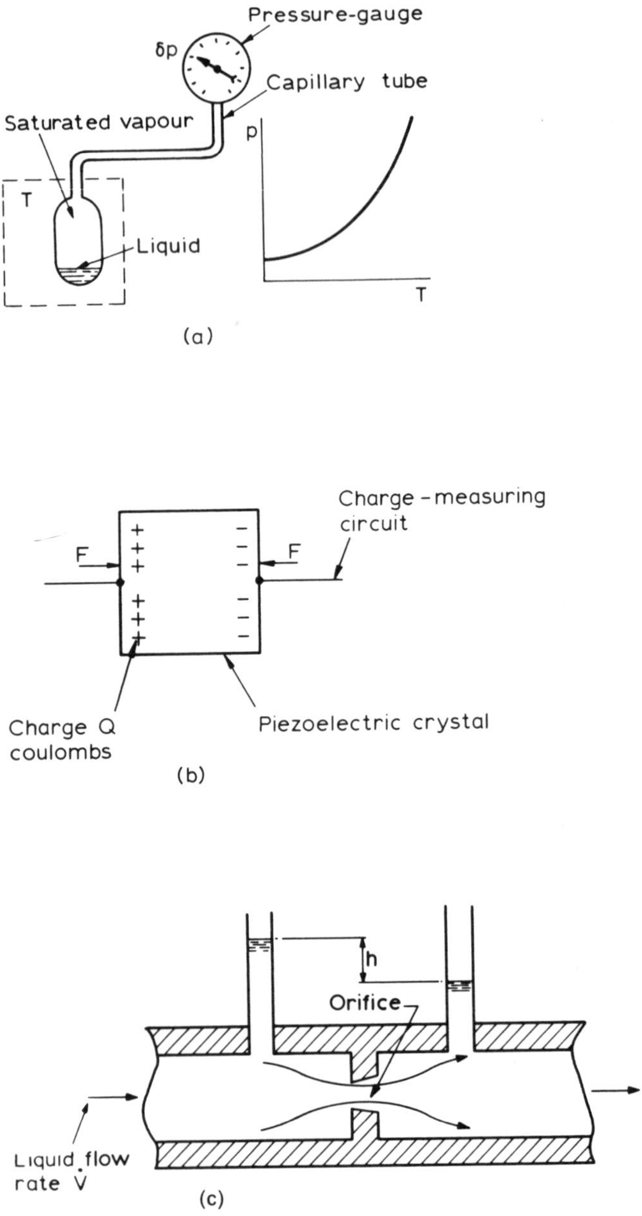

Fig. 1.4 (a) Vapour-pressure thermometer.
(b) Piezoelectric force transducer.
(c) Orifice plate for liquid flowrate measurement.

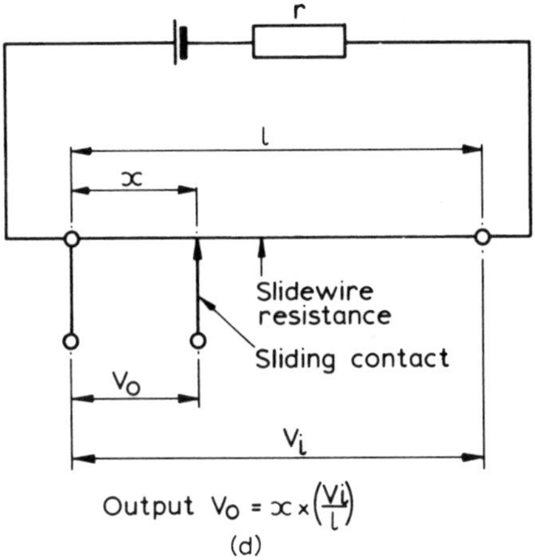

Fig. 1.4 (d) Voltage-dividing displacement transducer.

1.5 Tutorial and practical work

1.5.1 Describe an example of a system in each of the following categories:

(a) a system that aids the operator of a non-automatic machine-tool

(b) a workshop or inspection-room instrument that records a trace of the measured quantity

(c) a system that measures a variable and uses the measurement to control the variable without displaying it

(d) a system that gives out an audible alarm, at a pre-set level.

1.5.2 Describe and sketch transducers which convert:

(a) temperature to displacement
(b) temperature to e.m.f.
(c) rotational speed to e.m.f.
(d) e.m.f. to displacement
(e) pressure to displacement
(f) force to displacement
(g) displacement to pressure
(h) displacement to e.m.f.
(i) fluid flow rate to displacement.

In each case, state whether the output signal is proportional to the input signal.

1.5.3 Identify the sensing, conditioning and output elements of the following measurement systems:

(a) a simple mercury-in-glass thermometer
(b) a dial test-indicator

(c) the water-temperature measuring system of a motor-vehicle engine

(d) the force measuring and recording system of a Hounsfield Tensometer

(e) a fuel-tank level-gauge.

1.5.4 Describe an example of a measuring system in each of the following:

(a) where both the input and the output vary continuously (i.e. do not change in steps)

(b) where the input varies continuously, but the output varies in steps

(c) where the input varies in steps or pulses and the output varies in steps

(d) where the input consists of pulses and the output varies continuously.

2 *Specification of measuring-system performance*

2.1 Selection of an instrument

When we use or select an instrument or a measuring system, we must know something about its performance, or we may be completely misled by the readings taken with it. We may ask such questions as:

How nearly will it indicate the quantity to be measured?
Will it give the same reading every time the same thing is measured with it?
Will it give the same reading of the same quantity with different operators?
Will it give the same readings after a long time has elapsed?
Will readings be affected by changes of pressure, temperature and humidity etc. of the environment?
Is the range of the instrument suitable?
Will it respond well enough to changing inputs?
and so on.

A number of terms, used to describe instrument characteristics such as these are defined in BS 5233 : 1975 Glossary of terms used in metrology (Reference 1). The following conform to these definitions.

2.2 Accuracy and error

There is a strong temptation when taking measurements to accept that the measured values are correct. It must be appreciated that, except in the few cases where the quantity being measured is purely a count, e.g. of the number of components coming from a production line, *every* measurement has error. Accuracy may be defined as the nearness to the true value of the quantity being measured. It is usually specified numerically as the amount of the maximum error likely to occur, as a percentage of the full-scale deflection (f.s.d.) of the instrument. However, the true value of a quantity being measured can never be known exactly, and hence neither can the true error, or the true accuracy.

In practice, we *calibrate* an instrument by comparing its readings against the values of another instrument or device known to have much higher accuracy. This second instrument is a *measurement standard*, usually referred to as a standard. The value that it gives is a *standard value*. We may specify the error of indication of the instrument, from the calibration test, thus:

$$\text{error (at any point)} = \text{measured value} - \text{standard value} \qquad (2.1)$$

These error values may be positive or negative, and should be evenly distributed about the zero error line, as shown in Fig. 2.1(c). If they are more to the positive or to the negative side then adjustment of the instrument is necessary. The size of the band on each side of the zero error line which just contains all the values is found, and used to calculate the error percentage f.s.d. value for the instrument. For example, if a pressure gauge has a full-scale-deflection value of 100 bar, and if the error values are evenly distributed about zero error in a band ± 2 bar of the standard value. Then:

$$\text{error \% f.s.d. (maximum)} = \pm\frac{\text{maximum error in range}}{\text{full scale value}} \times 100\% \qquad (2.2)$$

$$= \pm\frac{2}{100} \times 100\%$$

$$= \pm 2\%$$

Hence the accuracy of the gauge would be specified as $\pm 2\%$ f.s.d. Fig. 2.1(a) shows the arrangement of a reference gauge and a gauge being calibrated against it, supplied with compressed air through a pressure

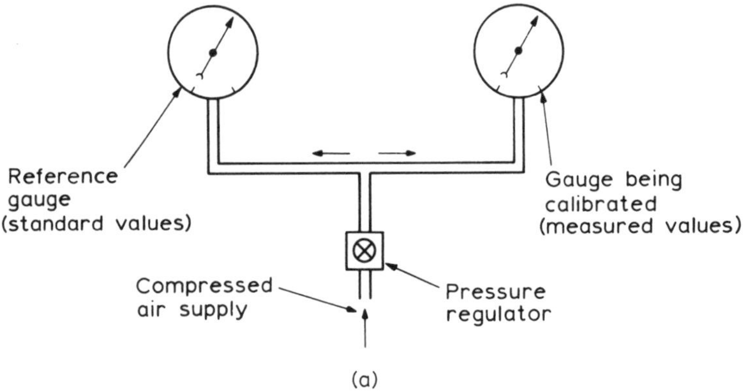

Fig. 2.1

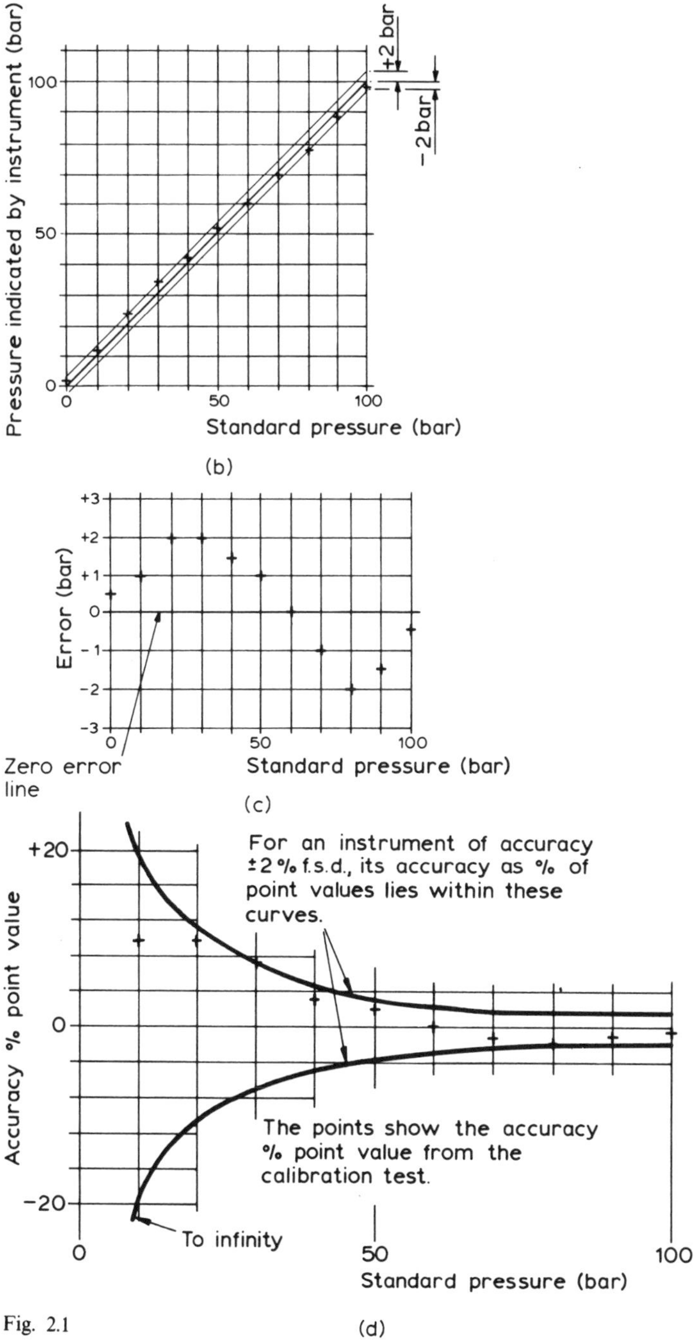

+2 bar
100
50
0
−2 bar
Pressure indicated by instrument (bar)
0
50
100
Standard pressure (bar)
(b)
+3
+2
+1
0
−1
−2
−3
Error (bar)
0
50
100
Zero error line
Standard pressure (bar)
(c)
+20
0
−20
Accuracy % point value
For an instrument of accuracy ±2% f.s.d., its accuracy as % of point values lies within these curves.
The points show the accuracy % point value from the calibration test.
To infinity
0
50
100
Standard pressure (bar)
(d)

Fig. 2.1

regulator. Fig. 2.1(b) shows the graph of measured values against standard values. Fig. 2.1(c) shows the errors plotted against standard values, and they are seen to be evenly distributed about a zero error line, i.e. the zero error line is the 'best straight' line through the points.

It must be appreciated that the error as *a percentage of the point value being measured* will be higher than the percentage f.s.d. accuracy of the instrument, except at the full-scale-deflection value, when it will be the same. For example, for the gauge of Fig. 2.1, at 20 bar the error could be ± 2 bar (as it could be at any value). As a percentage of the value being measured this is $(\pm 2/20) \times 100\% = \pm 10\%$. This is probably an unacceptable value of error in most situations. This value increases as we take readings lower down the scale, and increases towards infinity as we approach zero. Fig. 2.1(d) shows the theoretical percentage of point value error curve for this instrument and also the measured point values.

Not all instruments have accuracy quoted as percentage f.s.d. Slip-gauge sets (these are instruments in the wider sense) may have calibration charts which specify the error of each gauge, a quantity to be added to or subtracted from the value marked on the gauge. (It should be noted that even after making this correction, we still cannot know the gauge thickness *exactly*.) Similarly, some pyrometers may have their errors quoted at fixed points on the International Practical Temperature Scale (IPTS), such as the melting points and the boiling points of various substances.

The errors discussed up to now are due to the instrument. However, further errors occur due to various other factors.

(a) *Application error*: This is the change of the quantity being measured, due to applying the instrument. As examples:

(i) a micrometer applied to a thin ring will distort it,
(ii) a thermometer dipped in hot liquid will cool it,
(iii) a voltmeter applied to a circuit will take current, and alter the voltage.

(b) *Operating errors*: These may arise from a variety of causes such as failure to read the indicated value correctly in size measurement or failure to apply a measuring instrument squarely; or due to applying excessive pressure so that an instrument is strained. These operating errors are illustrated in Fig. 2.2. Reading errors arise due to difficulty in visually determining the fraction of a scale division at which a pointer aligns. Reading errors are worse if parallax is present, i.e. if the pointer and scale are not in the same plane. This is eliminated in many instruments, for example electrical multi-meters, by placing a mirror behind the pointer, so that when the mirror image of the pointer is not visible to the operator, he is looking squarely at the pointer and scale.

(c) *Environmental error*: This is error caused by changes of the surrounding pressure, temperature, humidity etc. It may be reduced by designing into the instrument compensation devices, or by controlling the measurement environment. For example, inspection rooms and

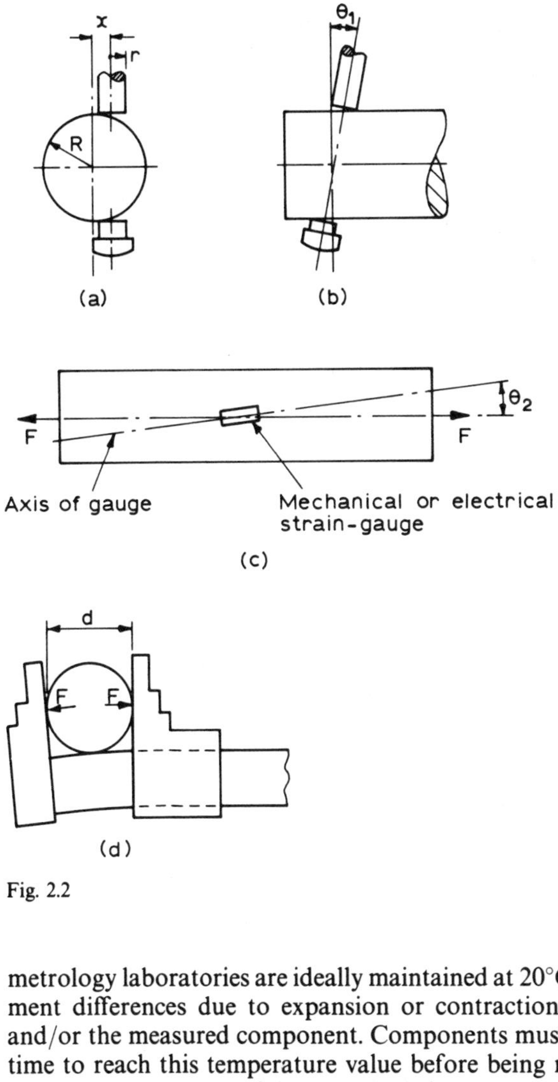

Fig. 2.2

metrology laboratories are ideally maintained at 20°C to avoid measurement differences due to expansion or contraction of the instrument and/or the measured component. Components must be given adequate time to reach this temperature value before being measured.

(d) *Dynamic error*: If the quantity being measured is changing or has recently changed, the output signal of the instrument will lag behind. For example, if a thermometer is placed suddenly in hot fluid, it will not reach the fluid temperature immediately, since heat must flow into the mercury and raise its temperature, which takes time. If insufficient time is allowed before taking a reading, *dynamic error* will occur, as shown in Fig. 2.3. In this case, the dynamic error is *transient*, i.e. it will die out. In other cases, where the input changes steadily, the output lags a fixed amount, relative to the input. This is *steady-state* error.

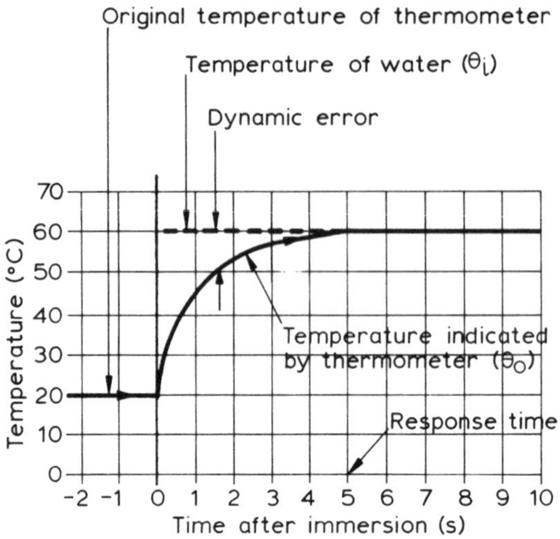

Fig. 2.3

It should be clear by now that accurate measurement is not easy, and that much care is necessary in the selection and use of instruments if a good standard of measurement is required.

2.3 Standards and calibration

The International System of Units (SI) defines seven *base units*, and many *derived units* are defined from these (see Appendix 1). The highest standard of either a base unit or a derived unit is called a *primary standard*. For example, the primary standard of mass (a base unit) is the mass of the international prototype of the kilogram, kept at Sèvres, Paris in the Bureau of Standards. Copies of this are kept throughout the world, in national standards laboratories and institutions of similar standing. The mass of each copy is not the same as that of the prototype, but the difference in each case is known very closely. The copies are referred to as *secondary standards*, and these are used to calibrate other masses, which in turn are used to calibrate more masses, and so on. Hence a chain of measurement standards trace back from any mass used for measurement to the primary standard.

The best standard of a particular quantity in a particular location may be kept as a *reference standard*. For example, in a factory, a high-grade set of slip gauges may be preserved and not put into general use, so that other gauges throughout the organisation may be calibrated against them. These other gauges are *working standards*, against which production measuring instruments may be checked.

Primary standards of length and time are based on wavelengths of radiation from particular substances under carefully specified conditions. However, with suitable equipment, these conditions may be reproduced anywhere, and there is not the disadvantage, as there is with mass, of having only one standard. Length gauges may be calibrated against the primary standard in an interferometer using a krypton 86 light source at a number of laboratories in the United Kingdom.

Standards of measurement are maintained by the work of such organisations as the National Physical Laboratory (NPL). The NPL co-operates with international organisations in the development of standards, offers advice on measurement in general, and carries out verifications of certain types of instruments and gauges. The British Calibration Service (BCS), although not running laboratories of its own, approves various laboratories for particular types of measurement, and these may then issue BCS certificates of calibration for instruments.

The important aspect of *traceability* of a measurement may be illustrated by using the example of an ordinary external micrometer. To calibrate this, it would probably have its readings throughout its range checked against piles of slip gauges from a reference set. These would in turn have been calibrated against a still higher standard, probably the primary standard, and a calibration chart would have been drawn up of the correction values to be added to or subtracted from the nominal thickness marked on each gauge. Hence the height of each pile of gauges is 'corrected', although it is still not the *exact* measurement of each pile, but is the standard value. The errors of the micrometer would be calculated from eqns. 2.1 and 2.2, as if each slip gauge pile height was correct, to give the percentage f.s.d. accuracy. This will not matter too

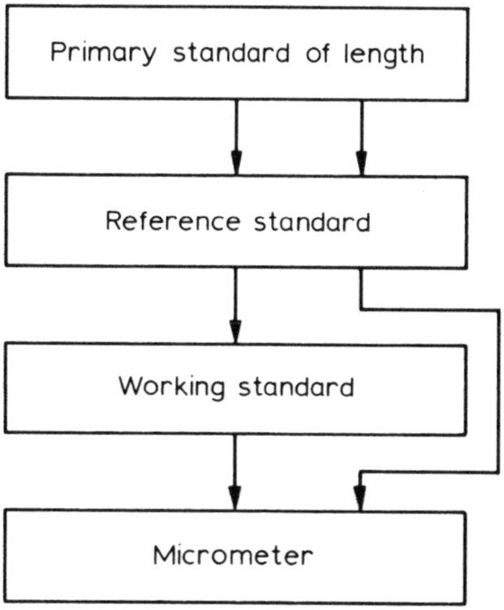

Fig. 2.4 Traceability of standards.

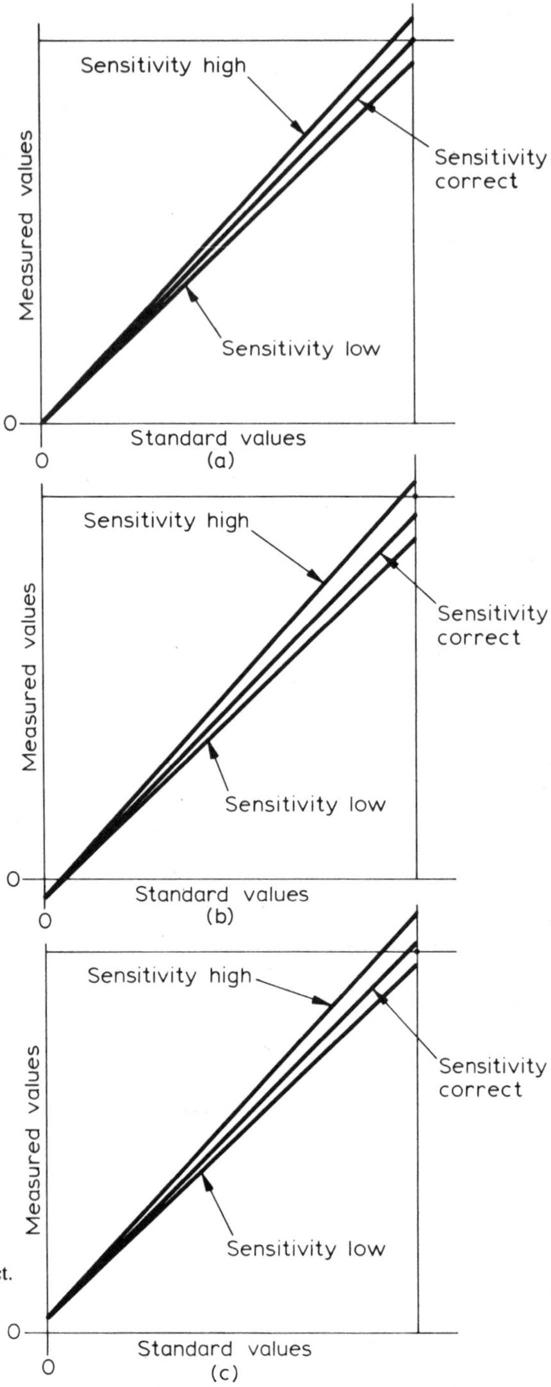

Fig. 2.5 (a) Zero correct.
(b) Zero low.
(c) Zero high.

much, since the closeness of the slip gauges to the true value is much better than the closeness of the micrometer readings to the slip-gauge values. Example 2.8.1 shows this numerically. The hierarchy of standards for this example is illustrated in Fig. 2.4. The micrometer could have been calibrated against either a working standard or a reference standard, and both routes are shown.

In some instruments errors detected during calibration may be corrected by adjustment. For example, ammeters and voltmeters frequently have a zero adjustment screw so that with the meter disconnected from the circuit, the pointer may be turned to the scale zero. If calibration at higher values shows the measured values to be proportionally higher or lower than the standard values, then the sensitivity may be adjusted if adjustment features are provided, as illustrated in Fig. 2.5. Bourdon-tube type pressure gauges usually have both zero adjustment and range adjustment, as shown in Fig. 2.6.

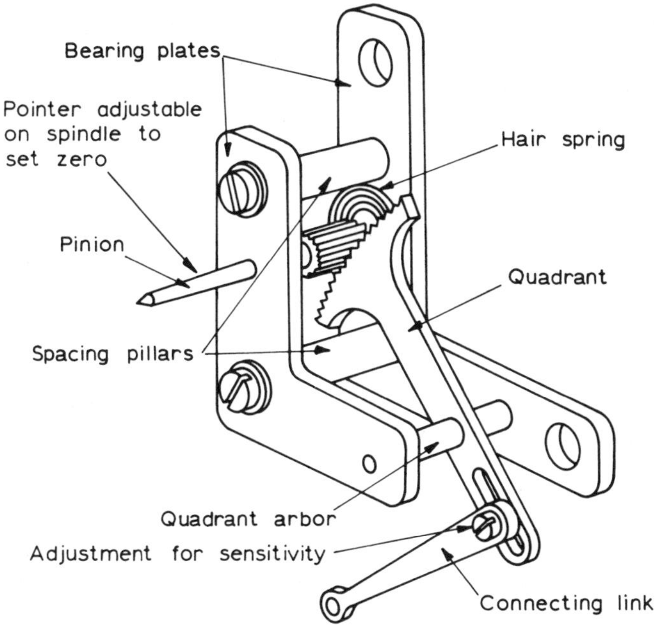

Fig. 2.6 Quadrant and pinion movement of Bourdon-tube pressure-gauge.

2.4 Repeatability, reproducibility and stability

It is necessary to know whether repeated measurements of the same quantity by the same or different instruments will give readings in close agreement. These terms refer to the closeness of repeated measurements, but under different conditions.

Repeatability is the closeness between successive measurements of the same quantity, with the same instrument, by the same operator, over a short time-span.

Reproducibility is the closeness between measurements of the same quantity, where the individual measurements are made under different conditions, for example:

(a) at different locations
(b) with different measuring instruments
(c) by different operators
(d) over longer time-periods
(e) under different conditions of instrument usage.

Stability is usually used to describe the ability of an instrument to maintain its standard over an extended length of time.

Hence we may say that the repeatability of the measurement of a 15 mm diameter by operator A at site B with micrometer C is ± 0.005 mm. In a wider situation, a firm may be concerned about the reproducibility of the measurement of, for example, a ring of diameter 30.0 mm which is produced in a number of factories, measured by different operators and instruments, but which must be controlled closely in size so that it is fully interchangeable within or even outside the group's products.

It must be appreciated that repeatability is not the same thing as accuracy. To quote from Reference 2, 'Accuracy is a measure of an instrument's ability to tell the truth, whereas repeatability is a measure of its ability to stick to the same story. Consequently, a good repeatability is no guarantee of good accuracy, although poor repeatability is a sure sign of poor accuracy.'

To take a practical example, a micrometer may read to ± 0.002 mm, and the same indicated value may be obtained every time the same diameter is measured, i.e. there is good repeatability. However, if the barrel or the anvil has been moved out of the correct position, the readings may *all* be inaccurate, although they will still be repeatable. In this case the error will be obvious, since the instrument will not read zero when the spindle and anvil are in contact. In other cases, the zero may still be correct and the inaccuracy not obvious. 'Drift' of instruments, i.e. changes of accuracy, may occur after a time, due to various causes such as wear, change of friction values, oxidisation of pyrometer elements etc., though precision may still be maintained.

2.5 Discrimination

Discrimination of a measuring instrument is its ability to respond to small changes of the quantity being measured (an alternative term *resolution* is used in some cases.)

Fig. 2.7 shows a coil of electrical conducting wire, with a sliding

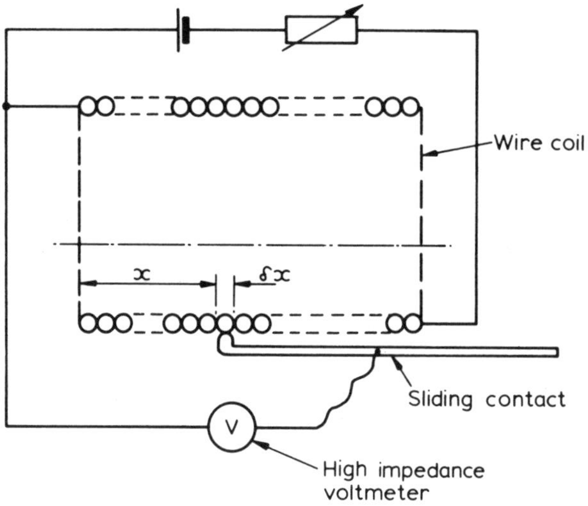

Fig. 2.7 Discrimination of a resistance-type displacement transducer.

contact, forming a displacement transducer, the output being a voltage proportional to the displacement x. However, the resistance does not change as the sliding contact moves from A to B, through distance δx. Hence δx is the discrimination of the transducer. The wire size would need to be reduced to reduce δx and hence improve the discrimination. Instead of a coil, continuous strips of conducting material, e.g. conductive plastic, are used to improve discrimination.

2.6 Sensitivity and range

Sensitivity of a measuring instrument is the relationship between the change in the quantity being measured, and the change in the measured value. Thus:

$$\text{Sensitivity} = \frac{\text{change in output of instrument}}{\text{change in quantity being measured}} \tag{2.3}$$

For example, a dial indicator may give one complete revolution of a pointer on a 20 mm radius scale for 1 mm displacement of the plunger. Hence:

$$\begin{aligned}\text{Sensitivity} &= \text{circumference of scale/plunger movement}\\ &= 2\pi \times 20\,\text{mm}/1\,\text{mm} = 126\end{aligned}$$

(a ratio without units in this case) i.e. the pointer moves 126 mm for every 1 mm movement of the plunger.

Other terms may be used to convey the same meaning, for example *amplification, gain and magnification*, the last being used when the output and input quantities are of the same kind. Example 2.8.3 shows a sensitivity calculation where the input and output quantities are not of the same kind.

In choosing an instrument for making a particular measurement a high sensitivity is desirable. In some cases this is done simply by choosing an instrument with a larger diameter scale. If the dial indicator previously referred to had a scale of radius 40 mm instead of 20 mm, then its sensitivity would be doubled. Also, if we use an instrument in a lower part of its scale, we are liable to get a smaller movement of the pointer than if an instrument of lower range had been chosen for the same scale size. Furthermore, in using an instrument in the lower part of its scale, the error as a percentage of the value measured may be large as shown in Section 2.2. On the other hand, if measurements are continually taken at the top of an instrument's range, there is a possibility of overloading it. For these reasons, a rule of thumb is sometimes adopted, of using an instrument in the middle third of its range. Fig. 2.8 shows some of these points.

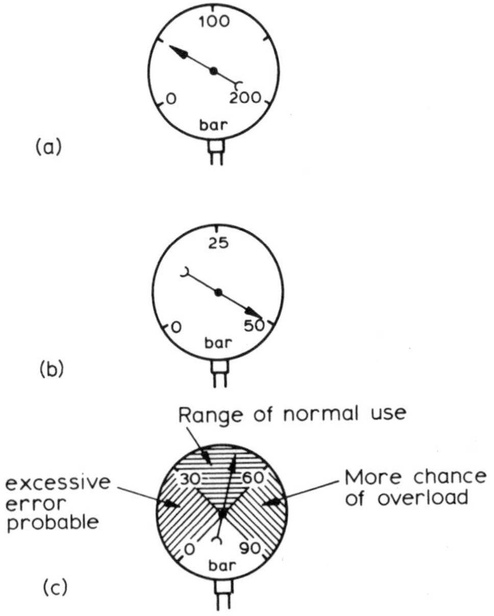

Fig. 2.8 Selection of a gauge to measure 50 bar.
(a) Excessive range, low sensitivity, high errors at low end of range.
(b) Exact range, most sensitive and low errors but liable to overload.
(c) Compromise.

2.7 Response time

Response time is defined as the time which elapses after a step change in the quantity measured, up to the point at which the measuring instrument indicates very nearly the quantity measured. A step change means a sudden change from one value of a measured quantity to another value, such as would occur if a thermometer at room temperature, say 20°C, were suddenly thrust into a fluid at 60°C, as shown in Fig. 2.3. The response time is the time from the step change to the moment when the thermometer indicates very nearly the temperature of the fluid. In some instruments, the indicated value may overshoot, i.e. become greater than the input, and oscillate before coming to rest, as indicated in Fig. 2.9. Response times are sometimes quoted for an instrument by the manufacturer. They are more important in some applications than in others. When using compressed-air size gauging, for example, it may take a second or so for the pressure gauge pointer or the manometer level to become steady, after placing a component in the measuring fixture. If the time is too long, throughput of components is reduced.

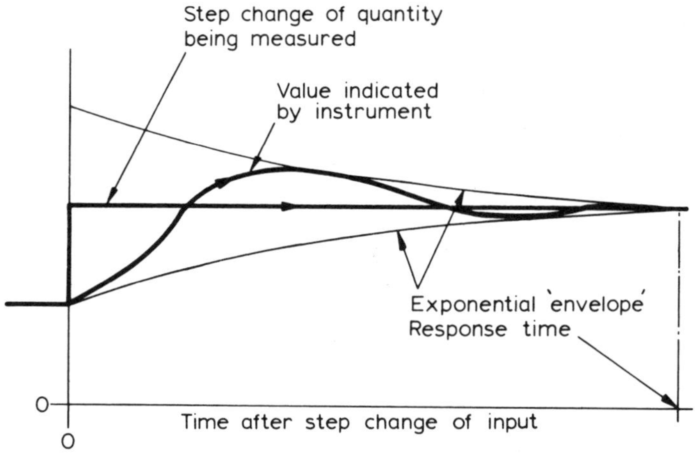

Fig. 2.9 Response of an underdamped instrument to a step change of input.

2.8 Worked examples

2.8.1 A micrometer reading to 0.001 mm over a range 0–25 mm was calibrated against a reference set of slip gauges for which a table of errors was available from the Statement of Calibration, and the differences determined as shown in the table. Plot the errors and determine the accuracy of the micrometer as a percentage of full-scale deflection.

A	*B*	*C* = *A* + *B*	*D*	*D* − *C*
Nominal size of slip-gauge (mm)	*Slip-gauge error* (mm)	*Slip gauge size* (mm)	*Micrometer reading* (mm)	*Error* (mm)
0	0	0	0	0
5.000 000	−0.000 002	4.999 998	5.003	+0.003 002
10.000 000	+0.000 002	10.000 002	10.000	−0.000 002
15.000 000	0	15.000 000	14.999	−0.001 000
20.000 000	0	20.000 000	19.997	−0.003 000
25.000 000	−0.000 002	24.999 998	24.999	−0.000 998

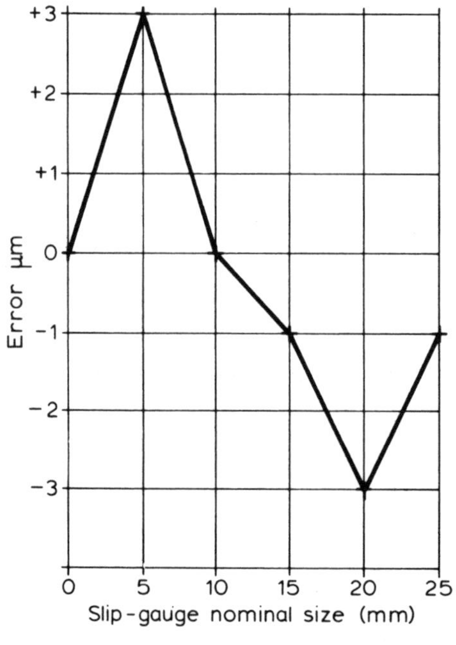

Fig. 2.10 Micrometer errors.

Fig. 2.10 shows the errors plotted against the standard sizes. The effect of the slip-gauge errors is seen to be small enough to be neglected in this case. The errors are seen to fall within the range $\pm 3\ \mu$m.
Hence:

$$\text{error percentage f.s.d.} = \frac{\pm 3 \times 10^{-6}}{25 \times 10^{-3}} \times 100\% = \pm 0.012\%$$

2.8.2 A voltmeter has a range 0–20 V and the manufacturer states its accuracy as $\pm 1\%$ f.s.d. For voltage values of 2, 4, 8, 12, 16 and 20, calculate at each the possible error as a percentage of point value and sketch the values on a graph.

$$\text{Possible error at any point} = \frac{20(\pm 1)}{100} = \pm 0.20 \text{ V}.$$

At a reading of 2 V

$$\text{error as percentage of point value} = \frac{\pm 0.20}{2} \times 100\%$$
$$= \pm 10\%$$

At a reading of 4 V

$$\text{error as percentage of point value} = \frac{\pm 0.20}{4} \times 100\%$$
$$= \pm 5\%$$

and so on. Fig. 2.11 shows the percentage errors graphically, and emphasises the dangers of using the lower parts of the range.

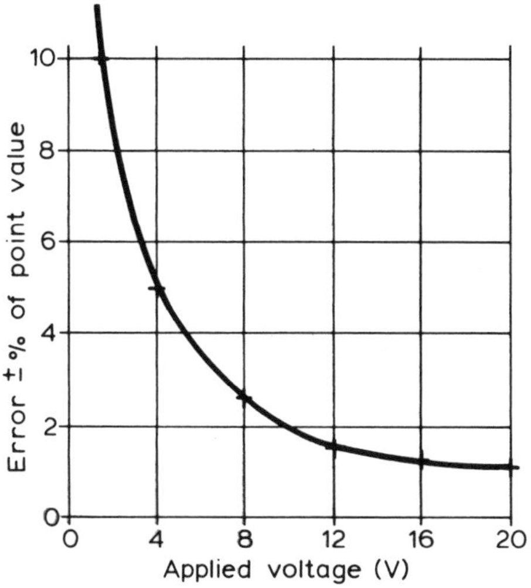

Fig. 2.11 Possible errors as percentage of point values.

2.8.3 A pressure gauge has a range 0–200 bar, and its scale extends over an arc of 75 mm radius for 270°. Calculate the sensitivity of the gauge in mm/bar and in m/Pa units.

$$\text{Sensitivity} = \frac{\text{change in output of instrument}}{\text{change in quantity being measured}}$$

$$= (\text{length of arc of scale})/(\text{range of scale})$$

$$= 2\pi \times 75 \times \frac{270}{360} \times \frac{1}{200}\ \text{mm/bar}$$

$$= 1.77\ \text{mm/bar}$$

$$= \frac{1.77}{1000} \times \frac{1}{100\,000}\ \text{m/Pa}$$

$$= 17.7 \times 10^{-9}\ \text{m/Pa}$$

2.9 Tutorial and practical work

2.9.1 Examine a number of instruments and/or their literature, which measure the same quantity, and note the values quoted in each case for the instrument's accuracy, repeatability, discrimination sensitivity, range and response time. Write notes comparing their performance and cost.

2.9.2 Discuss how the heating effect of the current passing through the moving coil of an ammeter or a voltmeter can affect the accuracy of the measurement.

2.9.3 Carefully examine the mechanism of a Bourdon-tube or other type of pressure gauge. Sketch and discuss briefly:

(a) the method (if any) of avoiding backlash between the teeth of the gears of the amplifying mechanism

(b) the method of adjusting the zero

(c) the method of adjusting the range.

2.9.4 Calibrate an external micrometer using the best slip-gauge set available.

2.9.5 Calibrate a dial test-indicator, devising a suitable method.

2.9.6 Determine the response time after a step change of input to instruments such as:

(a) U-tube manometer

(b) voltmeter

(c) thermometer

(d) motor vehicle fuel-level gauge

(e) air-jet measuring system.

2.9.7 Determine the difference in the readings of different operators measuring the same diameter with the same micrometer, not using the ratchet device.

2.9.8 Examine a number of external vernier gauges and micrometers of various types and note the discrimination in each case. Compare and discuss the values.

2.9.9 In addition to the types of error mentioned in this chapter, errors of measurement may also be classified as (a) *systematic* errors, i.e. those which are almost constant and of the same sign, and (b) *random* errors, i.e. those occurring accidentally, varying in magnitude and sign. Give examples of each kind of error. Discuss ways of detecting systematic and random errors in an instrument or system (remembering that an operator forms a part of many measurement systems).
2.9.10 Determine the application error when a micrometer is used to measure the diameter of a very thin ring.

2.10 Exercises

2.10.1 A wire wound resistance-type linear-displacement transducer was tested in conjunction with a 0–50 mm barrel-type precision micrometer head as shown in Fig. 2.12. The input voltage (v_i) was maintained constant, and the output voltage (v_o) was measured with a digital voltmeter for different values of spindle displacement (x) measured by the micrometer. Draw the error/displacement graph, and state the sensitivity of the arrangement. Specify the accuracy of the system (a) as a percentage of true value, (b) as a percentage of full-scale (or fiducial) value.

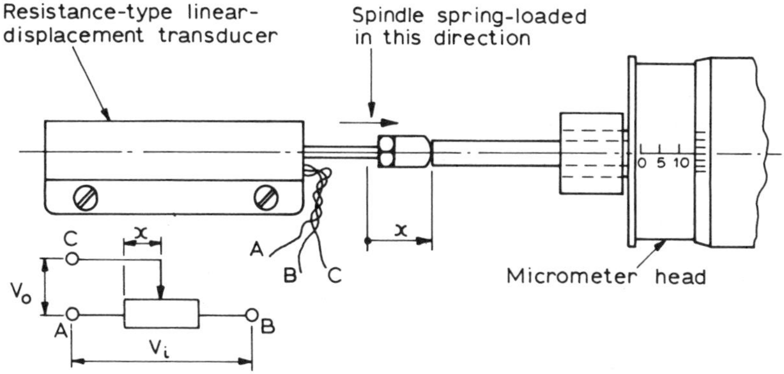

Fig. 2.12

Discuss the suitability of the transducer for use in a machine-tool position-control system to control dimensions to an accuracy of 0.10 mm.

Readings

x (mm)	0.000	2.000	4.000	6.000	8.000	10.000	12.000
v_o (volts)	0.000	2.01	4.00	6.01	8.03	10.01	12.00
x (mm)	14.000	16.000	18.000	20.000	22.000	24.000	26.000
v_o (volts).	13.99	15.98	17.99	20.00	22.02	24.01	26.02
x (mm)	28.000	30.000	32.000	34.000	36.000	38.000	40.000
v_o (volts)	28.03	30.01	32.00	33.99	36.00	37.99	39.97
x (mm)	42.000	44.000	46.000	48.000	50.000		
v_o (volts)	41.96	43.98	46.01	48.01	50.00		

2.10.2 A Bourdon-tube pressure-gauge has a scale from zero to 50 bar over an arc of 270°. The radius of the scale line is 100 mm. During a deadweight calibration test, the following values were observed:

Calibration pressure (bar)	*Scale value (bar)*	*Calibration pressure (bar)*	*Scale value (bar)*
0	0.0	30	30.1
5	5.0	35	35.3
10	9.8	40	40.2
15	14.8	45	45.1
20	19.9	50	50.0
25	25.1		

(a) Determine the sensitivity (i) as a ratio of pressures, (ii) as a ratio of length/pressure.

(b) Determine the maximum error as (i) percentage of scale value, (ii) percentage of full-scale (fiducial) value.

(c) Could the gauge be adjusted to comply with $\pm 0.5\%$ f.s.d. accuracy?

2.10.3 Fig. 2.1(a), (b), (c) shows three cases of wrong use of instruments. For each case calculate the percentage error in the measurement due to these wrong usages. State what type of error you would call these, and whether they are of a random or of a systematic type, (See 2.9.9).

2.10.4 (a) Explain how each of the following may affect the accuracy of the measurement made by an instrument:

(i) manufacturing limitations in the production of the instrument
(ii) operating errors
(iii) friction in the instrument.

In each case, choose two examples to illustrate your explanations, and state what measures may be taken to minimise or eliminate the errors.

(b) State, and illustrate with diagrams, what is meant by

(i) random errors
(ii) systematic errors, of measurement.

Choose two errors of each type to illustrate your answer.

(c) State what is meant by 'operator bias', making reference to parts (a) and (b) of the question.

2.10.5 The following five types of error can occur in measuring systems:

(a) parallax error
(b) application error
(c) error due to hysteresis of elastic elements
(d) error due to friction
(e) error due to environmental effects.

Select TWO of the above, and for each of these:
(i) state an example of an instrument where the type of error could occur
(ii) discuss how the error would occur in the example stated, and whether it would be random or systematic
(iii) discuss how the error might be reduced or eliminated, either at the design stage, or in manufacture, or in use.

2.10.6 (a) With reference to the measurement of length, discuss briefly what is meant by each of the terms:
(i) primary standard
(ii) traceability
(iii) calibration.

(b) Discuss briefly the difference between:
(i) 'accuracy' and 'precision'
(ii) 'sensitivity' and 'discrimination'
choosing a suitable measurement example to illustrate each case.

3 *Operating principles of common transducers*

A very large variety of physical principles is used in many different ways to provide elements which will sense the change of some quantity, and give an output signal which depends on that change. The term transducer was defined in Chapter 1, and some examples were discussed in Section 1.4. We now deal with some transducers in more detail.

3.1 Force-measuring transducers

3.1.1 Deflection of elastic elements

A common method of measuring the magnitude of a force is to observe the deflection of a coil spring to which the force is applied. Referring to Fig. 3.1, the extension (x) of the coil spring in a spring balance is proportional to the force (F) applied to it. Thus:

$$F = kx \tag{3.1}$$

where k is the *stiffness* or *rate* of the spring (N/m)
F is the force applied (N)
x is the extension (m).

The spring is an *elastic* element. Other elastic elements which are used to measure force are shown in Fig. 3.2, and eqn. 3.1 also applies to these. If we are concerned with designing an instrument, the value of the spring constant k in each case may be calculated from standard equations. For an existing instrument, it may be determined by experiment.

3.1.2 Piezoelectric force transducers

Compressive force applied to opposite parallel faces of certain crystals causes an excess of electrons at one of the faces and a shortage at the other as shown in Fig. 1.4(b). The crystal acts as a capacitor, and the separation of electrons constitutes a charge, as would occur if an e.m.f.

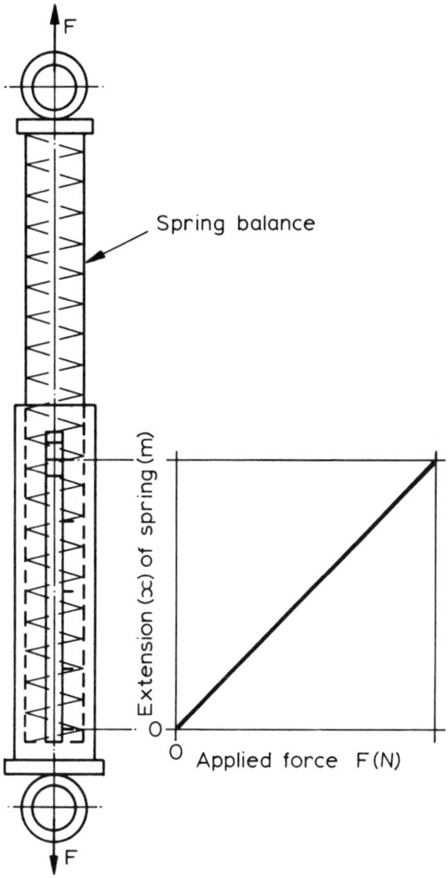

Fig. 3.1 The coil spring as a force-displacement transducer.

had been applied. The effect is found in quartz crystals, and also in crystals of some specially prepared salts such as barium titanate. In a piezoelectric transducer the crystals are usually protected by being enclosed in a stainless steel casing. A cross-section through a typical piezoelectric force transducer in the form of a washer is shown in Fig. 3.3(a). The transducer is used with a charge amplifier (a signal conditioning element) which has an input resistance R, and gives a voltage output (V_o).

Fig. 3.3(b) illustrates diagramatically the transducer with a force applied, the resulting separation of charge, and the connections to the charge amplifier. The output from the charge amplifier may be connected to an indicating, recording, alarm or control element. The transducer

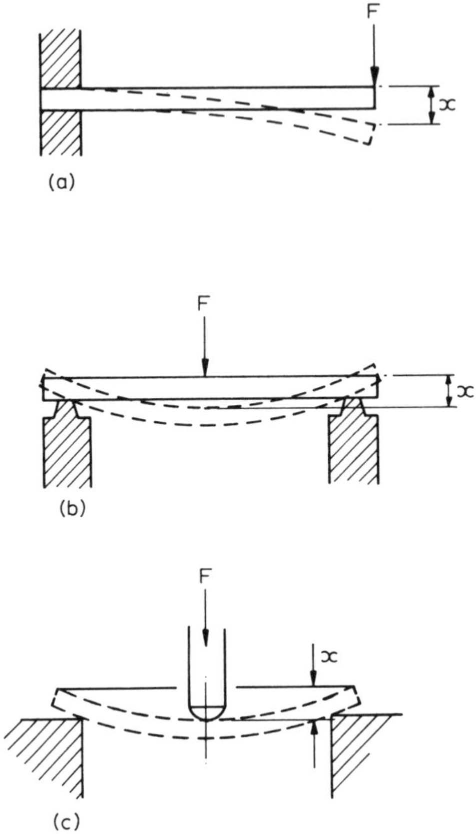

Fig. 3.2 Some elastic elements used for force measurement
(a) Cantilever.
(b) Simply-supported beam.
(c) Simply-supported diaphragm.

acts as a capacitor with its own source of e.m.f., and the equivalent circuit shown in Fig. 3.3(c) may be drawn. Fig. 3.3(d) shows a possible application, measuring the force in a cylinder-head stud.

The equivalent circuit shows that the charge on the crystal due to the force applied to it will cause a small current through the input resistance (R) of the charge amplifier, so that it is eventually dissipated. Fig. 3.4 shows the graph of force against time, when a force is suddenly applied and maintained, and the corresponding output voltage (V_o) against time graph. This latter is an *exponential decay* with a *time constant* $\tau = RC$ seconds (see eqn. 8.5). The decay of the output voltage means that piezoelectric systems are not suitable for long term measurements. The

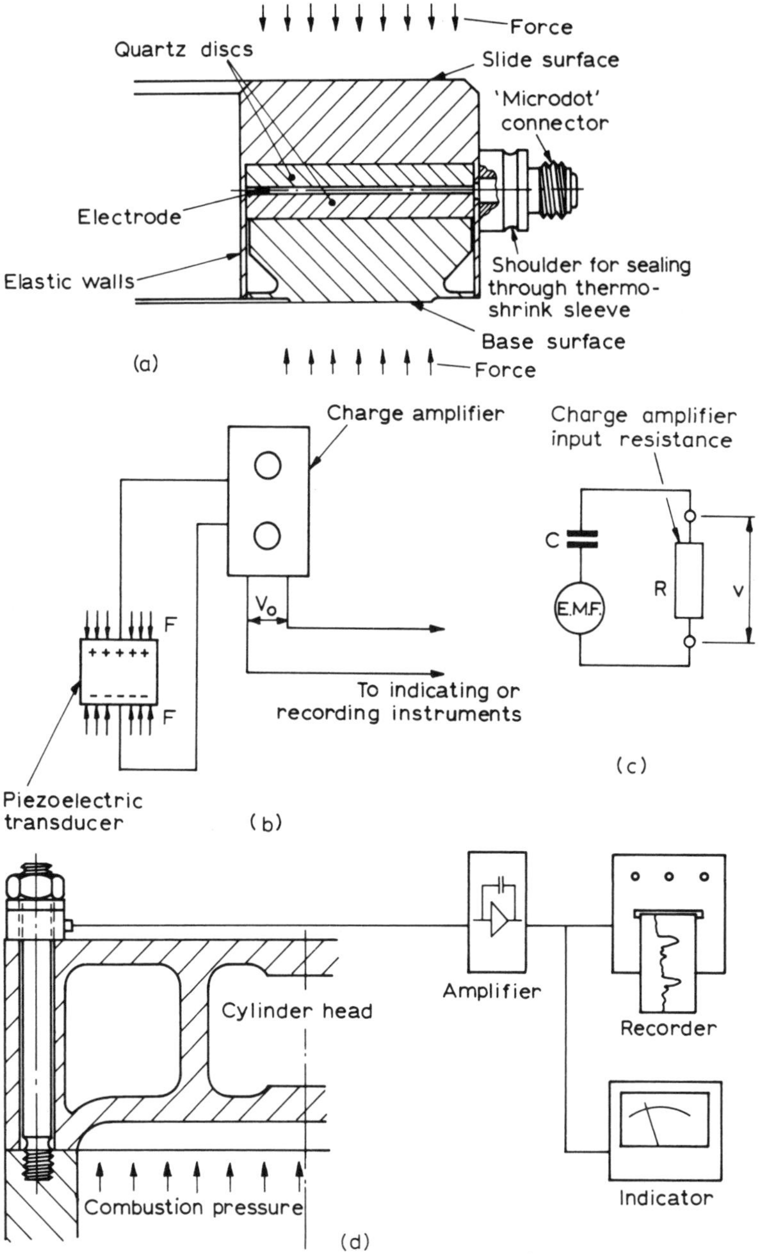

Fig. 3.3 Piezoelectric force-transducer and its application.
(a) Diagrammatic section of a quartz load washer.
(d) Measurement of force in a cylinder-head stud.

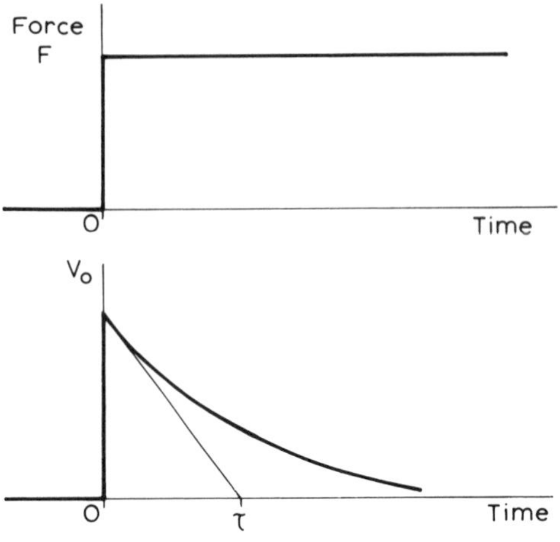

Fig. 3.4

duration of time depends on the particular transducer, some having decay of the order of 5% in 60 minutes, others decaying more rapidly, but in general they are more suited to very short term measurements, or for the measurement of dynamic forces. On many charge amplifiers, a switch with a *long* and a *short* position enables one of two different R values to be chosen, varying the time constant (τ). The short setting would be used for fluctuating forces, the long setting for static or slowly changing forces. When tested in a short-time test, a typical system shows a proportional relationship between the applied force (F) and the charge amplifier output voltage (V_o), as shown in Fig. 3.5.

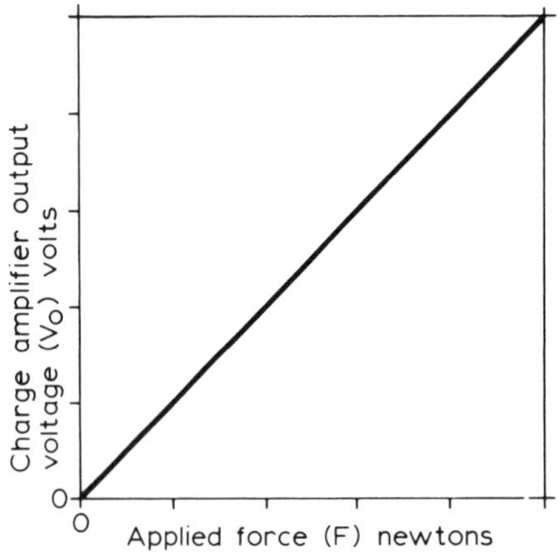

Fig. 3.5 Proportional relationship between input and output of a force-measuring system.

The sensitivity of the transducer plus charge amplifier system is:

$$\text{sensitivity} = \frac{\text{change of } V_o}{\text{change of } F} = \frac{\delta V_o}{\delta F} \quad \text{(volts/newton)}$$

Piezoelectric systems are robust and reliable, although care is necessary in screening cables, and maintaining electrical insulation.

3.2 Electrical-resistance strain gauges

When an electrical conductor is strained, it is found that a change of its resistance occurs, and the phenomenon is used to measure strain. If the unstrained resistance of a conductor is R, and due to a strain ε this changes by δR, then the strain may be calculated using the equation:

$$F\varepsilon = \frac{\delta R}{R}$$

or

$$\varepsilon = \frac{\delta R}{R} \times \frac{1}{F} \qquad (3.2)$$

F is the *strain sensitivity factor*, or for a gauge, the *gauge factor*, and a common value of this is 2, although it may vary from -12 for nickel, to 5 for iridium-platinum alloy. It should be noted that F has no units, being (fractional change of resistance)/(fractional change of length).

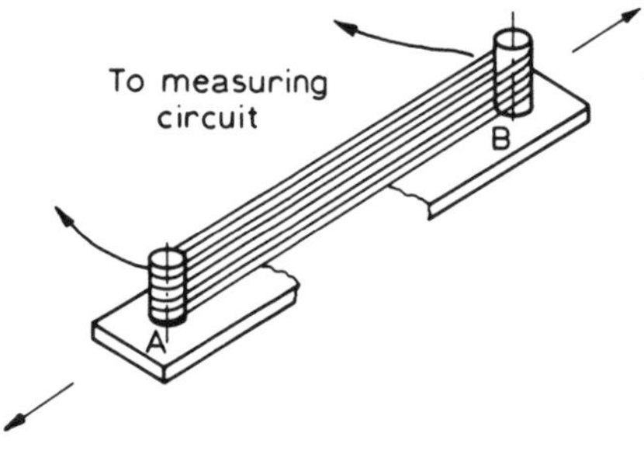

Fig. 3.6

Strain gauges may be of unbonded type, when thin wires of conductor may be arranged in a transducer in a way such as shown in Fig. 3.6. Movement apart of the points A and B causes tensile strain in the resistance wire, and hence an increase of its resistance. Most electrical strain gauges are of bonded type, that is they are bonded on to the surface whose strain is to be measured. Mounted in this way, they can measure compressive strain, causing a decrease of resistance, as well as tensile strain. Bonded gauges are of two main types, i.e. *wire and foil.* Wire gauges consist of a grid formed from very fine wire, and bonded to a stiff paper backing. Foil gauges are chemically etched from very thin metal foil, again bonded to a backing sheet, usually of thin plastic. Exploded and assembled views of both types are shown in Fig. 3.7.

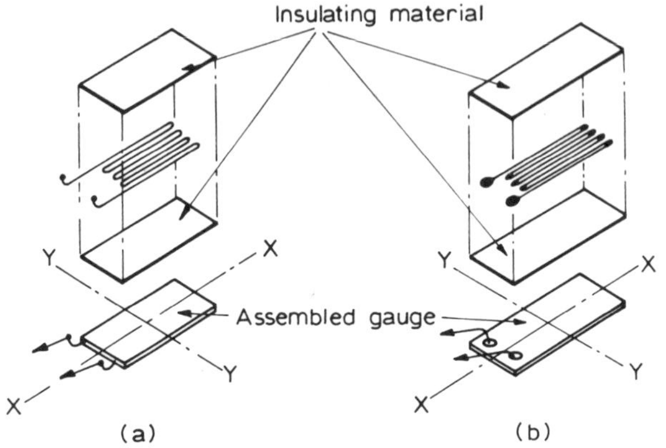

Fig. 3.7 Electrical-resistance strain-gauges: (a) Wire gauge (b) Foil gauge.

When a solid is stretched in tension, it reduces in size laterally, i.e. it has negative strain of about 0.3 of the positive longitudinal strain (0.3 is the value of *Poisson's ratio*). The end loops of a strain gauge suffer a change of resistance due to this negative lateral strain in the tested component, introducing an error. The effect is referred to as *cross-sensitivity*. In the foil gauges it is easy during manufacture to leave the end loops wide as shown Fig. 3.7(b), thus reducing the cross-sensitivity considerably.

The bonded strain gauge has a change of resistance because of the strain in its wire or foil element, but we are aiming to measure the strain of the material to which it is attached. Hence the strain of the gauge must be as nearly as possible the strain of the material, and to do this the gauge backing, either paper or plastic, must be bonded as closely as possible. If the adhesive is too thick, the strain of the gauge will be less than the strain of the material to which it is bonded. Fig. 3.8 illustrates a bonded strain gauge.

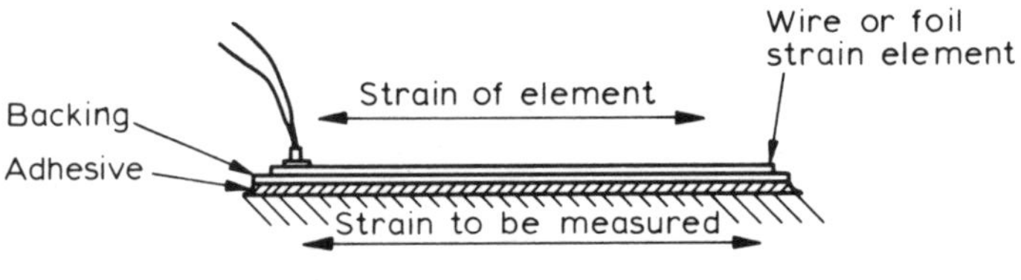

Fig. 3.8 Enlarged cross-section of a bonded strain-gauge.

Gauges may be made in quite large sizes, and down to about 2 mm in length. The very small sizes are more difficult to bond securely into a predetermined position, correctly aligned to measure strain in the required direction, but are needed where the strain is changing considerably in a short distance, such as in a fillet radius. It also requires a good technique to solder electrical connections on to the tabs of small gauges.

Different adhesives are available for bonding the various backing materials to a variety of surfaces, and it is advisable to follow the supplier's instructions in each case. However, the following general rules may be applied:

(a) clean the material which is to receive the gauge, so that it is free of oxides, grease or other contaminants

(b) clean the gauge surface to be bonded, using a suitable solvent

(c) apply adhesive evenly, apply the gauge to the material, and press firmly in place, removing any trapped air bubbles, and check the gauge for alignment

(d) allow the adhesive to cure for a suitable period before soldering on connections

(e) when dry, protect from the atmosphere with a suitable covering medium as recommended by the manufacturer.

Errors may occur if the adhesive thickness is excessive, and may also be caused due to different rates of thermal expansion of the materials of the component and of the gauge, as the temperature changes. If, for example, the temperature rises, and the gauge material would normally expand more than the component material, but cannot do so because it is bonded to the component, then this produces compressive strain in the gauge, which would be indicated in error as compressive strain in the component. One way of reducing this is by matching the thermal expansion co-efficients of the gauge and the component. Such gauges are termed *self-compensating*. A further method of temperature compensation is described in Chapter 4.

3.3 Thermistors

Thermistors consist of small pieces of *semiconductor* material made by sintering mixtures of metallic oxides of manganese, nickel, copper, cobalt, iron etc. The electrical resistance of a thermistor changes considerably with temperature, typically about ten times as much as the platinum or nickel used in resistance thermometers. Also, as temperature increases, the resistance of most thermistors reduces whereas the resistance of most metals increases. The large change of resistance with temperature makes the thermistor very suitable as a temperature transducer. It may be used to give a direct reading or recording of temperature, or it may be used in a control system to maintain a

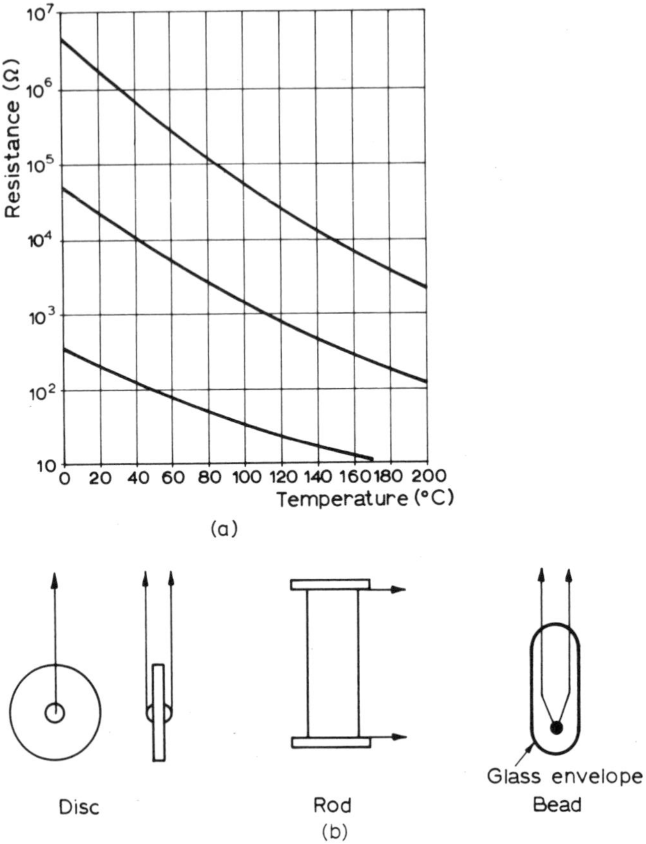

Fig. 3.9 (a) Typical R/T curves for thermistors.
(b) Typical thermistor forms.

temperature at a set value. Typical resistance/temperature curves are shown in Fig. 3.9(a).

The thermistor material has a very high resistance, and this enables very small transducers to be manufactured, in forms such as discs, rods, beads etc. Typical thermistor forms are shown in Fig. 3.9(b). The small mass of many of the thermistors means that they heat up or cool down very quickly, i.e. they have a good *response*, and this is a very advantageous feature in measurement and control systems. Since they have a large change in output, i.e. of resistance, for a small change in input, i.e. temperature, then they have a high sensitivity, another very advantageous feature. One disadvantage they suffer is that the change of resistance is not equal for equal changes of temperature, i.e. they are not linear, and this is shown by the curves of Fig. 3.9(a).

3.4 The l.v.d.t. displacement transducer

When an alternating e.m.f. of frequency f is applied to a coil A wound round an iron core as shown in Fig. 3.10(a), then an alternating e.m.f. at the same frequency is induced in coil B, wound round the same core. The amplitude (V_o) of the output e.m.f. depends on:

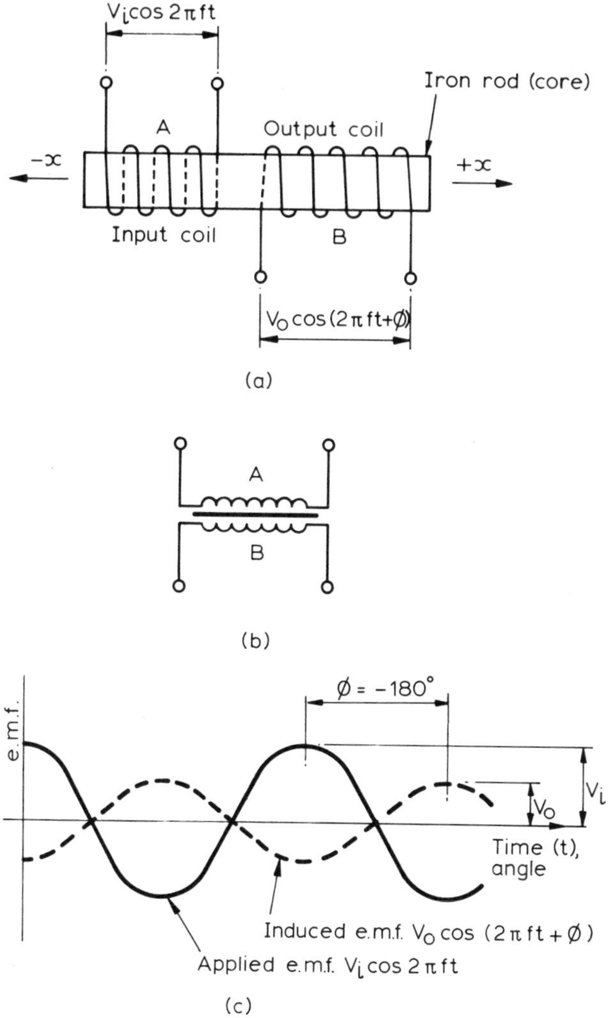

Fig. 3.10 Mutual inductance.
(a) The transformer effect.
(b) Symbol representation on circuit diagrams.
(c) Input and output e.m.f. relationships.

(a) the amplitude (V_i) of the input e.m.f.
(b) the number of turns in the coils A and B
(c) the amount of magnetic coupling, between A and B, provided by the core.

Movement of the rod in the $+x$ or $-x$ directions alters the amount of coupling, and hence the value of V_o for a given V_i. The output waveform lags the input waveform by one half-wavelength, i.e. ϕ is $-180°$.

The principle is used in a very useful displacement measuring instrument, the *linear variable differential transformer* (l.v.d.t.). A typical arrangement of a simple type is shown in Fig. 3.11 (a). The symbol shown in (b) represents a l.v.d.t. on circuit diagrams. There is an input coil A, and two output coils B and C connected in series. When the core is in the central position the coupling A to B is the same as A to C, giving identical induced e.m.f.s in B and C. Since the coils are wound so that these e.m.f.s oppose each other, they cancel out, and the output voltage at this position is zero, as shown in Fig. 3.12. When the core is moved to the left,

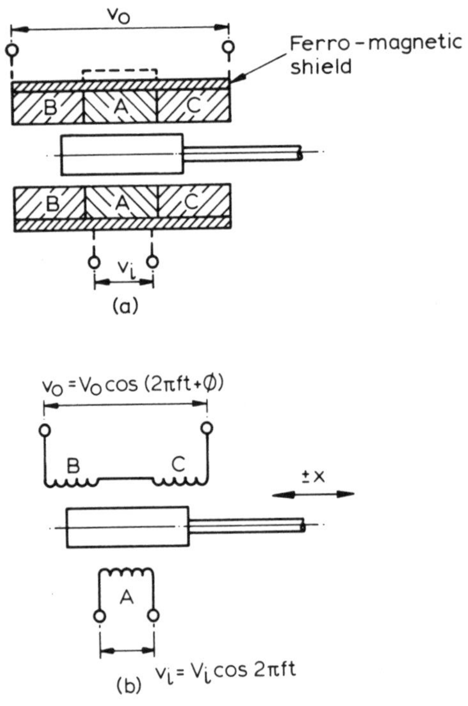

Fig. 3.11 Linear-variable-differential-transformer
(a) Cross-section.
(b) Circuit.

position Y, coupling increases between A and B, and reduces between A and C. There is now an output which lags the input by 90°.

When the core is displaced to the right by the same amount from 0, position Z, the e.m.f. induced in C is increased, and that in B reduced. The output waveform is identical with that of position Y, except that its phase is now 90° ahead of the input. Hence to distinguish whether or not an output voltage indicates a $+x$ or $-x$ displacement, the phase must be determined.

The alternating e.m.f. applied to the l.v.d.t. is referred to as a *carrier signal*. To enable the output from the l.v.d.t. to be read on a d.c. meter, the output must be *demodulated*, i.e. the carrier wave removed, leaving only the amplitude (V_0) of the output voltage. Fig. 3.13 shows schematically a signal conditioning system for doing this, the output from this being a direct e.m.f. proportional to displacement, as indicated.

To simplify the user's task in applying an l.v.d.t. to a measurement system, an electronic signal conditioning system such as that illustrated

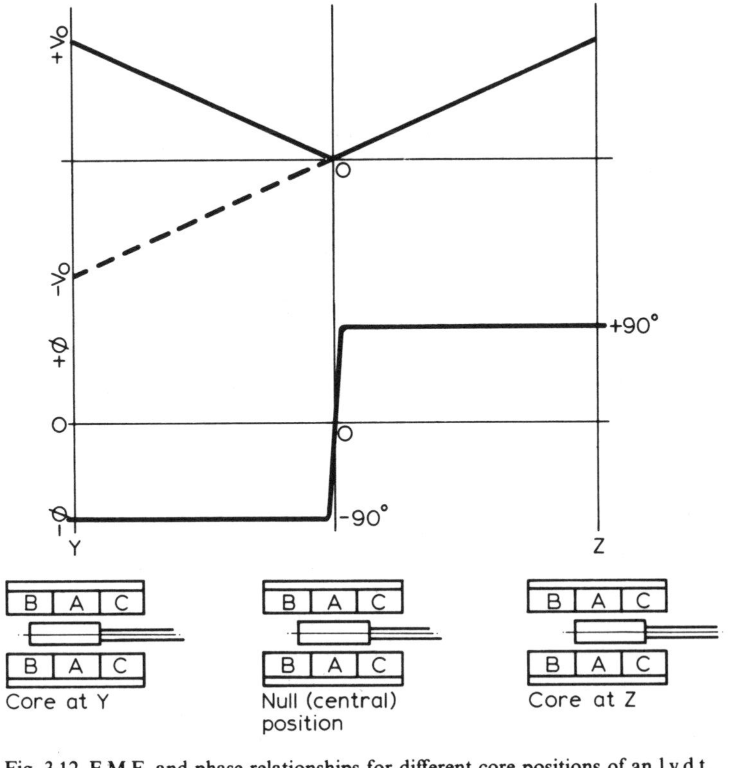

Fig. 3.12 E.M.F. and phase relationships for different core positions of an l.v.d.t.

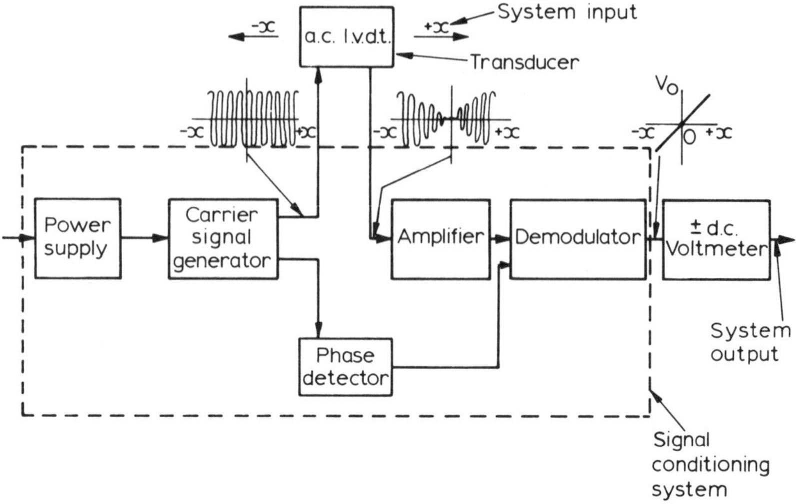

Fig. 3.13. An a.c. l.v.d.t. displacement-measuring system.

in Fig. 3.13 may be miniaturised and incorporated into the transducer body. The user supplies the transducer with a d.c. input, and the d.c. output is proportional to the core displacement, as with the a.c.l.v.d.t. The d.c.l.v.d.t. is thus used in exactly the same way as a resistance-type displacement transducer (see Exercise 2.10.1). Care must be taken to supply a constant d.c. input, or fluctuations in supply voltage may be interpreted as displacements of the core, in either the a.c. or the d.c. versions.

L.V.D.T.s may be made to measure very small displacements, such as ± 1 mm, or much longer displacements. The applications of these transducers are limited only by the ingenuity of the user. Reference 3 gives detailed information on the construction and application of l.v.d.t.s of various types.

3.5 Light-sensitive transducers

Hot surfaces such as those of a heated filament, a furnace, or the sun, emit electromagnetic radiation over a wide range of frequencies. The narrow band of these frequencies to which the human eye is sensitive (those of wavelengths 0.4 to 0.7 μm) we call visible light. Many types of transducer are available which respond to light, and some respond to ultra-violet and infra-red radiation, just outside the visible range. In industry there are many existing and potential applications for these, both in manufactured products for all spheres of use, and also in the equipment to produce them.

Many light-sensitive transducers use the properties of semiconductor materials for their operation. The energy of light rays falling on a semiconductor, or on semiconductors forming a diode or a transistor, may generate a small e.m.f. (the *photovoltaic effect*) produce a change in resistance (the *photoconductive effect*) or cause a current to flow (the *photoelectric effect*).

3.5.1 Photo-voltaic transducer

The *selenium cell* shown in Fig. 3.14 is the transducer used in many light meters. It does not need external power. The energy of the light falling on the selenium layer after passing through the thin metal film causes electrons to be released. These are collected by the metal collecting ring and pass round the external circuit. The current measured by the milliammeter increases with the illumination falling on the cell. The main disadvantage of this type of transducer is its low sensitivity.

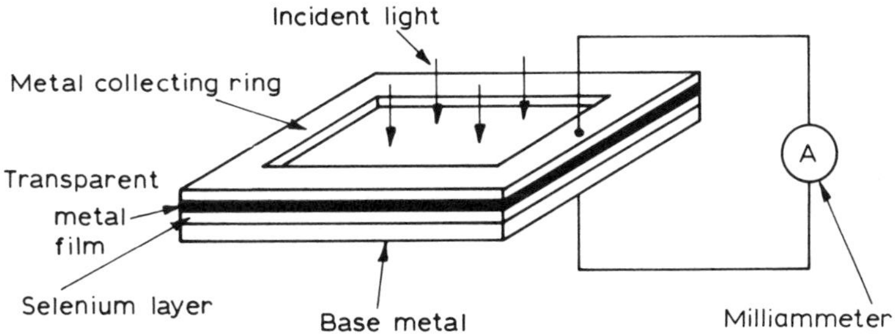

Fig. 3.14 Selenium cell in light meter.

3.5.2 Photoconductive transducer

An example of this type is shown in Fig. 3.15. The semiconductor material, commonly cadmium sulphide (CdS), but several others are used, is in the form of a thin film on a backing. Metal electrodes with interlocking fingers are deposited onto the semiconductor, and an e.m.f. is applied to these. With no incident light, the resistance is very high and current very small. With incident light, the resistance reduces, and the current increases as the illumination increases. The device is more sensitive than the photovoltaic cell described, and is widely used in cameras and other photographic equipment. Where the input is a fluctuating light, this transducer has a limit of about 100 Hz, after which it will not respond rapidly enough.

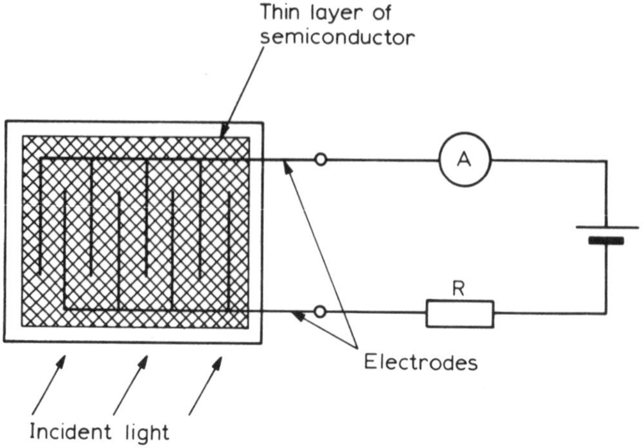

Fig. 3.15 Photoconductive transducer and circuit.

3.5.3 Photodiode and phototransistor transducers

Fig. 3.16 shows a light-sensitive semiconductor diode, i.e. a *photodiode* transducer, and its circuit. The photodiode consists of two types of semiconductor material fused together during manufacture. The transducer consists of a light-tight casing with a lens in the end which focusses the light rays on to the junction of a photodiode. With no light, a very small current flows. With light, increase in current is proportional to the illumination.

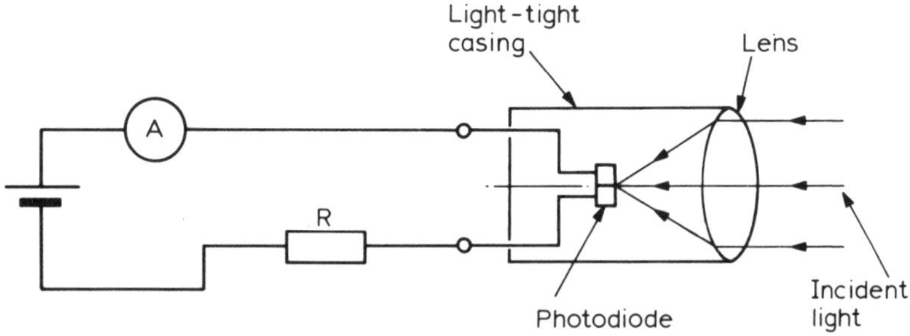

Fig. 3.16 Photodiode transducer and circuit.

Fig. 3.17 shows a phototransistor and circuit. In an ordinary transistor, the voltage applied across the emitter and the base controls the current i_e through the emitter, and light is kept out. In the phototransistor, light is allowed to fall on the base, and the light energy controls the current i_e. The voltage v_{eb} may be used to provide zeroing or biasing facilities.

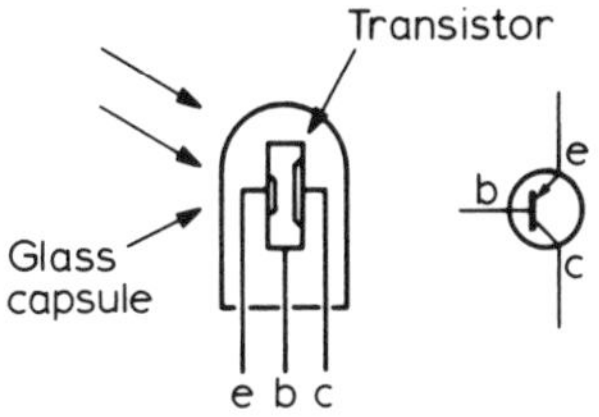

Fig. 3.17 Phototransistor and circuit.

Both photodiodes and phototransistors have a very rapid response. They may be made into very small and reliable light-sensitive transducers which can be very inexpensive, and they find numerous applications. A particularly neat and easily applied device is shown in Fig. 3.18. Mounted in one slotted block are a light source, typically a light-emitting diode (l.e.d.), the light from this illuminating a photodiode. An application of this to measure the speed of rotation of a shaft would necessitate a slotted opaque disc being attached to the shaft. As the shaft rotates, the slots cause alternate illumination and non-illumination of the photodiode, giving pulses of current. The output would be connected to a frequency meter, the measured frequency being proportional to rotational speed. Another application of l.e.d. and photodiode together, in a bank of eight pairs, is in the tape reading head for reading punched tape such as is used in numerically controlled machines, computers etc. In these examples, the transducers are functioning as light-operated switches, and this is typical of many other applications.

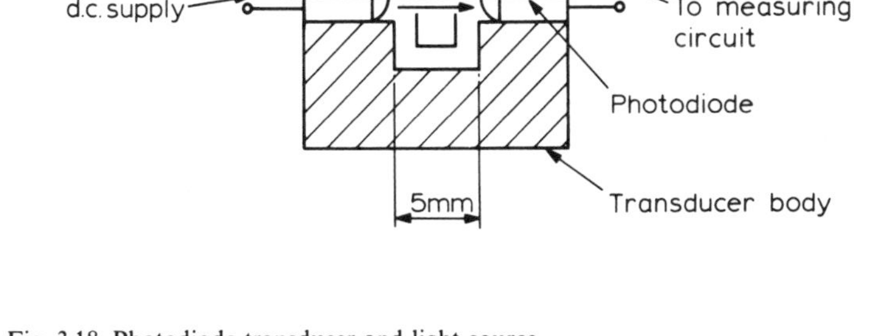

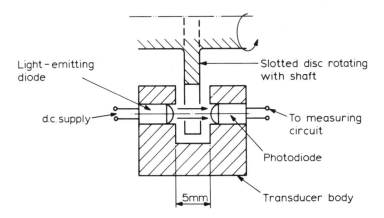

Fig. 3.18 Photodiode transducer and light source.

3.6 Worked examples

3.6.1 A spring balance, graduated 0–50 N over a scale length of 100 mm, was calibrated using laboratory masses stated by their manufacturer to be within ±0.1 % of their marked values. The following readings were taken:

mass (kg)	0.00	1.00	2.00	3.00	4.00	5.00
force reading (N)	0.0	9.5	19.5	30.0	39.5	49.0

Determine (a) the accuracy % f.s.d. of the balance
(b) the sensitivity of the balance
(c) the rate (k) of the spring.

(a) The error at each point is found by subtracting the force applied from the force reading, as shown in the following table, assuming g is the standard value of 9.80665 m/s^2:

Mass	(kg)	0.00	1.00	2.00	3.00	4.00	5.00
Force reading	(N)	0.0	9.5	19.5	30.0	39.5	49.0
Applied force	(N)	0.0	9.81	19.61	29.42	39.23	49.03
Error	(N)	0.0	−0.3	−0.1	0.6	0.3	0.0

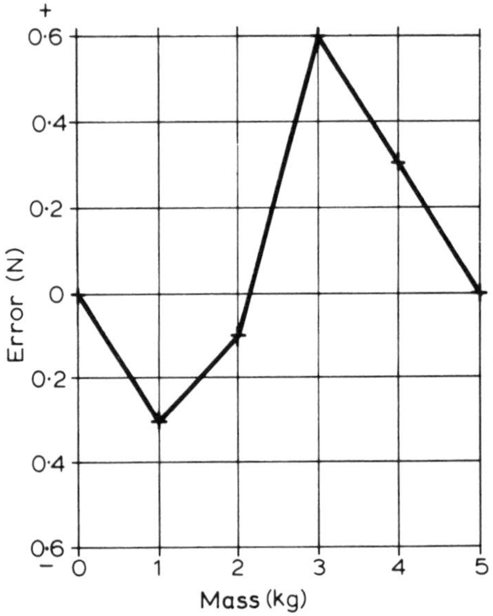

Fig. 3.19

The errors are shown in Fig. 3.19 plotted against the mass. The maximum positive error is 0.6 N, the maximum negative error 0.3 N. Adjustment of the zero, increasing the no load reading to 0.2 N approx, would give all errors within a band ± 0.5 N from the standard value. Then the accuracy may be calculated:

$$\text{accuracy \% f.s.d.} = \frac{\pm 0.5}{50} \times 100\,\%$$
$$= \pm 1\,\%$$

The standard against which the balance is calibrated is seen to be ten times as accurate as the balance.

(b)
$$\text{Sensitivity} = \frac{\text{output change}}{\text{input change}}$$
$$= \frac{100\,\text{mm}}{50\,\text{N}}$$
$$= 2\,\text{mm/N}$$

(c)
$$\text{Spring rate } (k) = \text{force to extend the spring by unit length}$$
$$= \frac{50\,\text{N}}{0.100\,\text{m}}$$
$$= 500\,\text{N/m}$$

3.6.2 The force on a cutting tool was tested using a dynamometer incorporating a simply-supported beam, as shown in Fig. 3.20. The dial

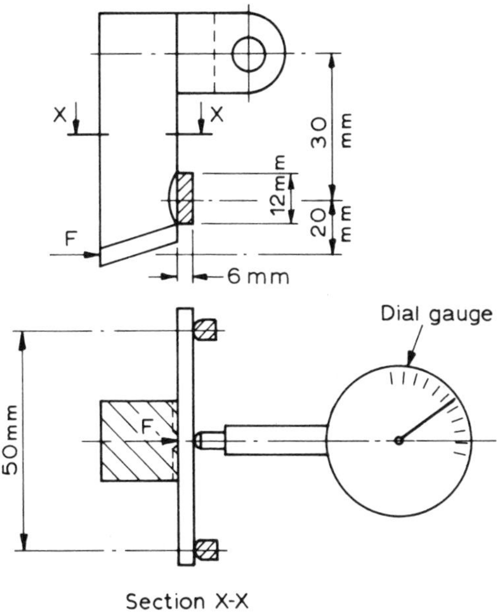

Fig. 3.20 Simply-supported beam as elastic-deflection element.

gauge indicated a deflection of the mid-point of the beam fluctuating between 0.05 and 0.06 mm during a test cut. The following readings were taken during a calibration test using a Hounsfield Tensometer as the standard:

Applied force	(N)	0	200	400	600	800	1000
Beam deflection	(mm)	0	0.020	0.040	0.060	0.075	0.095

Determine (a) the sensitivity of the dynamometer,
(b) the mean cutting force and its range of fluctuation.

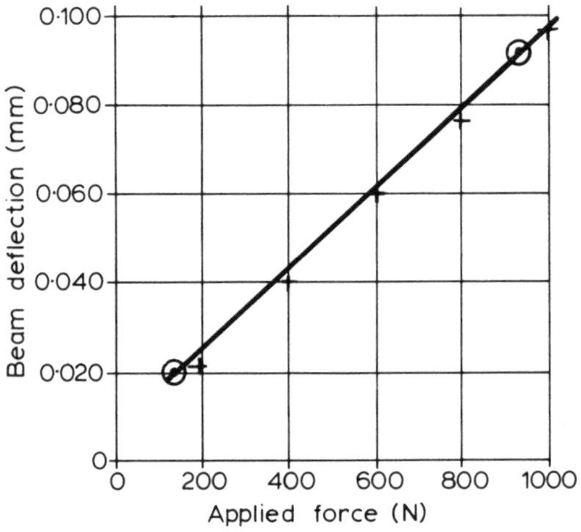

Fig. 3.21

Fig. 3.21 shows the points plotted on x-y axes, and the best straight line drawn through (estimated by eye). Using the points marked ⊙ the sensitivity is calculated.

(a)
$$\text{Sensitivity} = \frac{\text{change of beam deflection}}{\text{change of force } F}$$

$$= \frac{0.090 - 0.020}{940 - 180} \frac{\text{mm}}{\text{N}}$$

$$= 92 \times 10^{-6} \text{ mm/N}$$

It should be noted however, that the graph line does not pass through 0, 0, and hence care should be taken if this value is being used to find a force from a deflection value.

(b) From the graph, deflections of 0.050 mm and 0.060 mm correspond to forces of 500 N and 620 N respectively. Hence the cutting force is fluctuating between these values, with a mean of 560 N.

3.6.3 A bonded strain gauge has a gauge factor of 2.10 and a resistance of 99.85 Ω. Calculate the strain in the gauge when the resistance changes to 100.04 Ω.

$$\text{Change of resistance } (\delta R) = 100.04 - 99.85 = 0.19\,\Omega$$

$$\text{Eqn. 3.2 gives strain } (\varepsilon) = \frac{\delta R}{R} \times \frac{1}{F} = \frac{0.19}{99.85} \times \frac{1}{2.10} = 0.91 \times 10^{-3}$$

The strain in the material to which the gauge is bonded should be the same value, if the bonding is correct.

3.6.4 A strain gauge having a temperature co-efficient of linear expansion of $16 \times 10^{-6}\,°C^{-1}$ is bonded to a component of Duralumin, for which the co-efficient of linear expansion is $23 \times 10^{-6}\,°C^{-1}$. Calculate how much the strain appears to change when the temperature of the component rises by 80°C.

Let l be the length of gauge.

$$\text{Expansion of Duralumin} = l \times 23 \times 10^{-6} \times 80 = 1840l \times 10^{-6}$$

$$\text{expansion of gauge} = l \times 16 \times 10^{-6} \times 80 = 1280l \times 10^{-6}$$

Hence the gauge is stretched by

$$x = (1840 - 1280)l \times 10^{-6}$$
$$x = 560l \times 10^{-6}$$

$$\text{strain of gauge } (\varepsilon) = \frac{x}{l} = \frac{560l \times 10^{-6}}{l} = 0.56 \times 10^{-3}$$

(Example 4.5.10 also covers this topic.)

This is a large value, and without some kind of correction, the strain measurements made under varying temperature conditions would be hopelessly inaccurate.

3.6.5 A thermistor is to be chosen from one of the three whose characteristics are shown in Fig. 3.9(a). It is to measure temperatures between 80 and 120°C and the resistance at 100°C should be as near to 1 kΩ as possible. Select one, and calculate its approximate sensitivity over the required range.

The middle curve shows a resistance of just over 1 kΩ at 100°C. At 80°C the approximate resistance is 1.3 kΩ, and at 120°C, 0.8 kΩ. Hence the approximate sensitivity is given by:

$$\frac{0.8-1.3}{120-80} \times 10^{3} = -12\ \Omega/^{\circ}\mathrm{C}$$

This is a much higher sensitivity than that of a metal resistance element, and leads to correspondingly sensitive measurement and control systems.

3.7 Tutorial and practical work

3.7.1 Devise a method of measuring the force on the spindle of a dial test indicator (possibly using a beam balance?) at different values of deflection. Plot the force against deflection values and determine the law connecting the two.

3.7.2 Examine tool force and torque dynamometers and note how they work. Devise and carry out a calibration test on one, and determine its sensitivity.

3.7.3 Devise a dynamometer to measure the cutting force on a lathe tool using, for example, beam deflection or a piezoelectric force transducer.

3.7.4 Devise a way of using a piezoelectric force washer to measure both the compressive *and* the tensile forces in a moving link in a machine.

3.7.5 Examine strain gauges available to you, and from the manufacturers literature determine their recommended bonding procedure.

3.7.6 Measure the resistance of a thermistor transducer at different temperatures, and plot a graph of the readings.

3.7.7 Select a suitable l.v.d.t. from manufacturers lists and make a sketch design incorporating it into one of the following:

(a) an extensometer for tensile testing
(b) a size comparator
(c) a system to measure the mass of components
(d) a measuring system of your own choice.

Determine the sensitivity of the system in each case.

3.7.8 Examine light-sensitive transducers available, and the manufacturers' circuit diagrams for them. Devise a system incorporating one of them to do one of the following:

(a) count the number of holes rotation of a dividing-head
(b) count the number of small components coming down a chute
(c) indicate accept/reject in a simple size gauge
(d) measure the speed of a model vehicle on a laboratory air cushion track
(e) measure the rotational speed of an engine shaft.

3.8 Exercises

3.8.1 (a) The following table shows values of error from the manufacturer's calibration chart, relating to the beams of a Hounsfield Tensometer.

Percentage of full load	*Beam*						
	20 kN	10 kN	5 kN	2.5 kN	1.2 kN	600 N	300 N
0	0	0	0	0	0	0	0
10	+0.2	+0.2	+0.2	+0.2	+0.2	+0.2	+0.2
20	+0.2	+0.2	+0.2	+0.2	+0.1	+0.2	+0.2
30	+0.2	+0.2	+0.2	+0.2	+0.1	+0.1	+0.1
40	+0.1	+0.1	+0.2	+0.2	+0.1	+0.1	+0.1
50	+0.1	+0.1	+0.1	+0.1	+0.1	+0.1	+0.1
60	0	+0.1	+0.1	+0.1	0	+0.1	+0.1
70	0	0	+0.1	+0.1	0	+0.1	+0.1
80	0	0	+0.1	0	0	+0.1	+0.1
90	−0.1	0	0	0	−0.1	+0.1	+0.1
full load	−0.2	−0.1	0	−0.1	−0.2	+0.1	0

Determine, for each beam, the (i) accuracy percentage f.s.d.,
(ii) accuracy percentage point value.

(b) Give the reason why, in selecting a beam to test a given material, care should be taken to use a beam with stiffness neither too large or too small.

3.8.2 A piezoelectric force-washer system similar to that shown in Fig. 3.3 was calibrated using a Hounsfield tensometer. The following output voltages were recorded for the force values shown, taken immediately the force was applied.

Applied force	(N)	3 000	6 000	9 000	12 000	15 000
Output voltage	(V)	0.28	0.61	0.92	1.20	1.49

Determine (a) the sensitivity of the system,
(b) the accuracy percentage f.s.d.
(c) the accuracy percentage point value.

3.8.3 The maximum stress allowable in a steel component in tension is 100 MPa, and the modulus of elasticity of the material is 200 GPa. Calculate the maximum strain that will occur due to this stress, and also the change of resistance of a strain gauge of resistance 99.89 Ω and gauge factor 2.15 which is bonded to the surface, axially in line with the stress.

3.8.4 Calculate the *apparent* changes of strain and stress occuring in the steel component of Exercise 3.8.3 due to a temperature change from 20°C to 80°C if there is no temperature compensation, and the temperature co-efficients of linear expansion are 12×10^{-6} and $16 \times 10^{-6}\,°C^{-1}$ for steel and the strain gauge respectively.

3.8.5 A very sensitive temperature transducer is required to measure in the range 20°C to 40°C. Choose the most suitable one of those whose characteristics are shown in Fig. 3.9(a). State its mid-temperature-range resistance and calculate its approximate sensitivity, for the required range.

4 *Signal-conditioning elements*

The quantity being measured by an instrument or instrument system is sensed by the *primary transducer*. The transducer gives out a signal which is a function of its input signal, i.e. $\theta_o = f(\theta_i)$. It is desirable that $f(\theta_i)$ is $K\theta_i$, a simple linear relationship, but this does not apply in all cases. However, this output signal may be too small to drive indicating, recording or control elements directly, or it may be in a form which is not convenient for transmitting to other parts of the system. It also may be a different physical quantity from the output of other primary transducers in the system. For these reasons, the signal from the primary transducer is frequently *conditioned*, i.e., altered to a more suitable form. Typical elements which condition a signal are secondary transducers, amplifiers, electrical bridges, potentiometers, modulators and demodulators. Some of these conditioning elements are described in this chapter.

4.1 Secondary transducers

The output from some primary transducer may be a displacement, for example the displacement of a Bourdon tube due to applied pressure. This may be converted by a secondary transducer to a voltage. One device which could do this is the l.v.d.t., described in Section 3.4.

4.2 Amplifying elements

Amplification may be defined as increasing the magnitude of the signal without changing the kind of signal, though this is not strictly true in all cases. Amplification may be carried out by mechanical, fluid, optical, electrical devices etc., or by a combination of these.

4.2.1 Mechanical amplification

The simple lever device shown in Fig. 4.1(a) increases a small input movement (x) to give an amplified movement (X) on the scale. The operation of a pair of spur gears as in Fig. 4.1(b) is very similar, but the input and output quantities are continuous rotations (θ_i and θ_o).

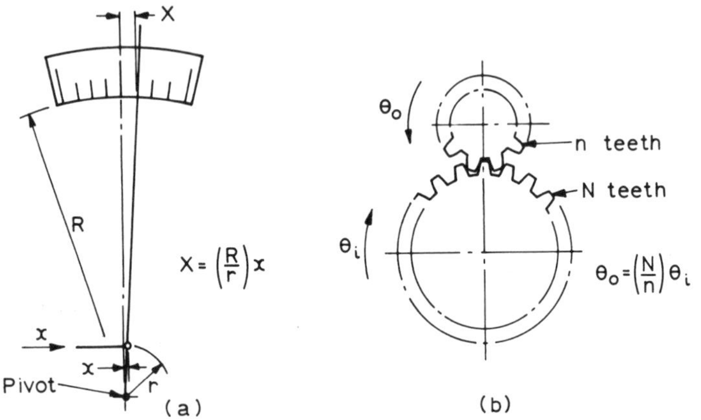

Fig. 4.1

Increased amplification may be obtained by using compound lever and compound gear train systems. In Fig. 4.2(a), the input signal, movement x_1, causes a rotation of the lever O_1A, and the movement (x_2) of A is transmitted to the second lever by a link AB. The movement (x_2) of AB is increased by the second lever O_2C to give an amplified output signal, movement (x_4). Similarly, in the compound gear train in Fig. 4.2(b) the amplification is carried out in two stages, and the signals are rotations which may be continuous.

Fig. 4.3 illustrates the Huggenberger extensometer, which uses a compound lever system to amplify the very small change of the gauge length due to the strain of the material to which it is attached. The instrument is clamped on to the material with sufficient force to ensure that the points A and B engage into the surface, and move with the surface as it strains. Point A is rigidly attached to the frame of the instrument, point B is at the end of lever L which is pivoted at P_1. For tensile strain as shown, the top of lever L moves to the left. The connecting link C, held in contact with the lever pivots P_2 and P_3 by the spring S, transfers the movement of P_2 on L to P_3 on the pointer. The pointer rotates about a fixed pivot P_4 on the frame of the instrument, and its end moves to the left along the strain scale. Since the ratios P_1P_2/P_1B and P_4D/P_4P_3 are both large, the movement of the pointer on the scale is much greater than the increase of the gauge length. A typical amplifi-

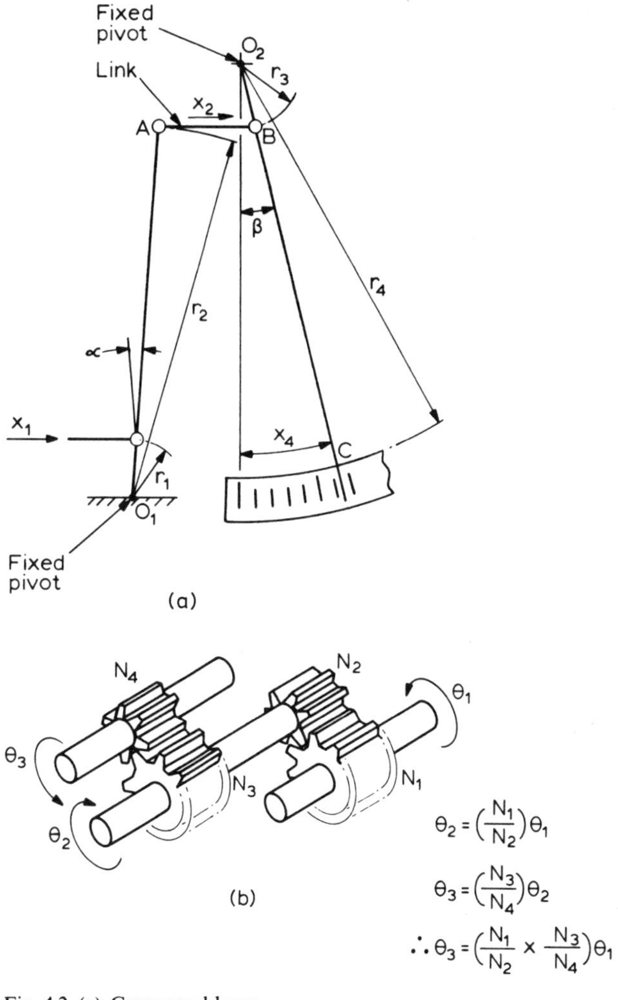

Fig. 4.2 (a) Compound lever.
(b) Compound gear train.

cation is 1000. Example 4.5.3 shows the method of calculating a particular value. It should be appreciated, however, that instruments are calibrated, and in the instrument case of each Huggenberger extensometer the calibration constant (n) is given. Thus:

$$\text{strain} = \text{change of scale reading}/n$$

Fig. 4.4 illustrates the mechanism of a dial gauge (also known as dial indicator or dial test-indicator). When the plunger A is displaced by a small amount (x), the rack gear B, engaged with spur gear C causes the

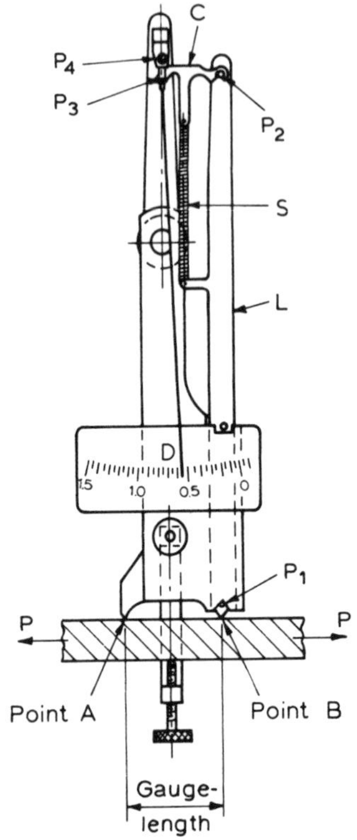

Fig. 4.3 Huggenberger extensometer.

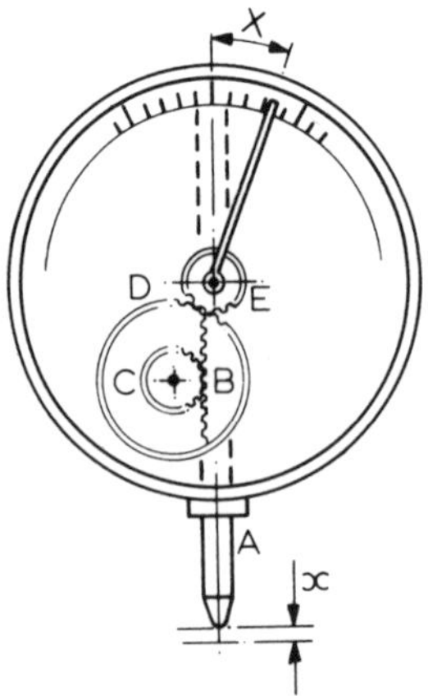

Fig. 4.4 Dial guage mechanism.

latter to rotate. The spur gear D on the same spindle as C is engaged with gear E on the pointer spindle, and the latter is rotated, moving the pointer along the scale by a larger amount (X). The British Standard BS907: 1965, 'Dial Gauges for Linear Measurement' emphasises that means should be taken to eliminate backlash between the gear teeth. One method is the use of a flat spiral spring which loads the teeth in the same direction, irrespective of the position or direction of motion of the plunger (see also Fig. 2.6). Example 4.5.4 shows how the amplification of a dial gauge mechanism may be calculated.

4.2.2 Fluid amplification

Fluid amplification is used very effectively in the Hounsfield tensometer testing machine. The force is applied to a test piece through a steel beam which deflects by a small amount. This deflection is amplified by the displacement of mercury from a cylinder into a glass capillary tube, as shown in Fig. 4.5. If x is the movement of the piston and X the movement of the mercury meniscus in the capillary tube then:

$$\left\{\begin{array}{l}\text{volume of mercury displaced}\\ \text{from cylinder}\end{array}\right\} = \left\{\begin{array}{l}\text{volume increase in}\\ \text{capillary tube}\end{array}\right\}$$

and

$$x \times A = X \times a$$

$$X = \frac{A}{a} \times x$$

and

$$X = \left(\frac{D}{d}\right)^2 x \tag{4.1}$$

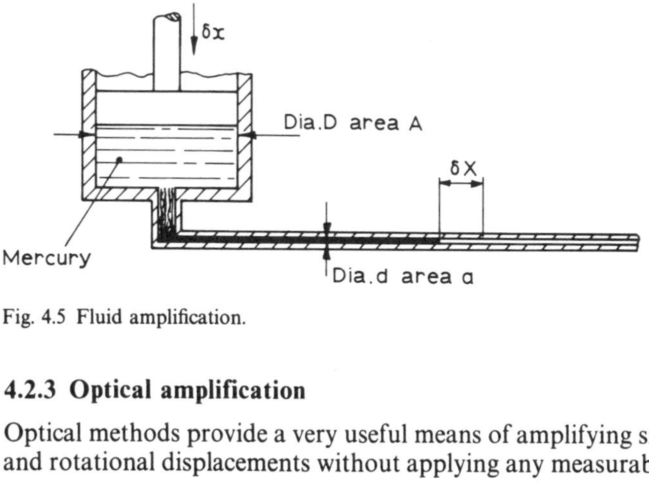

Fig. 4.5 Fluid amplification.

4.2.3 Optical amplification

Optical methods provide a very useful means of amplifying small linear and rotational displacements without applying any measurable force to

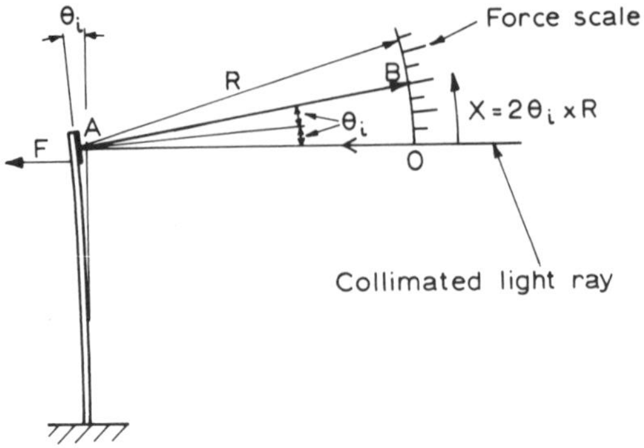

Fig. 4.6 Optical lever.

the displaced element. Fig. 4.6 shows a cantilever sensing the magnitude of the force F, giving as an output signal the slope $\theta = KF$ where K is a constant. Initially, when $F = 0$, the collimated light ray is reflected back by the mirror A along the same path to the scale zero. When the force (F) causes a slope (θ_i) of the end of the cantilever, the outgoing ray OAB is deflected through an angle $2\theta_i$, since both the angles of incidence and reflection at the mirror are equal to θ_i. The radius R may be increased to increase the scale deflection (X). Further mirror surfaces may be added, each one giving a further amplification. The principle may also be found applied in electrical instruments such as the spot galvanometer and the ultra-violet recorder.

4.2.4 Electrical amplifiers

If an a.c. signal is applied to a transformer, an a.c. signal of increased voltage is induced in the secondary coil, although the output power is slightly less than the input power. The effect is widely used, including incorporation into instrument systems.

However, electronic amplifiers are more widely used, and in these a separate power supply is provided so that the output power may exceed the input power if this is required. Fig. 4.7 illustrates the overall features of such an amplifier. The following definitions apply:

$$\text{gain} = \frac{\text{power output}}{\text{power input}} = v_o i_o / v_i i_i$$

$$\text{voltage amplification} = v_o / v_i$$

$$\text{current amplification} = i_o / i_i$$

Amplifiers may be divided into two broad types. D.C. amplifiers are capable of amplifying static, slowly changing or rapid, repetitive input

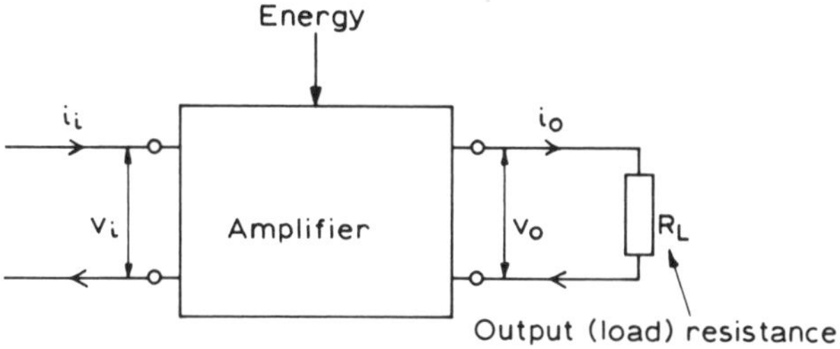

Fig. 4.7 Electrical amplifier.

signals. A.C. amplifiers are only capable of dealing with rapid, repetitive signals, but are usually simpler and cheaper when compared with the d.c. types. For both types of amplifier, their *frequency response* is important. Fig. 4.8 shows a graph of voltage amplification against frequency. It is seen that the v_o/v_i values fall off below and above certain frequencies. The amplifier should be operated within the flat frequency range for minimum distortion of the signal. Charge amplifiers are specially designed to have inputs from transducers whose output signal is an electric charge. Their output is voltage and in general they may be regarded as specialised voltage amplifiers (see Example 4.5.7). Where an amplifier is to drive devices taking current, such as ultra-violet recorders, some chart recorders, spot galvanometers etc., then an amplifier should be chosen which is capable of delivering the current required.

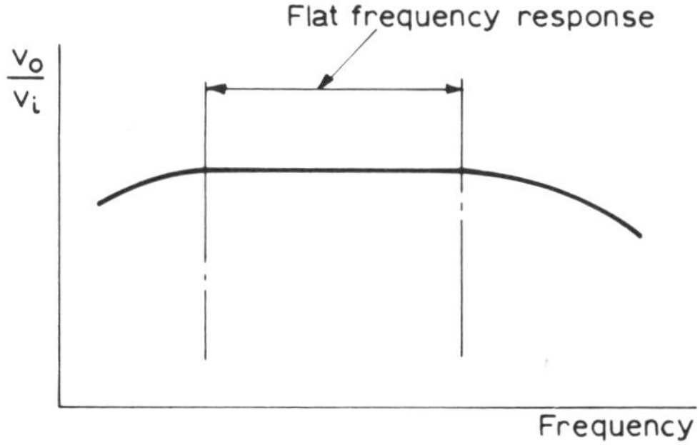

Fig. 4.8 Frequency response.

Amplification may be in several stages; for example there may be a pre-amplifier and then a main amplifier. Amplifiers may be separate units, either dedicated units (i.e. those designed for or incorporated into particular systems) or general purpose amplifiers. Amplifiers are frequently built into other instruments, such as bridge amplifiers, recorders, and oscilloscopes.

D.C. amplifiers used for steady signals, such as those from temperature-sensing transducers (e.g. resistance thermometers or thermocouples) may be fitted with trips. Thus they may be set so that pairs of contacts are made or broken at a set voltage and hence temperature, enabling motors, heaters, valves, etc., to be switched on or off for control purposes, or bells rung for alarm, etc.

4.3 The Wheatstone bridge and its application

For some primary transducers, such as the electrical resistance strain gauge described in Section 3.2, the output is a small change of resistance. A useful instrument for measuring this small resistance change, or for converting it to a voltage or current signal, is the Wheatstone bridge.

4.3.1 Null-type bridge

The null-type bridge is shown in its basic form in Fig. 4.9. The bridge consists of two fixed resistors R_1 and R_2, and a resistance R_4 whose value is to be measured. R_3 is a variable resistor whose value can be varied, and its magnitude precisely known. A constant voltage is applied to the points AC by means of the battery, of e.m.f. E, and the variable resistor. A sensitive galvanometer with a low internal resistance R_G is connected across the points BD. When the galvanometer current is zero, the bridge is *balanced*. This is obtained by varying R_3. At balance, $V_{BD} = 0$ and hence

$$V_{AB} = V_{AD} \quad \text{and} \quad V_{BC} = V_{DC}$$

$$\text{or} \quad I_1 R_1 = I_3 R_3 \quad \text{or} \quad I_2 R_2 = I_4 R_4$$

but $I_1 = I_2$ and $I_3 = I_4$ at balance and therefore

$$I_1 R_1 = I_3 R_3 \tag{4.3}$$

and

$$I_1 R_2 = I_3 R_4 \tag{4.4}$$

Dividing eqn. 4.3 by eqn. 4.4,

$$\frac{R_1}{R_2} = \frac{R_3}{R_4} \quad \text{and} \quad R_4 = \left(\frac{R_2}{R_1}\right) \times R_3 \tag{4.5}$$

This equation enables the value of R_4 to be found if R_1, R_2 and R_3 are known.

Frequently, as in the case of electrical strain gauges, the *change* of resistance due to a change of the measured quantity is required. Consider a strain gauge in a balanced bridge. Due to a strain being applied, its resistance changes from R_4 to $(R_4 + \delta R_4)$, which unbalances the bridge, this being shown by the galvanometer indicating a current flow. The

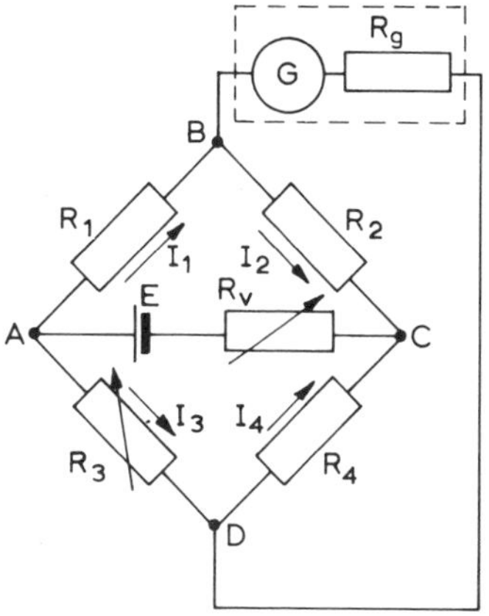

Fig. 4.9 Null-type Wheatstone bridge.

resistor R_3 must be altered to rebalance the bridge, and now becomes $(R_3 + \delta R_3)$. The equation of the bridge at rebalance is:

$$\frac{R_1}{R_2} = \frac{R_3 + \delta R_3}{R_4 + \delta R_4}$$

or

$$R_4 + \delta R_4 = \frac{R_2 R_3}{R_1} + \frac{R_2 \delta R_3}{R_1}$$

But the initial balance gives $\dfrac{R_2 R_3}{R_1} = R_4$

$$\therefore \qquad \delta R_4 = \left(\frac{R_2}{R_1}\right)\delta R_3 \qquad (4.6)$$

Eqn. 4.6 is seen to be of the same form as eqn. 4.5, but uses *changes* of R_3 and R_4.

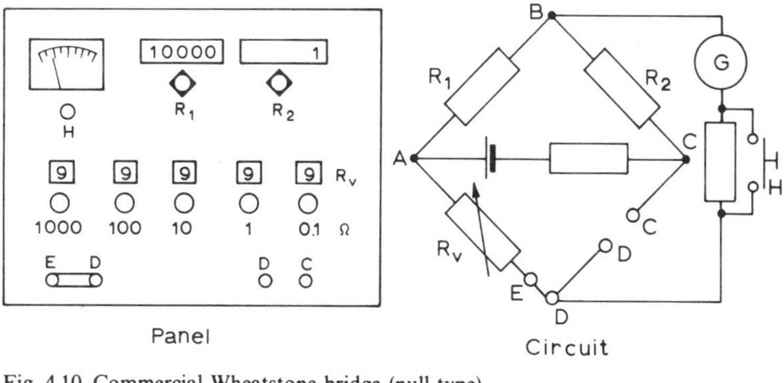

Fig. 4.10 Commercial Wheatstone bridge (null type).

A general purpose commercial bridge as shown in Fig. 4.10 may have R_3 variable up to say 10 000 Ω in 0.1 Ω steps, and also the ratio (R_2/R_1) variable in decade steps from say 10 000 : 1 to 1 : 10 000. This will enable measurements of resistance from 1 Ω to 100 MΩ to be made to five significant figures. Assuming the R_2/R_1 ratios are correct, the percentage accuracy of the measurements can be no better than the percentage accuracy of the set values of R_3. This bridge is not well suited to measure small changes of resistance, and for strain gauge work specialised bridges are used.

Rebalancing a bridge as the measured variable changes can be a laborious and time consuming task, becoming impossible for rapidly changing input signals. Hence the Wheatstone bridge is frequently used as a voltage-sensitive or a current-sensitive bridge, in which cases the small unbalance of the bridge is measured.

4.3.2 Voltage-sensitive bridge

If the galvanometer of Fig. 4.9 is replaced by a high-impedance voltage measuring instrument such as a valve voltmeter or a cathode-ray oscilloscope, or by a high-impedance chart recorder, then negligible current is taken from the points BD when the bridge becomes unbalanced. It may be shown (Ref. 4) that the voltage V_{BD} is nearly proportional to the change of resistance δR_4. Thus, if initially $R_1 = R_2 = R_3 = R_4$ (or very nearly):

$$V_{BD} = \frac{V_{AC}}{4} \times \left(\frac{\delta R_4}{R_4}\right) \tag{4.7}$$

This shows that it is necessary to maintain V_{AC} at the correct value, otherwise its changes may be mistaken for changes in R_4. A convenient instrument for strain measurement is the bridge-amplifier, illustrated in Fig. 4.11. This supplies the direct voltage V_{AC} and controls it to the set value. A pre-amplifier and amplifier with variable amplification settings amplify the small unbalance voltage V_{BD} to a suitable level for indicating or recording instruments.

4.3.3 Current-sensitive bridge

In this variation of the bridge, the small current from points BD operates a galvanometer, e.g. a spot galvanometer for direct strain reading, or the miniature galvanometer of an ultra-violet recorder. The current is approximately proportional to the change of resistance, δR_4. If, initially, $R_1 = R_2 = R_3 = R_4$ (or very nearly) then:

$$\text{galvanometer current } I_g = \frac{V_{AC}}{4KR_4} \times \left(\frac{\delta R_4}{R_4}\right) \tag{4.8}$$

where

$$K = \left(\frac{R_g}{R_4}\right) + 1.$$

Fig. 4.11 Fylde bridge-amplifier.

4.3.4 Strain measurement

Fig. 4.12(a) shows an electrical resistance strain gauge bonded longitudinally to a bar which is to be subjected to tension. The bridge is balanced by adjusting R_3 until the galvanometer reads zero, with force $P = 0$. The bridge may be of null-type, voltage-type or current-sensitive type, and so the change of output resistance, voltage or current is a measure of the change (δR_4) of the strain gauge resistance. The strain may be calculated as shown in Example 4.5.9.

4.3.5 Temperature effects in strain bridge circuits

The electrical resistance of most metals varies with temperature change, hence all of the resistances of a bridge, including the sensing one, may change as the temperature varies. The temperature change of a strain gauge may change the resistance R_4 by as much as or more than the typical change due to strain (see Example 4.5.11). Also, if the expansion of the material to which the gauge is bonded due to temperature change is greater than that of the gauge, the gauge will be subjected to tensile strain due to this temperature change, and further error results. (It also works in reverse if the material expands less than the gauge would.)

To overcome these defects, two things may be done. Firstly, the gauge may be chosen to have a temperature expansion co-efficient the same as the material to which it will be bonded. Secondly, a *dummy gauge* may be

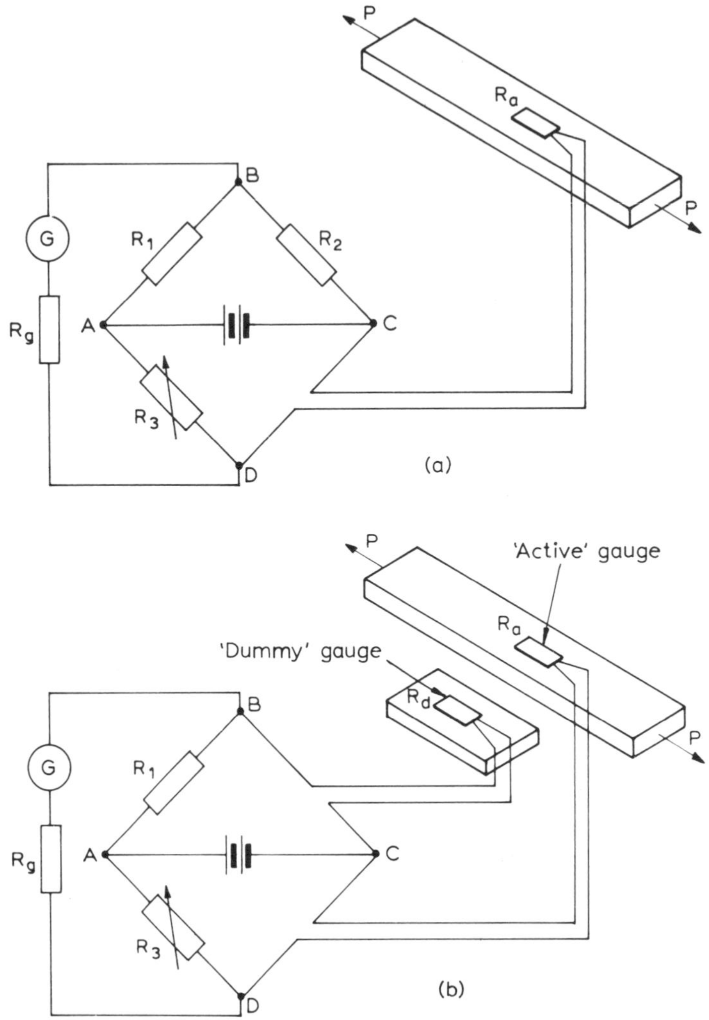

Fig. 4.12 (a) Strain-measuring bridge.
(b) Temperature-compensated strain-measuring bridge.

used to compensate for temperature effects. Consider the bridge circuit of Fig. 4.9, and assume all resistors are initially the same value. If R_2 and R_4 increased by the same small amount then V_{BC} would still remain the same as V_{DC} and the bridge would remain balanced. Hence if R_2 is a second strain gauge, bonded to the same material as R_4, and maintained at the same temperature as R_4, then the temperature of both may change from that at initial balance, without unbalancing the bridge. The bridge is now unbalanced only due to change of strain altering R_4, provided the other resistors R_1 and R_3 stay at the same temperature as each other, and R_1, R_2 and R_3 have no strain applied to them. Fig. 4.12(b) shows the arrangement. The strain gauge used for temperature compensation only is usually referred to as a 'dummy' gauge.

4.3.6 Temperature and strain effects in temperature-measuring bridges

Wheatstone bridges are frequently used for temperature measurement. The temperature-sensing primary transducer may be a resistance element, such as a platinum resistance thermometer, or a foil-type element similar to a strain gauge, or a resistance film deposited on ceramic or glass, etc. Or it may be a semiconductor element such as a thermistor. The change, δR_4 of the resistance of the sensing element due to its temperative change, unbalances the bridge. However the bridge may also be unbalanced by change of resistance of R_1, R_2 and R_3 and the connecting leads, caused by temperature changes: the bridge may also be unbalanced by strain in any of the resistances, especially those of foil type. Care should be taken in using the latter type to eliminate or balance out strain effects. Fig. 4.13 shows a bridge circuit where the primary transducer is a platinum resistance element whose resistance is R_s, and the resistance of its leads is R_L. To avoid error due to the change of resistance of the leads, compensating (dummy) leads with resistance R'_L and connected into the adjacent arms of the bridge are run near the active leads. When R_L changes due to temperature, R'_L changes by the same amount, and the bridge is not unbalanced by this effect.

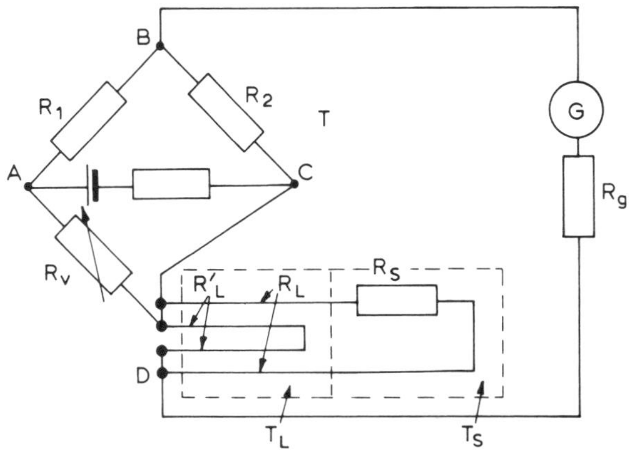

Fig. 4.13 Temperature-compensated temperature-measuring bridge.

4.4 Potentiometer

The term *potentiometer* is often used rather loosely to mean a variable resistance. In measurement work two types of potentiometer are used, the voltage-dividing type and the voltage-balancing type, and the basic element in these is usually a straight or coiled wire or strip of conducting material.

4.4.1 Voltage-dividing potentiometer

Fig. 4.14(a) shows a circuit consisting of a source of e.m.f., a variable resistor, and a resistance wire AB of length l. A sliding contact C may connect anywhere along l, at x from A. If no current is taken through the contacts at A and C, then the current (I) is the same through ACB.

$$V_{AB} = IR_{AB} \quad \text{and} \quad V_{AC} = IR_{AC}$$

and

$$\frac{V_{AB}}{V_{AC}} = \frac{IR_{AB}}{IR_{AC}} = \frac{R_{AB}}{R_{AC}}$$

Also, if the resistance of the wire is proportional to its length, then:

$$R_{AB} = \text{constant} \times \text{AB}$$

$$R_{AC} = \text{constant} \times \text{AC}$$

Hence

$$\frac{V_{AB}}{V_{AC}} = \frac{\text{constant} \times \text{AB}}{\text{constant} \times \text{AC}}$$

and

$$\frac{V_{AB}}{V_{AC}} = \frac{\text{AB}}{\text{AC}}$$

or

$$\text{AC} = \frac{\text{AB}}{V_{AB}} \times V_{AC}$$

Hence

$$x = \left(\frac{l}{V_{AB}}\right) V_{AC} \tag{4.9}$$

Thus, if V_{AB} is maintained at a constant value, V_{AC} may be measured, and is proportional to the distance x. The circuit may be used to meausre displacements, and forms the basis of resistance-type displacement transducers. The main requirements for accuracy are:

(a) the value of V_{AB} must be maintained constant

(b) no current must be taken by the voltmeter connected to AC, hence a high-impedance instrument must be used

(c) the resistance of the wire must be proportional to length.

A single length of wire is not usually used in displacement transducers, but a strip of conducting plastic material is used in one type. More common is a coil of wire, and this is indicated in Fig. 4.14(b). In addition to the requirements (a), (b) and (c) above, the coil must be evenly wound.

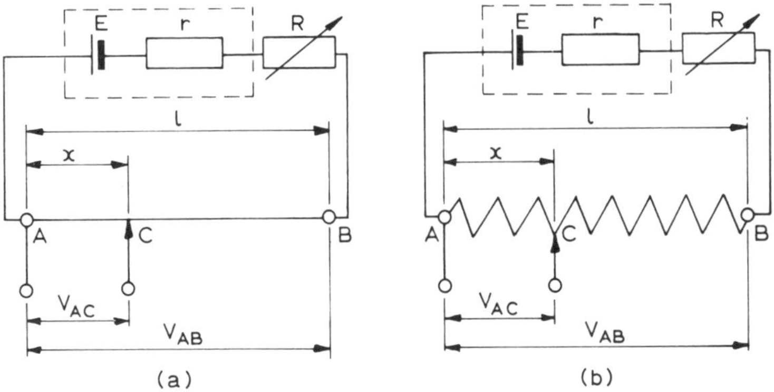

Fig. 4.14 Voltage-dividing potentiometer.

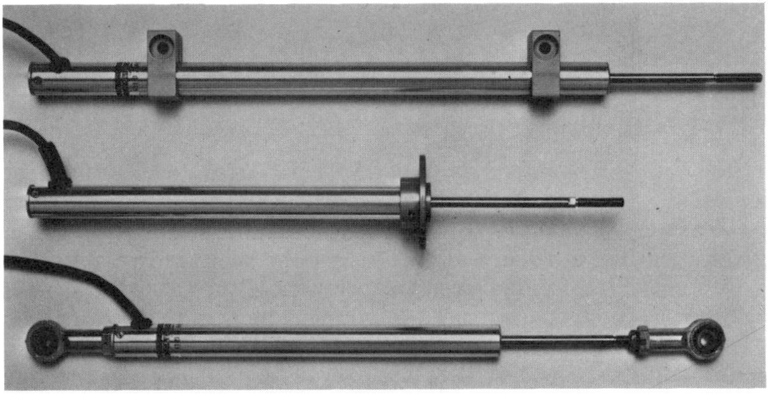

Fig. 4.15 Resistance type displacement transducer.

Example 4.5.12 shows calculations relevant to this type of transducer, and Fig. 4.15 shows typical displacement transducers suitable for industrial use. See also Fig. 2.7.

4.4.2 Voltage balancing potentiometer

Fig. 4.16(a) and (b) show circuits similar to those of Fig. 4.14, but including a galvanometer G. The requirement is to accurately measure an applied e.m.f. or p.d., denoted V. With V applied to AC through the galvanometer, contact C is moved along the resistance wire until the galvanometer reads zero. At this condition, V is equal to V_{AC}, and V_{AC} may be calculated using the measured values x and V_{AB} (note that the positives of E and V are connected together). However, for accurate measurements, a standard source of e.m.f. is introduced. This is the standard cadmium cell SC, shown in Fig. 4.16(b). The cell has an e.m.f. of

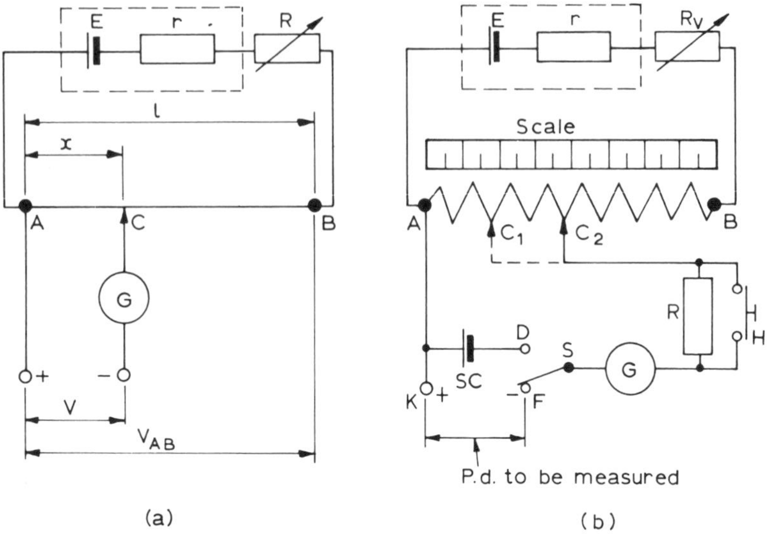

Fig. 4.16 Voltage-balancing potentiometer.

1.0186 V at 20°C, and for a particular cell, e.m.f. versus temperature data are usually available, as shown in Fig. 4.17.

To use the standard cell, the circuit is as shown in Fig. 4.16(b). The two-way switch is connected to DS and the slider moved until the galvanometer reads zero. By depressing button H, the resistor R is short-circuited, and the final balance position may be found more precisely. The balance distance is AC_1. The two-way switch is then altered to FS, connecting in the e.m.f. or p.d. to be measured, and balance is obtained at AC_2. In each of these balances, the same current (I) is flowing through the slidewire, hence:

$$V_{SC} = IR_{AC1} \quad \text{with the standard cell.}$$

$$V = IR_{AC2} \quad \text{with the e.m.f. to be measured.}$$

Hence
$$\frac{V}{V_{SC}} = \frac{IR_{AC2}}{IR_{AC1}} = \frac{R_{AC2}}{R_{AC1}}$$

If the resistance is proportional to the length of wire, then:

$$\frac{V}{V_{SC}} = \frac{\text{constant} \times AC_2}{\text{constant} \times AC_1}$$

$$V = \left(\frac{AC_2}{AC_1}\right) \times V_{SC} \qquad (4.10)$$

Thus the value of V may be found from the known value of V_{SC}, multiplied by a ratio of lengths along the slidewire, as shown in Example

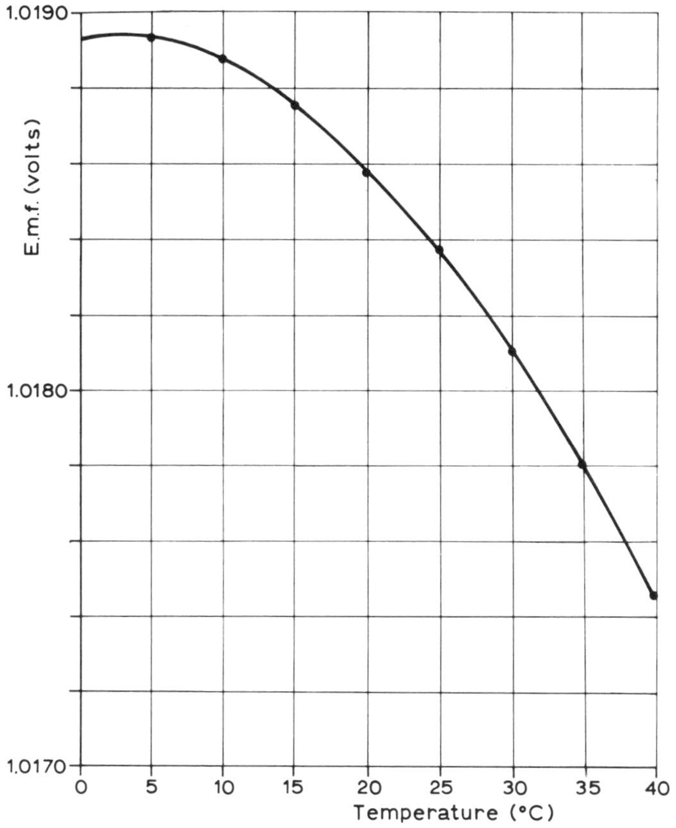

Fig. 4.17 Temperature/e.m.f. characteristics—Weston cell.

4.5.13. The small e.m.f. of the standard cell limits the method to low voltage d.c. measurement, although several standard cells may be connected in series to give a larger V_{SC} value. The method may be applied to the measurement of any small e.m.f. or to a small change of voltage over part of a circuit. It is widely used for the measurement of the thermocouple e.m.f.s in temperature measurement. The instruments used for this contain a standard cell, and the balancing is usually carried out by an automatic mechanism. The temperature value may be read directly from the scale, as indicated in Fig. 4.16(b).

4.5 Worked examples

4.5.1 The following lengths apply to the compound lever system shown in Fig. 4.2(a): $r_1 = 5$ mm, $r_2 = 100$ mm, $r_3 = 6$ mm, $r_4 = 120$ mm.

Calculate the amplification of the system.

$$\text{angle } \alpha = \frac{x_1}{r_1} = \frac{x_2}{r_2} \text{ rad and hence } x_2 = x_1\left(\frac{r_2}{r_1}\right) \qquad (1)$$

$$\text{angle } \beta = \frac{x_2}{r_3} = \frac{x_4}{r_4} \text{ rad and hence } x_4 = x_2\left(\frac{r_4}{r_3}\right) \qquad (2)$$

Substituting from eqn. 1 in eqn. 2:

$$x_4 = x_1 \times \frac{r_2}{r_1} \times \frac{r_4}{r_3}$$

$$\text{Amplification } \frac{x_4}{x_1} = \frac{r_2 r_4}{r_1 r_3}$$

$$= \frac{100 \times 120}{5 \times 6}$$

$$= 400$$

4.5.2 The following tooth numbers apply to the spur gears in the compound gear train shown in Fig. 4.2(b). $N_1 = 30$, $N_2 = 10$, $N_3 = 60$, $N_4 = 10$. Calculate the amplification of the system.

$$\theta_2 = \theta_1 \times \frac{N_1}{N_2} \qquad (1)$$

and

$$\theta_3 = \theta_2 \times \frac{N_3}{N_4} \qquad (2)$$

Substituting from eqn. 1 in eqn. 2:

$$\theta_3 = \theta_1 \times \frac{N_1}{N_2} \times \frac{N_3}{N_4}$$

$$\text{Amplification } \frac{\theta_3}{\theta_1} = \frac{30 \times 60}{10 \times 10}$$

$$= 18$$

4.5.3 The dimensions of a Huggenberger strain gauge such as that of Fig. 4.3 were measured and found to be: AB = 25 mm, BP_1 = 3 mm, P_1P_2 = 136 mm, P_3P_4 = 4 mm, P_4 to scale line = 100 mm, distance from 0 to 1.0 along the scale line = 25 mm. The given gauge constant for the instrument is $n = \dfrac{\text{indicated strain}}{\text{actual strain}} = 1016$.

Calculate the amplification of the lever system, and relate it to the manufacturer's constant.

Let the movement of B relative to A be x_1

Let the movement of P_2 be x_2

Let the movement of the pointer at the scale be x_3.

Then $$x_2 = x_1 \times \frac{136}{3} \qquad (1)$$

and $$x_3 = x_2 \times \frac{100}{4} \qquad (2)$$

Substituting from eqn. 1 in eqn. 2:

$$x_3 = x_1 \times \frac{136}{3} \times \frac{100}{4}$$

$$\text{Amplification } \frac{x_3}{x_1} = \frac{136 \times 100}{3 \times 4} = 1130$$

By calculation, $$n = \frac{\text{indicated strain}}{\text{actual strain}}$$

$$= \frac{x_3}{x_1} \quad \text{since the gauge and scale lengths are the same}$$

$$= \frac{x_1 \times 1130}{x_1}$$

$$= 1130$$

The difference between the manufacturer's *n* value and the calculated one is due to the crude and inaccurate measurement of all of the distances (using dividers and rule), and the manufacturers value of *n* by calibration would not be disproved by this test.

4.5.4 In a dial gauge mechanism as in Fig. 4.4 the plunger has a rack with teeth of 0.5 mm pitch, engaging with a spur gear having 30 teeth. Calculate the required gear ratio N_3/N_4 if one rotation of the pointer occurs for 1 mm travel of the plunger.

Input x = 1 mm = 1/0.5 tooth pitches.
= 2 tooth pitches.

$$\text{Rotation of shaft 1 is } \theta_1 = \frac{2}{30} = \frac{1}{15} \text{ rev}$$

$$\text{Rotation of shaft 2 is } 1 = \frac{1}{15} \times \frac{N_3}{N_4}$$

$$\text{Hence required gear ratio} = \frac{N_3}{N_4} = 15$$

4.5.5 In a fluid amplification device such as shown in Fig. 4.5, the diameters were $D = 25$ mm and the capillary bore $d = 1$ mm. Calculate the amplification of the system.

$$\text{Amplification} = \frac{\text{movement of fluid meniscus in tube}}{\text{movement of plunger in cylinder}}$$

$$= \frac{\delta X}{\delta x} = \frac{A}{a}$$

$$\therefore \quad \text{amplification } \frac{\delta X}{\delta x} = \frac{\pi}{4} D^2 \times \frac{4}{\pi d^2}$$

$$= \frac{D^2}{d^2}$$

$$= \left(\frac{D}{d}\right)^2 = \left(\frac{25}{1}\right)^2 = 625$$

4.5.6 Fig. 5.5 shows the optical amplification system of an ultra-violet recorder. The collimated light ray reflects from the mirror of the miniature galvanometer on to a light-sensitive paper at 100 mm radius from the mirror. Calculate the sensitivity of the arrangement in mm/rad. If θ_1 is the deflection of the mirror, then:

$$\text{deflection of reflected ray is } \theta_2 = 2\theta_1 \qquad (1)$$

$$\text{Also, scale deflection is } x = \theta_2 \times R \qquad (2)$$

$$\text{Sensitivity} = \frac{\text{change of output signal}}{\text{change of input signal}}$$

$$= \frac{x}{\theta_1} = \frac{2\theta_1 \times R}{\theta_1}$$

$$= 2R$$

$$= 2 \times 100$$

$$= 200 \text{ mm/rad}$$

4.5.7 A piezoelectric force transducer was connected to a charge amplifier. When the given sensitivity of the force transducer is set on the sensitivity dial of the amplifier, and the gain set to 1000, the overall sensitivity of the system should be 1 mV/N. Determine the accuracy of the system if the following readings were obtained using an accurate force standard:

Applied force	(*N*)	0	300	600	900	1200	1500
Output	(*V*)	0	0.298	0.592	0.896	1.200	1.496

A graph of voltage against force shows very little deviation from a straight line of slope 1 mV/N passing through the origin. A typical error as a percentage of the point value, calculated using eqn. 2.2 is:

At 300 N, the output voltage should be 300 N × 1 mV/N = 0.300 V.

Hence voltage error = 0.298 − 0.300 = −0.002 V.
Error percentage point value = −(0.002/0.300) × 100 %
= −0.67 %

Carrying out a similar calculation for each test point gives:

Applied force (N) :	0	300	600	900	1200	1500
Accuracy of point value (%) :	0	−0.67	−1.33	−0.44	0	−0.27

The point accuracy is seen to be within ±1.3 %.

4.5.8 A resistance R_4 was connected to the points DC in the Wheatstone bridge shown in Fig. 4.10. At null balance, $R_v = 25\,491\ \Omega$, $R_1 = 10\,000\ \Omega$ and $R_2 = 1\ \Omega$. Calculate the value of R_4.

At balance, $$\frac{R_1}{R_2} = \frac{R_v}{R_4} \quad \therefore \quad R_4 = \frac{R_2}{R_1} \times R_v$$
$$= \frac{1}{1\,000} \times 25\,491 = 25.491\ \Omega$$

N.B. This number of significant figures can only be included in the answer if R_1, R_2 and R_v are each accurate to the same number.

4.5.9 In a strain-gauge Wheatstone bridge, the four arms were $R_1 = 10\,000\ \Omega$, $R_2 = 100\ \Omega$, $R_3 =$ variable, $R_4 = 99.80\ \Omega$, the strain gauge initial resistance. At initial balance, with zero strain, R_3 was 9981 Ω, and this increased to 10 002 Ω when the bridge was rebalanced after the strain was applied. Calculate the change of resistance of the strain gauge, and the strain if the gauge factor (F) was 2.1.

By eqn. 4.6 $\delta R_4 = \left(\frac{R_2}{R_1}\right)\delta R_3$ where δR_4 is the change of resistance of the gauge
and δR_3 is the change of R_v

$$\delta R_3 = 10\,002 - 9981$$
$$= 21\ \Omega$$

$$\delta R_4 = \frac{100}{10\,000} \times 21$$
$$= 0.21\ \Omega$$

By eqn. 3.2, strain $$\varepsilon = \frac{\delta R_4}{R_4} \times \frac{1}{F}$$
$$= \frac{0.21}{99.8} \times \frac{1}{2.1}$$
$= 1.00 \times 10^{-3}$ and is tensile, since R_3 and hence R_4 have increased

4.5.10 A strain gauge having a strain factor $F = 2.1$ has a strain of $+10^{-3}$ applied to it. If the gauge resistance and all of the other resistances have an initial resistance of 100 Ω calculate,

(a) the change of value of R_3 to rebalance a null-type bridge,

(b) the output voltage of a voltage-sensitive bridge if the voltmeter resistance is very high, and the bridge supply is 4 V

(c) the output current of a current-sensitive bridge if the galvanometer resistance is 250 Ω, and the bridge supply is 4 V.

(a) By eqn. 3.2,

$$\text{strain } \varepsilon = \frac{\delta R}{R} \times \frac{1}{F}$$

$$\delta R = \varepsilon R F$$

$$= +10^{-3} \times 100 \times 2.1$$

i.e.

$$\delta R_4 = +0.21\,\Omega$$

By eqn. 4.6, this is also the required change δR_3 for rebalance

(b) By eqn. 4.7,

$$V_{BD} = \frac{V_{AC}}{4}\left(\frac{\delta R_4}{R_4}\right)$$

$$= \frac{4}{4} \times \left(\frac{+0.21}{100}\right)$$

$$= 2.1\,\text{mV}$$

(c) By eqn. 4.8,

$$K = \left(\frac{R_g}{R_4}\right) + 1$$

$$= \left(\frac{250}{100}\right) + 1$$

$$= 3.5$$

$$I_g = \frac{V_{AC}}{4KR_4} \times \left(\frac{\delta R_4}{R_4}\right)$$

$$= \frac{4 \times 0.21}{4 \times 3.5 \times 100 \times 100}$$

$$= 6\,\mu\text{A}$$

4.5.11 An electrical-resistance strain-gauge of resistance 120 Ω and gauge factor (F) of 2.0 is bonded to steel having an elastic limit stress of 400 MN/m^2 and modulus of elasticity (E) of 200 GN/m^2. Calculate the change of resistance (a) due to a change of stress equal to 1/10th of the elastic range, (b) due to an increase of temperature of 20°C if the gauge material is Advance alloy.

Temperature co-efficients
of expansion —steel: 12×10^{-6}/°C
Advance alloy: 16×10^{-6}/°C

Temperature co-efficient of resistance — Advance alloy: $20 \times 10^{-6}/°C$

(a) Change of stress $= 400 \times 10^6/10 = 40 \times 10^6$ N/m^2

$$\begin{aligned}\text{Change of strain} &= \theta/E \\ &= 40 \times 10^6/(200 \times 10^9) \\ &= 200 \times 10^{-6}\end{aligned}$$

By eqn. 3.2

$$\begin{aligned}\delta R &= \varepsilon R F \\ &= 200 \times 10^{-6} \times 120 \times 2.0 \\ &= 0.048\,\Omega\end{aligned}$$

(b) (i) The resistance change due to the temperature co-efficient of resistance (α) of the gauge is:

$$\begin{aligned}\delta R &= R\alpha\delta T \\ &= 120 \times 20 \times 10^{-6} \times 20 \\ &= 0.048\,\Omega\end{aligned}$$

(ii) The free expansion of the gauge would be more than that of the steel due to the same temperature rise, and hence the gauge, constrained to move with the steel, has negative strain: Considering a unit length, strain of gauge is

ε = free expansion of steel − free expansion of Advance alloy

$$\begin{aligned} &= 12 \times 10^{-6} \times 20 - 16 \times 10^{-6} \times 20 \\ \therefore \quad \delta R &= \varepsilon R F \\ &= (12 - 16) \times 20 \times 10^{-6} \times 120 \times 2.0 \\ &= -0.019\,\Omega\end{aligned}$$

The changes of resistance due to temperature change are seen to be of the same order as the changes due to the measured strains likely to be encountered, and if uncompensated will lead to the unacceptable errors. In this example, the change due to differential expansion partly offsets the change due to co-efficient of resistivity, but the effects are additive in some metal combinations.

4.5.12 A resistance-type displacement transducer such as shown in Fig. 4.15 has a stroke of 100 mm and its resistance over this length is 1000 Ω. If a system using the transducer is to have an overall sensitivity of 0.1 V/mm calculate the potential difference V_{AB} which must be applied, the current through the coil, and the power dissipated by the coil.

The circuit diagram is that shown in Fig. 4.14(b)

Equation 4.9 gives

$$x = \left(\frac{l}{V_{AB}}\right) V_{AC}$$

or

$$\text{sensitivity } \frac{V_{AC}}{x} = \frac{V_{AB}}{l}$$

and

$$\frac{0.1}{1.0} = \frac{V_{AB}}{100}$$

$$V_{AB} = 10\text{ volts.}$$

Note that this does not depend on the resistance of the coil.

Current through coil is $I = V/R_{AB}$

$$= 10/1000$$
$$= 10\,\text{mA}$$

Power dissipated by the coil is $P = VI$

$$= 10 \times 10 \times 10^{-3}$$
$$= 0.1\,\text{W}$$

Note that the higher the resistance, the less power it has to dissipate, and the errors due to temperature effects are likely to be smaller.

4.5.13 In measuring an e.m.f. E a one-metre wire potentiometer was used, and the first balance distance AC_1 with the standard cell connected was 98.5 mm. With E connected, the balance distance was measured as 80.5 mm. If the cell characteristics were as shown in Fig. 4.17 and the room temperature was 19°C, determine the value of E.

The circuit is that shown in Fig. 4.16(b).

By eqn. 4.10,
$$E = \frac{AC_2}{AC_1} \times V_{sc}$$

and from the graph V_{sc} is 1.0186 volts.

Hence
$$E = \frac{80.5}{98.5} \times 1.0186$$
$$= 0.832\,\text{V}$$

Note that, although the standard cell e.m.f. is given to five significant figures, the distances are only measured to the nearest half millimetre, and hence the best estimate of E is 0.83 V in this case.

4.6 Tutorial and practical work

4.6.1 Measure the relevant lever lengths of a Huggenberger extensometer and calculate the amplification. Compare this with the constant given for the gauge.

4.6.2 For a Hounsfield Tensometer measure (a) the fluid amplification ratio for the mercury indicator and (b) the mechanical amplification of the automatic recording mechanism, and compare the two.

4.6.3 Determine the amplification ratio of a pressure gauge mechanism.

4.6.4 Sketch a system of mirrors to give an amplification of eight times the angular change $\delta\theta$ of the input ray.

4.6.5 Examine the electronic amplifiers used in your laboratory (or works) instrument systems. Note from their literature the gain, frequency range, effect of load resistance, etc., and so compare their performance.

4.6.6 Examine the circuit diagrams of d.c. bridges used for measurement in your laboratory work, and determine whether they are null-type or current-sensitive or voltage-sensitive types. Compare their ranges.
4.6.7 Investigate the effect of using two electrical resistance strain gauges, either (a) side by side, or (b) longitudinally in line, connected in series with each other and bonded to a link in tension and connected into the arm DC of a Wheatstone bridge. Is the sensitivity increased by using the two gauges?
4.6.8 Investigate the effect of connecting two strain gauges, one on each side of a cantilever aligned longitudally and opposite to each other, one connected into arm DC, one into arm BC, of the Wheatstone bridge shown in fig. 4.12(b). Is the sensitivity increased by using the two gauges? Is the bridge temperature-compensated?
4.6.9 Discuss the effect of the heating of the resistance wires of bridge circuits during and after balancing the bridge.
4.6.10 Examine available literature for resistance type linear and angular displacement transducers and compare their stated resistance, range, discrimination and accuracy.
4.6.11 Using a 1 metre wire potentiometer, measure the e.m.f.s of two cells individually, then combined in series, and discuss any discrepancies in the results.

4.7 Exercises

4.7.1 Calculate the amplification of a compound lever arrangement where lever O_1AB has a fixed pivot O_1 and lever CO_2D has a fixed pivot O_2. Both levers are initially parallel and connected by a link BC at 90° to their axes. $O_1A = O_2C$, and $O_1B = CD = 5 \times O_1A$. The input is a small movement of A, and the output is at D.
4.7.2 In a dial gauge mechanism similar to that of Fig. 4.4, the rack B has a tooth pitch of 0.40 mm and engages with wheel C with 25 teeth. Wheels D and E have 40 and 8 teeth respectively and the scale is 50 mm diameter. Calculate: (a) the movement of the plunger to cause one rotation of the pointer, (b) the amplification X/x.
4.7.3 A Huggenberger type extensometer has a constant $n = 500$. Determine the constant of similar models of the extensometer, but modified in the following ways:
(a) *all* dimensions are increased by the factor 1.5
(b) the gauge and scale lengths remain the same, but the lever system is increased in size, as a whole, by the factor 1.5
(c) The lever lengths P_1P_2 and P_3D *only* (Fig. 4.3) are increased by the factor 1.5, all other sizes remaining the same.
4.7.4 In a fluid amplification system as in Fig. 4.5 the amplification is to be 1000. If the capillary tube is 1.00 mm diameter, calculate the required cylinder diameter.

4.7.5 In a spot galvanometer the distance from the mirror to the scale is 250 mm. Calculate the movement of the spot when the input current causes a change of angle of the mirror of 1°.

4.7.6 A strain gauge of resistance 99.5 Ω and gauge factor 2.1 is bonded to a steel strip, a similar gauge being bonded to a piece of the same type of steel for temperature compensation as shown in Fig. 4.12(b). The resistances R_1 and R_2 are each 100 Ω, the force P is zero at initial bridge balance, and the bridge supply voltage is constant at 4.00 V. If force P is now applied such that a uniform stress of 320 MPa exists in the steel strip calculate:

(a) the strain in the steel,
(b) the change of resistance of the strain gauge,
(c) the output V_{BD} of a voltage-sensitive bridge,
(d) the output I_g of a current-sensitive bridge

The modulus of elasticity E for the steel used is 200 GPa.

4.7.7 A strain gauge manufactured from Advance alloy is bonded to a tie-bar made from Duralumin alloy. Calculate the strain that would be indicated due to an increase in temperature of 30°C above that at bridge initial balance, if the gauge resistance is 100 Ω and the gauge factor 2.1, considering

(a) temperature co-efficient of resistance effects
(b) differential expansion effects
(c) (a) and (b) combined.

Temperature co-efficient of expansion —Duralumin: 23×10^{-6}/°C.
—Advance: 16×10^{-6}/°C.
Temperature co-efficient of resistance —Advance: 20×10^{-6}/°C.

4.7.8 A linear-displacement transducer is of the wire-wound type with a stroke of 0.150 m and resistance of 6 kΩ. If a regulated supply of 20 V d.c. is applied over the ends of the coil calculate:

(a) the sensitivity of the arrangement
(b) the current through the coil
(c) the heat dissipated by the coil.

4.7.9 The current flowing through a standard 1 Ω resistor during the calibration of an instrument was determined by measuring the voltage across the resistor with a voltage-balancing potentiometer, consisting of a straight one-metre slide wire and a Weston standard cell. Sketch the arrangement.

With a constant voltage applied to the ends of the slide wire the standard cell, of e.m.f. 1.0186 V, balanced the voltage across 980 mm of wire, and immediately afterwards, the voltage across 652 mm of wire balanced the voltage across the standard resistor. Calculate the current through the standard resistor.

5 *Indicating and recording devices*

In Chapter 4, methods and devices for conditioning the signal from a primary transducer were discussed. After conditioning the signal may be displayed or recorded, it may operate an alarm or it may operate a control of some kind. In this chapter some of the devices for displaying and recording measurements are discussed.

5.1 Mechanical pointers

Many instruments have completely mechanical systems, for example, the Bourdon tube pressure gauge (Fig. 6.14), the Huggenberger extensometer (Fig. 4.3), pressure recorder (Fig. 1.2). In these instruments, indication is by a mechanical pointer, and the final amplification is provided by the length of the pointer from its pivot to the scale. Errors may arise in these movements due to friction at the pivots, and the response may be sluggish due to the inertia of the moving parts. They are not usually suitable for the indicating or recording of rapidly changing signals.

5.2 Electromechanical movements

In many instruments an electrical signal is converted to the mechanical movement of a pointer. The basic electromechanical movement is the D'Arsonval galvanometer, the elements of which are shown in Fig. 5.1. The current i_{AB} flows in a coil positioned in a radial magnetic field, the latter being due to either a permanent magnet as shown or, less usually, an electromagnet. The interaction of the current in the longitudinal parts of the coil with the radial magnetic field causes a tangential force (F) on the conductors and hence a torque (T). After the spindle has rotated through an angle θ, this electromagnetic torque is balanced by the torque (T') from the springs. The flat spiral springs illustrated are typical of

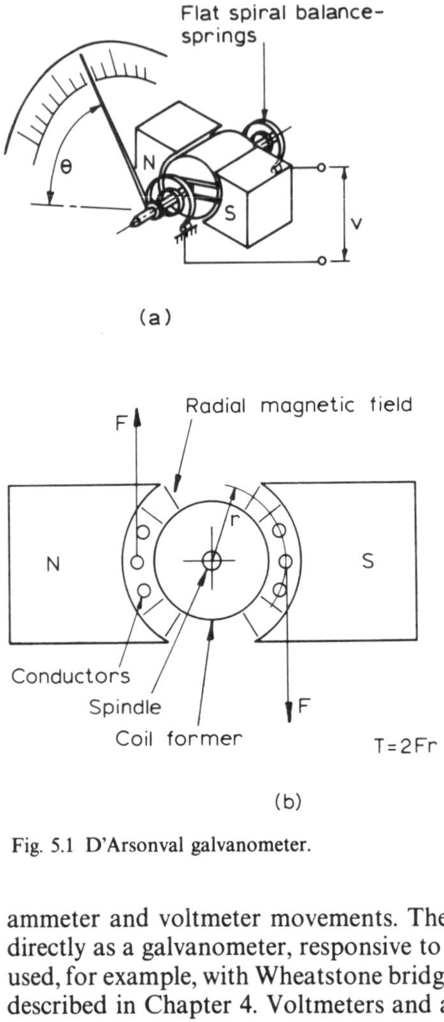

Fig. 5.1 D'Arsonval galvanometer.

ammeter and voltmeter movements. The type illustrated may be used directly as a galvanometer, responsive to very small currents. It may be used, for example, with Wheatstone bridge and potentiometer circuits as described in Chapter 4. Voltmeters and ammeters may be obtained by connecting suitable resistances in series or in parallel with the galvanometer coil. Errors occur in these instruments due to friction in the bearings, even though these may be high quality jewelled pivots. The inertia of the moving parts may cause a slower response than is desirable, if rapidly changing signals are to be applied.

Recorders may use a similar electromechanical movement, but with a writing arm instead of a pointer, as shown in Fig. 5.2. The writing is usually carried out by the slow flow of ink from a reservoir through a capillary tube, by a fibre-tipped pen or by heated stylus. In addition to the bearing friction drag there is friction at the writing point, and the increased inertia due to the pen further retards the response.

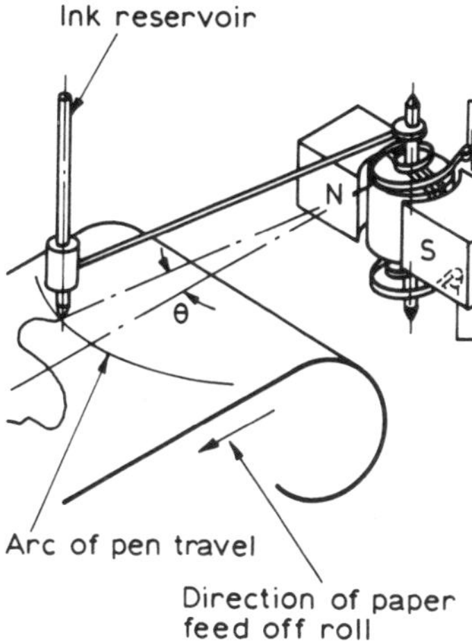

Fig. 5.2

5.3 Miniature galvanometer movements

Galvanometers of very small size have been developed, which incorporate features to overcome the disadvantages discussed in the previous section. The moment of inertia of the rotating parts, ($I = \sum mr^2$) is approximately proportional to the fourth power of the radius. Hence reduction of the size of the moving parts greatly reduces

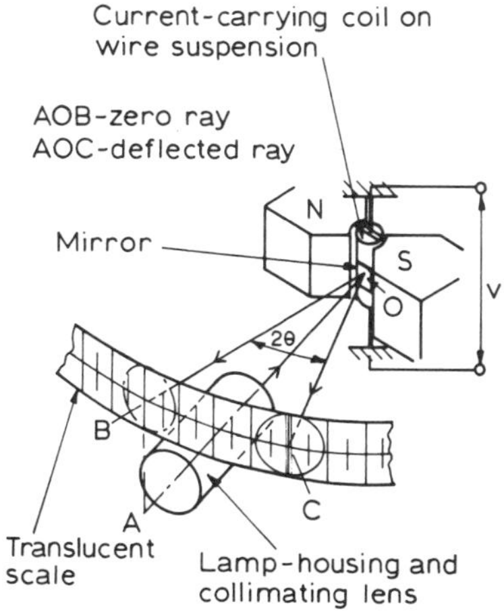

Fig. 5.3

the moment of inertia, giving a much more rapid response. The moment of inertia is further reduced, and writing friction eliminated, by using a mirror attached to the moving coil. Instead of a pointer or writing arm, the mirror deflects a light ray. Bearing friction is eliminated by supporting the coil former on taut wires fixed at their ends, which twist when the electromagnetic torque (T) is applied to the coil. The wires also provide the restoring torque (T') which equals T when the coil deflects through an angle θ, and carry the current to and from the coil. Fig. 5.3 shows the principle applied in a *spot galvanometer* movement. A collimated light ray is directed on to the mirror. As the coil is deflected through an angle θ, the reflected light ray is deflected through an angle 2θ, and the spot is deflected along the transparent scale by a distance depending on the radius (see Section 4.2.3).

A very slender type of miniature galvanometer has been developed for use in multi-channel light-sensitive recorders. The arrangement is shown in Fig. 5.4.

5.4 Ultra-violet recorder

The schematic arrangement of an ultra-violet recorder is shown in Fig. 5.5. The light from an ultra-violet source is directed as a collimated ray on to the mirror of the miniature galvanometer and is reflected on to the ultra-violet sensitive paper roll. As with the spot galvanometer, the reflected ray is deflected by 2θ for a coil deflection θ. A typical recorder would utilise six or more miniature galvanometers, mounted side by side in a permanent magnet block, each of them rotatable for zeroing on to any part of the recording paper, the latter being 100 mm or more in width. The paper speed is usually variable in steps over a wide range.

A galvanometer is selected for use in an ultra-violet recorder according to the sensitivity and range required for the measurement to be made, and the maximum current that it may safely carry, as illustrated by Example 5.9.1. The maximum frequency that may be recorded depends upon the frequency response of the galvanometer used. The speed of the paper must be sufficient to spread out the recorded trace along the time axis, when the recorded frequency is high.

5.5 Y-t recorders

Industry uses a very large number of recorders which plot variables continuously against time over long periods. These may utilise strip charts, or in many cases circular charts such as the recorder of Fig. 1.2. Charts may be designed to be replaced at 24 hour or 7 day intervals, or as required to suit production schedules or shift systems etc. Typical

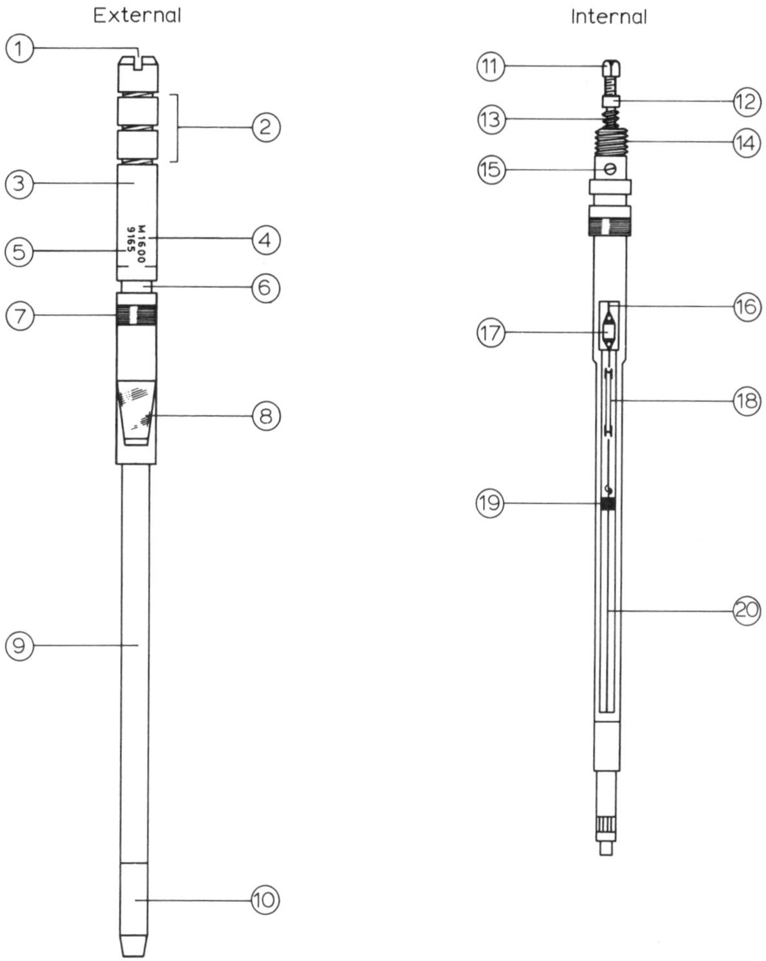

Key

External

1 Zero adjustment slot
2 Colour coded rings
3 Top cap
4 Engraved type no.
5 Engraved serial no.
6 Collar
7 Insulator
8 Lens
9 Outer body
10 Bottom cap

Internal

11 Plunger
12 Tension nut
13 Tension spring
14 Top boss
15 Locking screw
16 Upper suspension
17 Mirror
18 Coil
19 Damping reservoir
20 Lower suspension

Principal dimensions

Upper body diameter	3.3 mm
Lower body diameter	2.4 mm
Overall length	68.2 mm

Fig. 5.4 Miniature galvanometer (by courtesy of Micro Movements Ltd.).

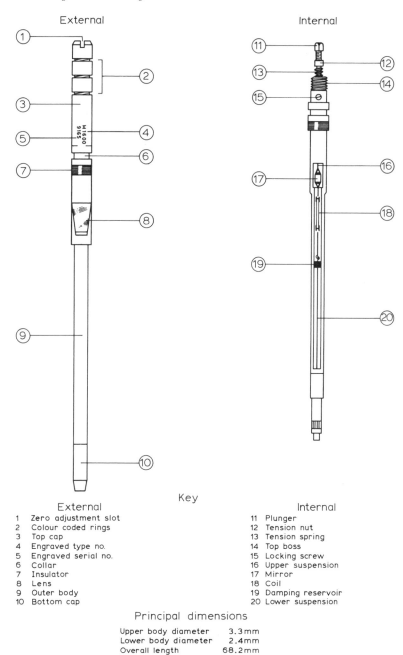

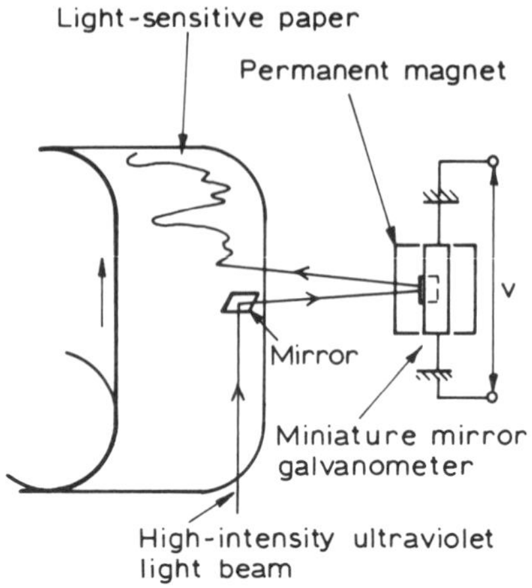

Fig. 5.5

variables recorded are the temperatures and pressures at different points in a process-control system, the temperatures of heat treatment furnaces, ovens, baths, etc., and the wind-speed and direction, rainfall, etc., at environmental stations. The primary transducers sensing such variables, together with some suitable conditioning elements if necessary, must provide the recorder with a change in voltage (mV), a change in current (mA), or a change in resistance (mΩ), in each case proportional to the change of the measured variable. Each channel of the recorder must be suitably arranged for, and calibrated with, the connected measuring system. The recorder is often *multiplexed*, i.e. the instrument selects each measuring channel in turn, connecting it to the indicating and recording system and making a recording mark, often in a distinctive colour, before passing on to the next channel. Some recorders work on the voltage-balancing potentiometer principle, (see Section 4.4.2) and incorporate a standard cell so that calibration is maintained continuously.

Typical multi-channel chart recorders are illustrated in Fig. 5.6, and an example of their use is demonstrated in Section 5.9.2.

5.6 *X-Y* plotters

In many instances, two measured variables need to be plotted, one against the other. They could be plotted individually against time on separate *Y-t* traces, and then the readings combined, eliminating time. However, it is more convenient to record them on an *X-Y* plotter of the type illustrated in Fig. 5.7(a). An input voltage which is a function of the *X* variable is connected to the *X* input of the plotter, and the *X*

Fig. 5.6 (a) Circular-chart recorder.

amplification set to a suitable value, and similarly for the Y value. The output of each amplifier is connected to a position control system which causes an X deflection of the pen proportional to the X input voltage, and a Y deflection proportional to the Y input voltage (see Fig. 5.7(b)). An example of the use of the X-Y plotter is shown in Section 5.9.3.

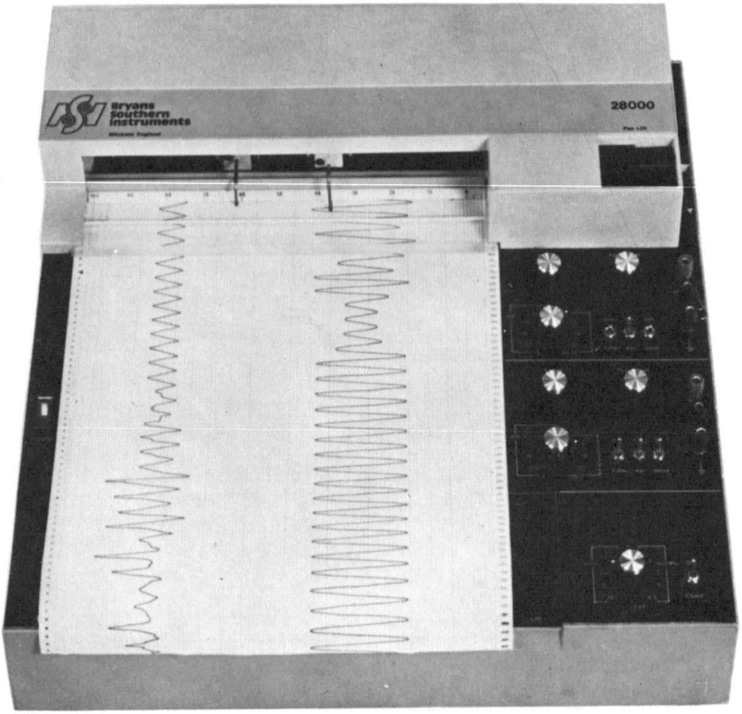

Fig. 5.6 (b) Strip-chart recorder.

Some models of the X-Y plotter have the facility for moving the pen steadily in the X direction at a preset rate, thus enabling them to be used in either an X-Y or a Y-t mode. These are known as X-Y-t plotters. An X-Y plotter is illustrated in Fig. 5.6(d).

Modern trends are towards the storage of information electronically in integrated-circuit (i.c.) systems. The data stored may be inspected at a later time by displaying it on a visual display unit (v.d.u.). Such systems may well prove to be sufficiently reliable and cost-effective so that they replace the X-Y plotters and Y-t recorders etc. described in this chapter.

5.7 Cathode ray oscilloscope

The technician student at higher level will already be familiar with the operation and use of the cathode ray oscilloscope (c.r.o.). Fig. 5.8 shows the essential features involved in displaying a continuous trace, the one shown being for an input of sinusoidal form. However, any signal that repeats at regular time intervals may be displayed, and measurements

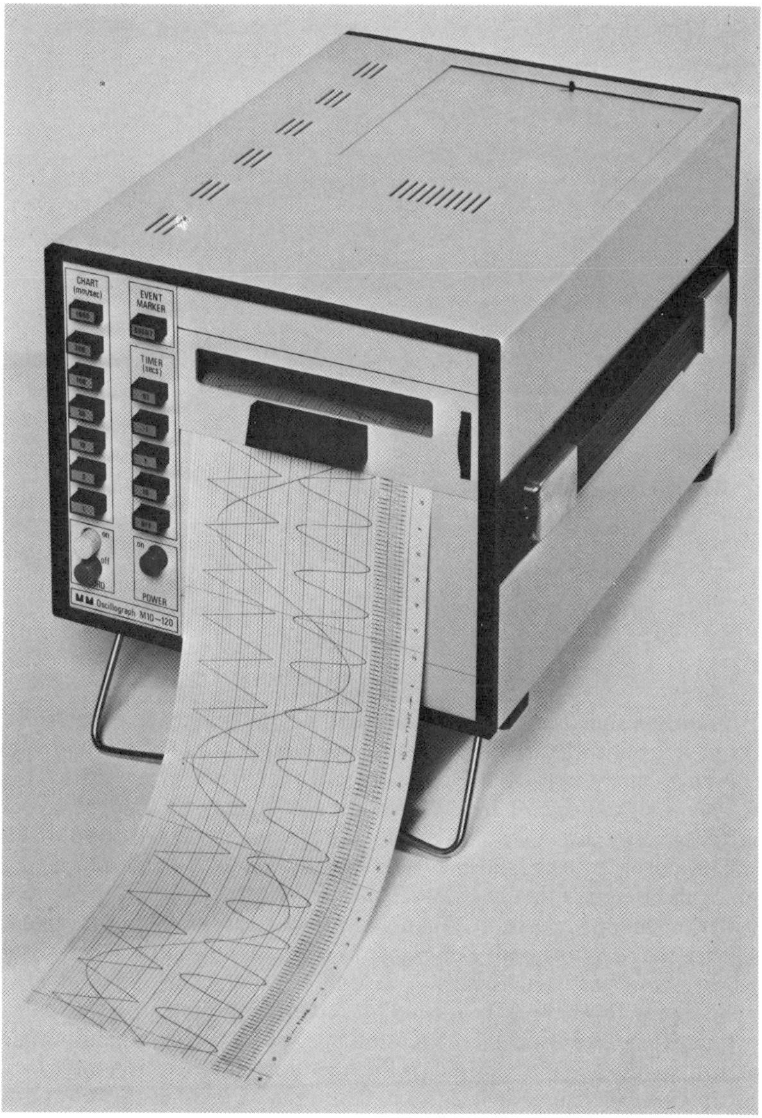

Fig. 5.6 (c) Light beam chart recorder.

made of such features as voltage values at points on the trace, the periodic time of repetitive signals, the time between pulses, the time span of pulses, and so on. The use of the c.r.o. in such measurements is illustrated in Example 5.9.4.

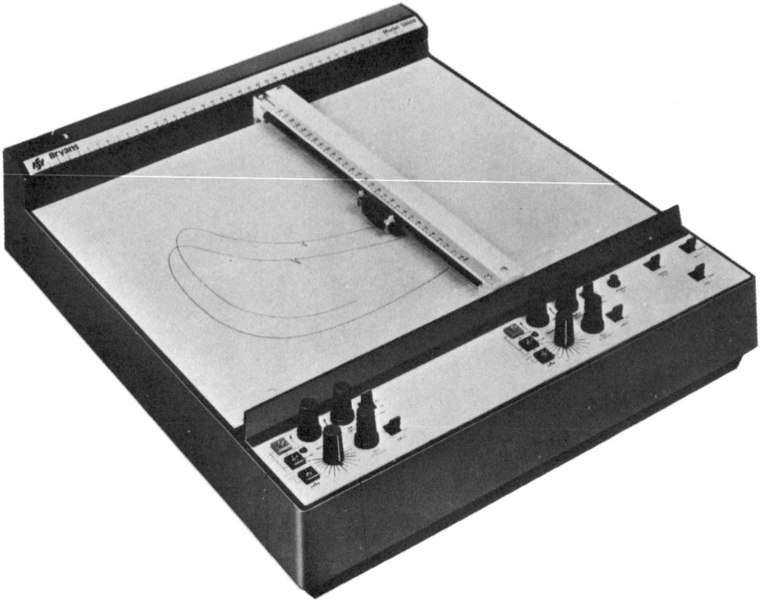

Fig. 5.6 (d) X-Y recorder.

Transient signals, such as the vibration due to an impact, may also be displayed, but these are not repetitive and disappear rapidly. To provide a permanent record of the c.r.o. trace, either from a repetitive or a transient signal, one of the following methods may be used. Polaroid instant picture cameras are available with a pyramid shaped hood which engages over the c.r.o. screen. These may have a fixed-focus lens, and a binocular eyepiece that enables the user to view the trace on the screen, with the camera in position. When the required trace is stable, the camera shutter may be operated. For transient signals, the shutter is left open whilst the event takes place. A second method is to use a *storage oscilloscope*, this having the facility for retaining the image on the screen for an extended period. The retention may be started by operating the control at any instant required by the operator. Thus the best trace may be obtained of a signal which is fluctuating from cycle to cycle. A third method due to modern digital and integrated circuit technology can now provide means of storing transient and cyclic data, and devices for storage and retrieval of these are now available.

The c.r.o. is basically an X-Y display device, and in most oscilloscopes, there is a facility for feeding in an X signal to trigger off the built-in timebase.

C.R.O.s with two or four independant traces with the same timebase are commonly used, and are convenient for displaying two or more

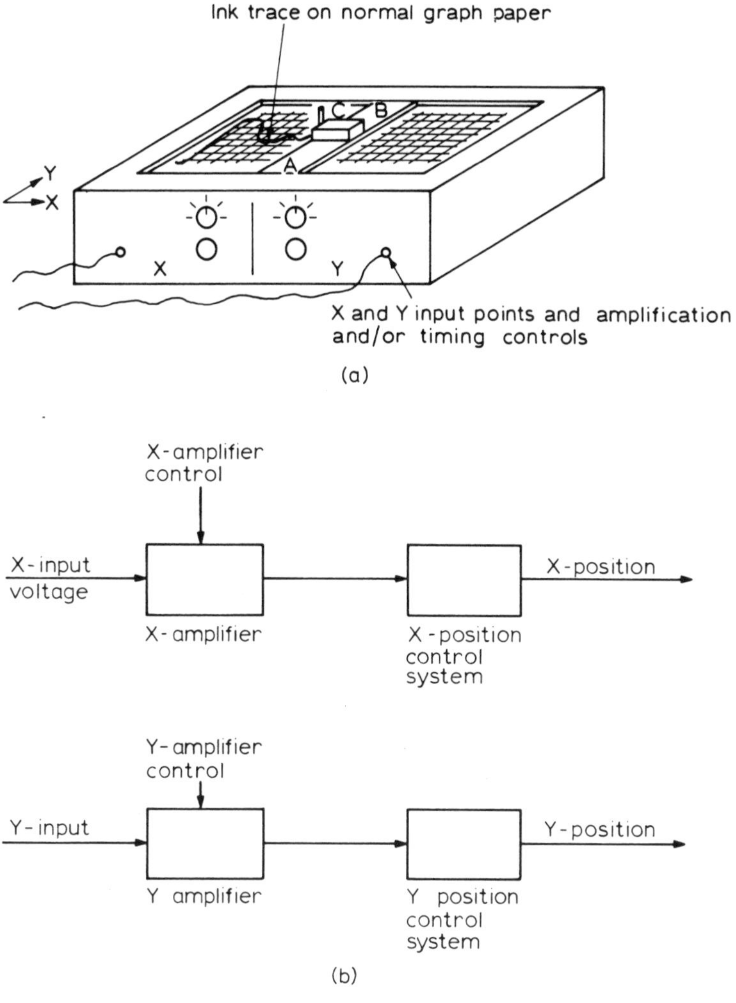

Fig. 5.7 (a) X-Y recorder.
(b) X-Y recorder schematic system.

separate but connected variables, for example: the injection pressure and the cylinder pressure of a diesel engine; the input voltage wave and the output voltage wave of an electronic amplifier; the vibration of a machine tool and the vibration of the floor on which it is mounted.

The main advantages of the c.r.o. may be summarized thus:

(a) it is able to display static, slowly changing and rapidly changing signals

(b) it responds almost instantaneously

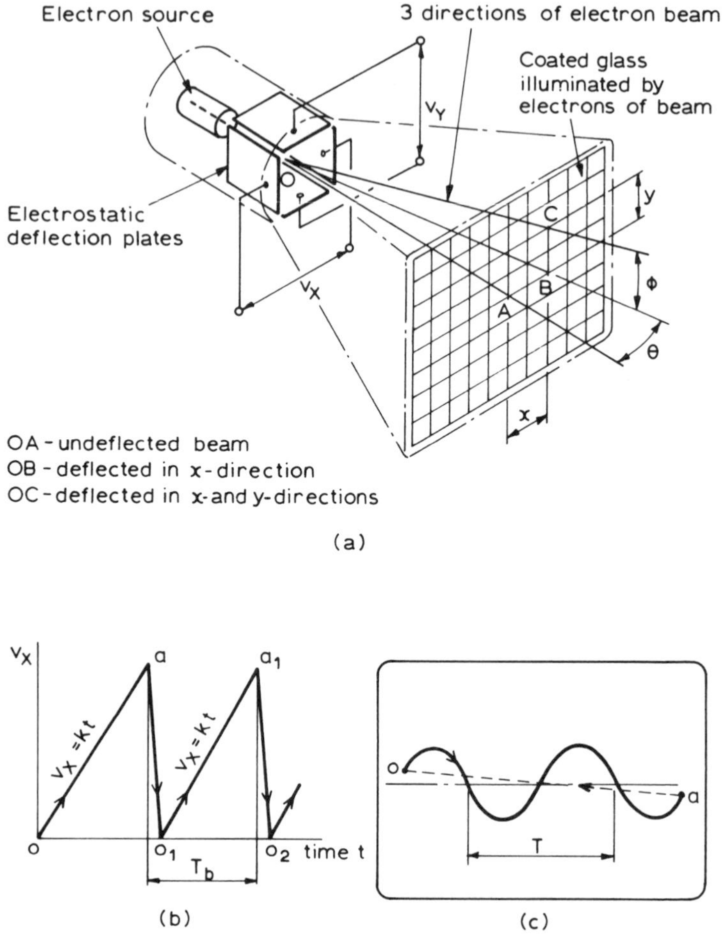

Fig. 5.8 Cathode-ray oscilloscope.
(a) Cathode-ray tube.
(b) 'Sawtooth' voltage wave.
(c) Trace of continuous wave.

(c) it has a very high input resistance and hence does not cause application error

(d) voltage and time measurements may be made easily with reasonable accuracy

(e) a wide range of sensitivities may be set on both voltage and time axes giving a wide range of measurement

(f) the voltage and time calibration may be easily checked.

5.8 Response of indicators and recorders

It is desirable that all changes of the measured variable should be followed exactly by the measuring or recording instrument, but this is only possible with slowly changing signals. The speed with which mechanical systems respond depends to a large extent on the following factors:

(a) the amount of mass or rotational inertia in the system
(b) the stiffness of the system
(c) the damping of the system, that is, the amount of energy dissipated during its motion.

These factors combine to give the system a *natural frequency* of oscillation, and a *damping ratio*, and the response of a system may be determined from these values.

Damping in an instrument is caused by the dissipation of energy, usually at a rate proportional to the speed of movement of mechanical parts, or viscous friction due to fluid motion, or due to the current

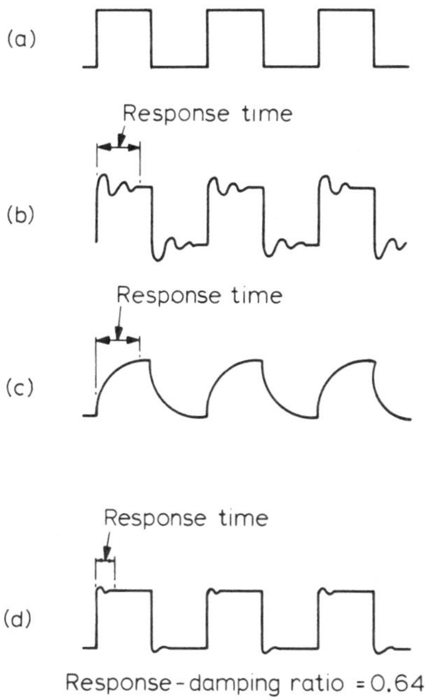

Fig. 5.9 Response and damping ratio.
(a) Square-wave input and ideal response.
(b) Response-damping ratio less than 0.64.
(c) Response-damping ratio more than 0.64.
(d) Response-damping ratio = 0.64.

flowing through an electrical resistance. The damping ratio is a convenient ratio defined as: (actual damping in a system)/(damping for just no overshoot). The optimum damping ratio for general use is 0.64, since this gives a flat frequency response (see Chapter 9), together with a relatively short response time, with a first overshoot of about 5% after a step input (see Example 5.9.5). Damping is inherent in the design and construction of instruments, but some recorders have adjustable damping, variable by the user.

The response of an instrument may be determined by feeding into it a square wave, i.e. a succession of positive and negative step changes, as shown in Fig. 5.9, trace (a). Trace (b) shows a response with a damping ratio of less than 0.64, trace (c) shows the response with a damping ratio of more than 0.64, (in fact 1.0 or more, see Chapter 9) and each of these has a longer response time than when the damping ratio is 0.64, trace (d).

The damping ratio of an instrument may be determined experimentally by observing the first overshoot, and using graphical data such as that shown in Fig. 5.10. The response time may be found by timing with a stopwatch, or from a time trace etc. The methods are demonstrated in Example 5.9.5.

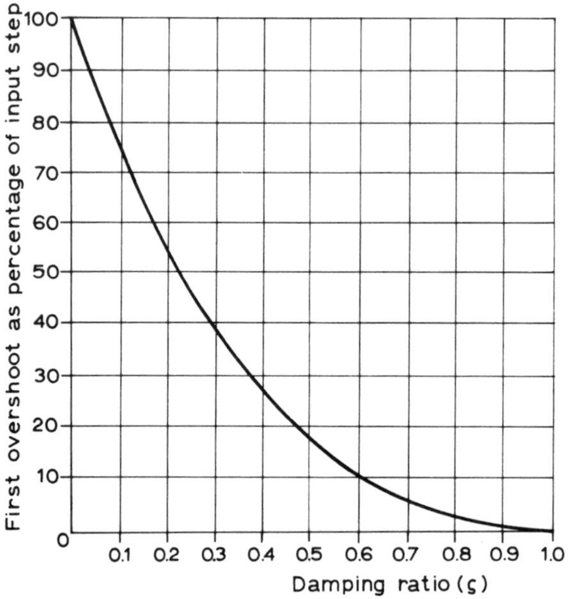

Fig. 5.10

The responses of instruments to steadily changing, i.e. *ramp*, inputs or to sinusoidal inputs are shown in Fig. 5.11. In (a) it is seen that, where the input changes steadily, the output will eventually settle down to a *steady-state error*, lagging by a constant value. In (b) it is seen that, where the

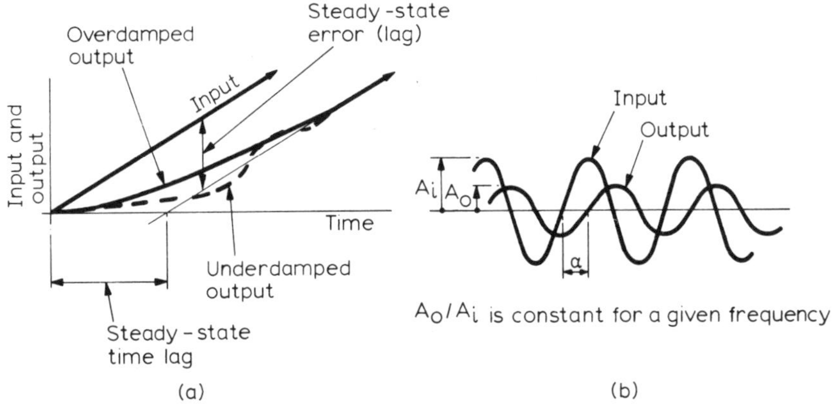

Fig. 5.11 The response of instruments to ramp and sinusoidal inputs.

input is a constant sinusoidal signal, the steady-state output amplitude (A_o) is a constant proportion of the input amplitude A_i and the output lags the input by a constant phase angle (α). Where the measured frequency is near the natural frequency, A_o may be larger than A_i.

These errors which occur due to instrument response must always be taken into account in interpreting readings. If a rapidly changing signal is to be displayed or recorded, then an instrument with a short response time must be selected. The c.r.o. uses an electron beam for indication. Since the mass of an electron is extremely small, then inertia effects are negligible, and the response time of the instrument is in the region of a few microseconds. Light-sensitive recorders use miniature galvanometers with very low moments of inertia, although still considerably more than the electrons of the c.r.o. The response time of these galvanometers depends on the natural frequency and damping ratio values, but may be typically in the region of a few milliseconds. Normal sized pointer and writing-arm electromagnetic movements have much larger moment of inertia values, and may have response times in the region of a second. *Y-t* and *X-Y-t* recorders may have position control systems for the pen, which operate on either analogue or digital methods, but the response is similar to that of the electromagnetic writing instruments described.

The value of the natural frequency of miniature galvanometers is supplied by the manufacturer, but to obtain the optimum damping ratio of 0.64, a suitable external resistance network must usually be included in the circuit.

Fig. 5.12 shows a circuit for connecting a driving source, through a matching network of resistors, R_1, R_2 and R_3, to a galvanometer.
R_L is the optimum load resistance for the driving source.
R_s is the output resistance of the driving source.

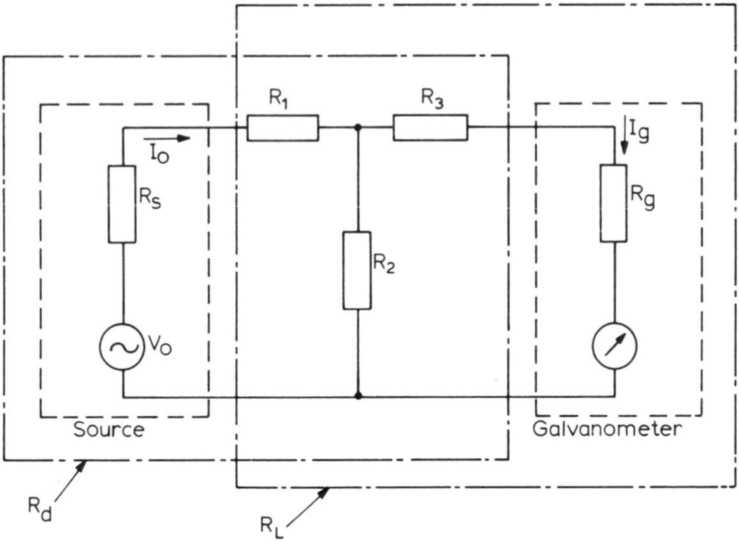

Fig. 5.12 Galvanometer matching network.

R_g is the galvanometer resistance.
R_d is the damping resistance required for the galvanometer.
R_1, R_2 and R_3 are the network resistances to give the required R_L and R_d values.

Then
$$R_L = R_1 + \frac{R_2(R_3 + R_g)}{R_2 + R_3 + R_g} \tag{5.1}$$

and
$$R_d = R_3 + \frac{R_2(R_1 + R_s)}{R_1 + R_2 + R_s} \tag{5.2}$$

If: d is the required deflection for a given driving source voltage V_o, or a given output current I_o, S is the *reciprocal sensitivity* of the galvanometer (mA/cm) for a given optical system and I_g is the current through the galvanometer, then

$$I_g = S \times d \tag{5.3}$$

Let
$$C = \frac{I_g}{I_o} = \frac{S \times d}{I_o}$$

i.e
$$C = \frac{Sd(R_s + R_L)}{V_o} \tag{5.4}$$

Solving eqns. 5.1 to 5.4 gives:

$$R_1 = R_L - \left\{ \frac{1-C}{\dfrac{1}{C(R_g+R_d)} - \dfrac{C}{R_L+R_s}} \right\} \quad (5.5)$$

$$R_2 = \frac{R_L - R_1}{(1-C)} \quad (5.6)$$

$$R_3 = \frac{R_2(1-C)}{C} - R_g \quad (5.7)$$

In carrying out the above calculations for the values of the network resistances, the following are obtained:

(a) the required sensitivity for the measurement to be made

(b) the required damping resistance specified by the manufacturer to obtain a damping ratio of 0.64

(c) the optimum load resistance for the source supplying the galvanometer.

Example 5.9.6 is an example of such a calculation.

Some miniature galvanometers are specifically designed for use at higher frequencies, and these are provided with internal fluid damping. For these, the resistance of the source has little effect. Fig. 5.13 shows a table of typical values of the characteristics of miniature galvanometers.

Type	*Natural frequency* (Hz)	*Flat response* (Hz)	*Terminal resistance* $R_g(\Omega)$	*Damping resistance* $R_d(\Omega)$	*D.C. sensitivity (reciprocal)* (mA/cm)	(mV/cm)	*Maximum safe current* (mA r.m.s)
A	20	12	47	350	0.0005	0.0235	10
B	40	25	37	250	0.0015	0.055	10
C	100	60	80	250	0.0025	0.20	10
D	150	100	90	250	0.005	0.45	10
E	400	270	120	250	0.050	6.0	20
F	800	600	34	250	0.250	8.5	20
G	1600	1000	35	250	0.40	14.0	30
H	3300	2000	35	fluid	4.00	140	75
J	5000	3000	35	fluid	10.0	350	75
K	8000	5000	42	fluid	15.5	650	75

Fig. 5.13 Characteristics of some miniature galvanometers.

5.9 Worked examples

5.9.1 A pressure transducer is connected to a signal conditioning system, giving a combined sensitivity of 0.50 mA/bar, and the measure-

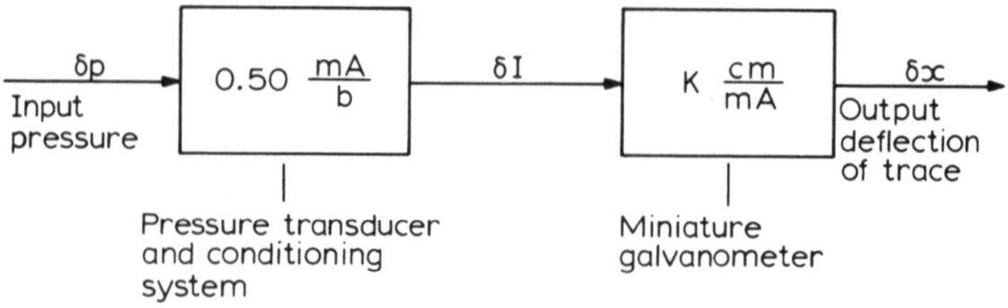

Fig. 5.14

ment is to be recorded on a u.v. recorder. Select from the table in Fig. 5.13 a suitable miniature galvanometer so that pressures up to 100 bar may be recorded on a chart width of between 100 and 150 mm. Determine (a) the actual overall sensitivity ($\delta x/\delta p$), (b) the chart width used, and (c) the maximum current through the galvanometer. The system may be represented as in Fig. 5.14.

(a) $$\text{Overall sensitivity} = \frac{\text{change of output}}{\text{change of input}}$$

$$\frac{\delta x}{\delta p} = \frac{10\,\text{cm}}{100\,\text{bar}} = 0.50\left(\frac{\text{mA}}{\text{bar}}\right) \times K\left(\frac{\text{cm}}{\text{mA}}\right)$$

hence $$\frac{1}{K} = 5.0\,\frac{\text{mA}}{\text{cm}}$$

(N.B. – the sensitivities in Fig. 5.13 are the ratios: input/output, i.e. *reciprocal sensitivities.*)

Galvanometer H has nearest to the required sensitivity. The actual sensitivity will be:

$$\frac{\delta x}{\delta p} = 0.5\left(\frac{\text{mA}}{\text{bar}}\right) \times \frac{1}{4.0}\left(\frac{\text{cm}}{\text{mA}}\right)$$

$$= 0.125\,\text{cm/bar}$$

(b) $$\text{Chart width used} = 100 \times 0.125 = 12.5\,\text{cm}$$

(c) Maximum current through

$$\text{the galvanometer} = 100\,\text{bar} \times 0.50\left(\frac{\text{mA}}{\text{bar}}\right) = 50\,\text{mA}$$

This is well within the galvanometer's current limit.

5.9.2 A strip-chart recorder receives one signal, from a force transducer, which is proportional to the mass of substance per metre of a conveyer belt and another signal, from a tachogenerator, which is proportional to the speed of a conveyor belt. The overall sensitivities are:

force sensitivity: 0.05 cm/kg
speed sensitivity: 5.0 cm s/m (i.e. 5 cm per m/s)
chart speed: 1.0 cm/min

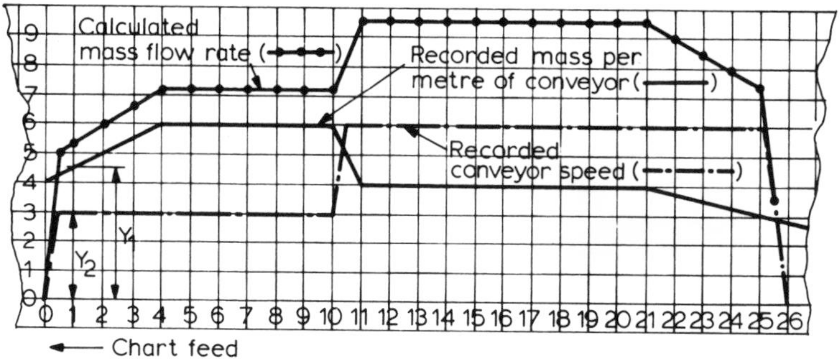

Fig. 5.15

Fig. 5.15 shows the recorded traces over a period of 26 min. The chart grid consists of 1 cm squares. Calculate:

(a) the mass flow rate at 1 min intervals
(b) the total mass conveyed during the period
(c) the average mass flow rate in tonnes per hour (t/h)
(d) the maximum mass flow rate in tonnes per hour (t/h)
(a) Example of mass flow rate calculation, for $t = 1$ min:

$$\text{mass flow rate} = \left\{\frac{Y_1}{Y_1 \text{ sensitivity}}\right\} \times \left\{\frac{Y_2}{Y_2 \text{ sensitivity}}\right\}$$

$$= \left\{4.5\,\cancel{\text{cm}} \times \frac{1}{0.05}\left(\frac{\text{kg}}{\cancel{\text{cm}}}\right) \times \left(\frac{1}{\cancel{\text{m}}}\right)\right\} \times \left\{3.0\,\cancel{\text{cm}} \times \frac{1}{5.0}\left(\frac{\cancel{\text{m}}}{\cancel{\text{cm}}\,\text{s}}\right)\right\}$$

$$= 54\ \text{kg/s}$$

Further similar calculations produce values which are marked on the trace and joined, as shown.
Mass flow rate scale sensitivity: 0.10 cm s/kg (as drawn).

(b) One square under the mass flow rate curve represents $10\left(\frac{\text{kg}}{\text{s}}\right) \times 60\ \text{s} = 600\ \text{kg}$

Total number of squares under mass flowrate curve = 207
Hence total mass conveyed in 26 min is 207 × 600 = 124 200 kg

(c) Average mass flow rate $= \dfrac{207 \times 600}{1000} \times \dfrac{60}{26}$

$= 287\,\text{t/h}$

(d) Maximum mass flow rate from calculated values $= 96\,\text{kg/s}$

$= 96 \times 3600 \times 10^{-3}\,\text{t/h}$

$= 346\,\text{t/h}$

5.9.3 A hydraulic piston was fitted with a force transducer and a displacement transducer, the outputs from which, after suitable conditioning, were fed as voltages to the *Y* and *X* axes of an *X*-*Y* plotter. The overall sensitivities were; force: 10^{-3} cm/N, displacement: 100 cm/m. The *X*-*Y* plot obtained during a stroke, illustrated in Fig. 5.16, was found to have the following values: maximum height 15.5 cm, overall length 28.0 cm, area 174 cm^2, mean height 6.2 cm.

Calculate: (a) the maximum force exerted during the stroke
(b) the average force exerted during the stroke
(c) the work done during the stroke
(d) the average power if the time for the stroke was 1.5 seconds.

(a) Maximum force exerted during stroke $= \dfrac{\text{maximum trace height}}{\text{force sensitivity}}$

$= 15.5\,\text{cm} \times \dfrac{1}{10^{-3}}\left(\dfrac{\text{N}}{\text{cm}}\right)$

$= 15.5\,\text{kN}$

(b) Average force exerted during stroke $= \dfrac{\text{average trace height}}{\text{force sensitivity}}$

$= 6.2\,\text{cm} \times \dfrac{1}{10^{-3}}\left(\dfrac{\text{N}}{\text{cm}}\right)$

$= 6.2\,\text{kN}$

(c) Total work done during stroke $= \sum(\text{force} \times \text{distance})$

$$= \frac{\text{area of graph}}{\text{force sensitivity} \times \text{displacement sensitivity}}$$

$$= 174\,\text{cm}^2 \times \frac{1}{10^{-3}}\left(\frac{\text{N}}{\text{cm}}\right) \times \frac{1}{100}\left(\frac{\text{m}}{\text{cm}}\right)$$

$= 1740\,\text{J}$

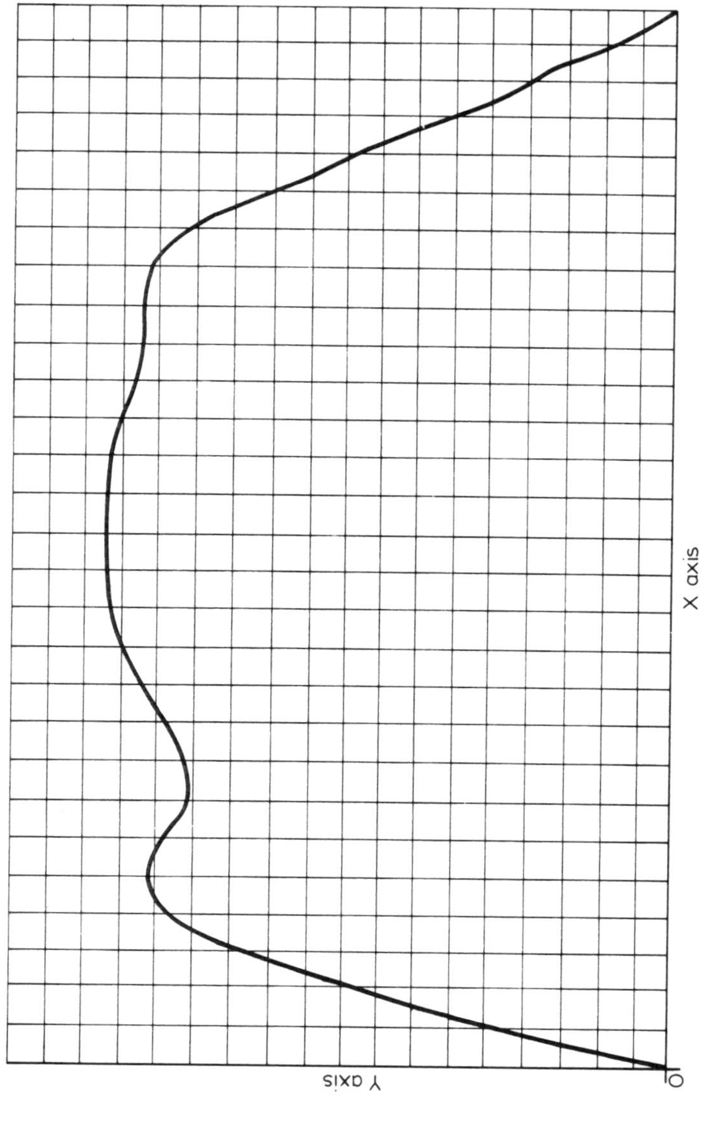

Fig. 5.16 X-Y plot of force against displacement.

$$\text{or, total work done} = \text{force} \times \text{distance} = 6.2\,\text{cm} \times \frac{1}{10^{-3}}\left(\frac{\text{N}}{\text{cm}}\right) \times 28\,\text{cm} \times \frac{1}{100}\left(\frac{\text{m}}{\text{cm}}\right)$$

$$= 1740\,\text{J}$$

(d)

$$\text{Average power} = \frac{\text{total work done}}{\text{time taken}} = \frac{1740\,\text{J}}{1.5\,\text{s}} = 1160\,\text{W}$$

(If there is no feature on the X-Y plotter to measure the time of the stroke, then a separate measurement of the time may be needed).

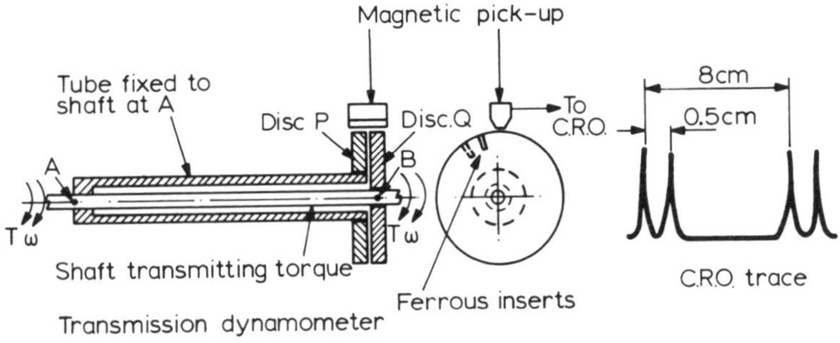

Fig. 5.17

5.9.4 Fig. 5.17 shows schematically a *transmission dynamometer*, i.e. a device for measuring the torque in a rotating shaft without absorbing the power transmitted. It operates by measuring the twist between points A and B of a slender shaft transmitting torque. The twist and hence the torque, is measured whilst the shaft is rotating, by determining the relative rotation of disc Q, connected to point B on the shaft, and disc P, connected by a tube to point A. The discs are made of a non-magnetic material, and each has a thin insert of ferrous material as shown. Initially, with no torque in the shaft, the inserts are in line, and cause only one pulse as they pass the magnetic pick-up (see Section 6.1.2). As the shaft AB twists, the inserts move apart, causing two pulses per revolution. Under steady conditions of power transfer, the trace shown in Fig. 5.17 was observed on the oscilloscope, with the timebase reciprocal sensitivity set at 5 ms/cm. If the torque sensitivity of the transducer is 3.6×10^{-3} rad/N m calculate:

(a) the shaft speed
(b) the torque transmitted by the shaft

(c) the power transmitted by the shaft.

$$\text{Time for one rotation} = 8\,\text{cm} \times 5\,\text{ms/cm} = 40\,\text{ms}$$

(a)
$$\text{Shaft speed} = \frac{1}{40 \times 10^{-3}} = 25\,\text{rev/s.}$$
$$= 50\,\pi\,\text{rad/s}$$

(b)
$$\text{Torque transmitted} = \frac{\text{angle of twist}}{\text{torque sensitivity}}$$
$$= \frac{0.5}{8} \times 2\pi\,\text{rad} \times \frac{1}{3.6 \times 10^{-3}}\left(\frac{\text{N m}}{\text{rad}}\right)$$
$$= 109\,\text{N m}$$

(c)
$$\text{Power transmitted} = T\omega = 109 \times 50\pi = 17\,\text{kW}$$

5.9.5 When a step input of 10 V was suddenly applied to a voltmeter, the following was observed:

(i) it settled, after oscillation, to indicate 10 V
(ii) its first overshoot was to 11 V
(iii) the pointer appeared to reach 10 V after approximately 1 s.

Determine for the instrument:

(a) the steady-state error (if any)
(b) the damping ratio
(c) the response time.

(a) Since the instrument indicated 10 V for an input of 10 V, then there is no observed steady-state error.

(b) The percentage

$$\text{first overshoot} = \left(\frac{\text{maximum voltage} - \text{input voltage}}{\text{input voltage}}\right) \times 100\,\%$$
$$= \left(\frac{11 - 10}{10}\right) \times 100\,\% = 10\,\%$$

Referring to Fig. 5.10, a first overshoot of 10 % corresponds to an approximate damping ratio of 0.6.

(c) The response time is the time to reach a steady value, i.e. 1 second.

5.9.6 A miniature galvanometer, of the type E as listed in Fig. 5.13, is to be used with an ultra-violet recorder and matched with an amplifier with an output resistance $R_s = 50\,\Omega$, for which the optimum load resistance $R_L = 450\,\Omega$. For an amplifier output voltage $V_o = 5$ V the required trace deflection is 10 cm. Calculate the required resistance values R_1, R_2 and R_3 in the matching network.

The sensitivity of the galvanometer, from Fig. 5.13, is 0.050 mA/cm.

Hence the maximum galvanometer current $I_g = 10\,\text{cm} \times 0.050\left(\frac{\text{mA}}{\text{cm}}\right)$

$$= 0.50\,\text{mA}$$

$$\text{Amplifier output current } I_o = \frac{\text{amplifier output voltage}}{\text{total circuit resistance}}$$

$$= \frac{5}{50+450} = 10\,\text{mA}$$

By eqn. 5.4: $$C = \frac{I_g}{I_o} = \frac{0.5}{10} = 0.05$$

By eqn. 5.5: $$R_1 = R_L - \left\{\frac{1-C}{\dfrac{1}{C(R_g+R_d)} - \dfrac{C}{(R_L+R_s)}}\right\}$$

$$= 450 - \left\{\frac{1-0.05}{\dfrac{1}{0.05(120+250)} - \dfrac{0.05}{(450+50)}}\right\}$$

$$= 432\,\Omega$$

By eqn. 5.6: $$R_2 = \frac{R_L - R_1}{1-C} = \frac{450-432}{1-0.05} = 18.9\,\Omega$$

By eqn. 5.7: $$R_3 = \frac{R_2(1-C)}{C} - R_g$$

$$= \frac{18.9(1-0.05)}{0.05} - 120 = 239\,\Omega$$

Suitable values of the resistances would be $R_1 = 430\,\Omega$, $R_2 = 19\,\Omega$, $R_3 = 240\,\Omega$.

These should give (i) a damping ratio of about 0.64

(ii) a sensitivity $\dfrac{\delta x}{\delta V_o} = \dfrac{10}{5} = 2\,\text{cm/V}$

(iii) a load resistance $R_L \approx 450\,\Omega$ for the amplifier

(iv) maximum galvanometer current $I_g = 0.5\,\text{mA}$, safely below the maximum given (20 mA r.m.s.)

5.10 Tutorial and practical work

5.10.1 Examine the specification of indicating instruments of various types and compare:
(a) sensitivities, (b) damping ratios, (c) frequency response, (d) type of damping, (e) speed of trace and (f) type of input signal required.
5.10.2 By applying step inputs, or a square wave input, to the following types of instrument, determine the approximate value of the damping ratio using the first overshoot value, and of the response time:
(a) pointer instruments such as ammeter, voltmeter, or pressure gauge
(b) writing instruments, e.g., temperature recorders, general *Y-t* recorders, *X-Y* and *X-Y-t* recorders, recording Hounsfield Tensometer
(c) ultra-violet recorder with different miniature galvanometers.
5.10.3 Using manufacturers literature, select recorders suitable for the continuous recording of (a) furnace temperatures using thermocouple sensors, (b) the forces measured by a lathe tool dynamometer, (c) the pressure in the cylinder of an internal combustion engine.

5.11 Exercises

5.11.1 A multichannel *Y-t* recorder using a strip chart 20 cm wide has the following settings available:

Sensitivity (reciprocal) : 500, 50 and 5 mV/cm; 500 and 50μ V/cm.
Chart speed : 0.5, 1.0, 2.0, 5.0 and 10 mm/s, 1.0, 2.0, 5.0 and 10 mm/min.

State the settings that should be used for recording in the following situations, and calculate the *Y* sensitivity and the maximum *Y* displacement on the chart, in each case.
(a) The output from a resistance type displacement transducer is 10 mV/mm, and the stroke is 750 mm. The time of the stroke is expected to be about 10s, and a displacement-time graph is required.
(b) The outputs from a number of platinum resistance thermometers are to be connected, each through an amplifier, to a recorder. The output of each amplifier is a change of 0.1 V for each degree celsius change of temperature. Room temperatures in the range 10°C to 30°C are to be recorded on a continuous basis for energy audit purposes.
5.11.2 The hydraulic pressure in a system is expected to fluctuate between 0 and 300 bar, at frequencies up to 50 Hz. It is to be measured using a piezoelectric pressure transducer, which with its charge amplifier, has a combined sensitivity of 10 mV/bar. Select from the miniature galvanometers listed in Fig. 5.13 one suitable for recording the pressure on an ultra-violet chart width of not more than 100 mm. Calculate the actual overall sensitivity of the system, and the chart width used.
5.11.3 The graph Fig. 5.18 shows the water-thermometer readings θ_1 at

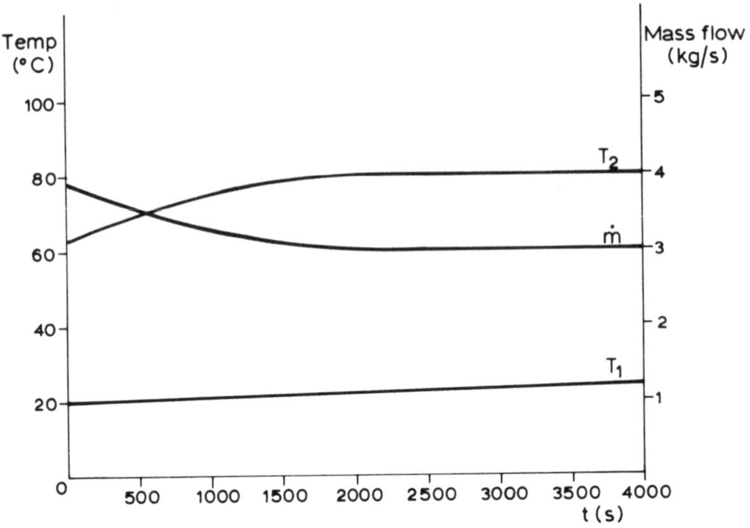

Fig. 5.18

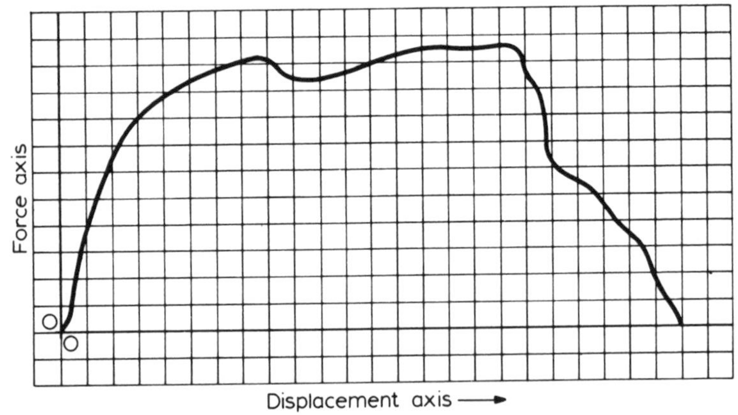

Fig. 5.19

inlet to and θ_2 at outlet from a heat exchanger on test, together with the rate of water flow through the exchanger as measured by a flowmeter, each against a base of time. Calculate the rate of heat dissipation in watts at 500 second intervals, and determine the maximum heat-transfer rate.

5.11.4 Fig. 5.19 shows the trace obtained using an X-Y plotter during the testing of a pneumatic cylinder in a mechanism. A piezoelectric force transducer, connected through a charge amplifier to the Y axis of the plotter, produces an overall force sensitivity of 2.0 cm/kN. The resistance

type displacement transducer, with associated conditioning circuits, is connected to the *X* axis, producing an overall displacement sensitivity of 0.5. The graph grid consists of 1 cm × 1 cm squares.
Calculate:

(a) the maximum force exerted during the stroke
(b) the total work done by the piston rod during the stroke
(c) the average force exerted during the stroke
(d) the average power exerted if the stroke takes 2.5 s.

5.11.5 Calculate the torque and power being transmitted by the dynamometer of Example 5.9.4 when the timebase sensitivity is set to 10 ms/cm and the c.r.o trace measurements are: distance between adjacent pulses 0.5 cm, distance between pulse pairs, 6 cm.

5.11.6 When a step input of 6 V was applied to a *Y-t* recorder the final displacement was 6.0 cm, and the first overshoot was to 6.2 cm. Determine the damping ratio of the instrument on this setting.

5.11.7 A miniature galvanometer, of the type C listed in Fig. 5.13, is to be driven by an amplifier whose output resistance is 150 Ω, and whose optimum load resistance is 150 Ω. For an amplifier output of 120 mV the required deflection is 10 cm. Calculate the values required for R_1, R_2 and R_3 in the network of Fig. 5.12 to provide the specified damping resitance and also satisfy the above requirements.

6 *Measuring systems and their calibration*

6.1 Frequency-measuring methods and systems

Frequency involves a number of 'events', each of which may be represented by a pulse of voltage, etc., and a time period. In its general sense, it may include such measurements as: the rotational speed of a shaft, the frequency of vibration of a structure, the rate at which components are leaving a production line, as well as the frequency of electrical voltages or currents, or of sound waves. Some instruments for frequency measurements are portable, for example an electrical frequency meter or a hand tachometer. Others may be 'dedicated', i.e. built into the machine, such as the tachometer measuring the engine speed in a vehicle, or a built in frequency meter in an electrical system. The following methods are used in frequency-measuring instruments and systems.

6.1.1 Mechanical tachometers

Fig. 6.1(a) shows a mechanism which senses rotational speed. As the whole assembly rotates with shaft A, the masses B move out, compressing the springs C. At a particular steady speed of rotation (ω) the spring force equals the force required for the centripetal acceleration of each mass. As the masses move out, the bell crank levers D cause the sleeve E to rise. The movement (x) of the sleeve is a function of the angular velocity, but not a linear one. A typical relationship between ω and x is illustrated in Fig. 6.1(b). The movement of the sleeve may be used directly to indicate speed (on a non-linear scale), or as shown, the movement may be amplified by a gear train. Alternatively, it may be used to control speed or other variables. The method is used more in control systems than for measurement, but in both of these applications has tended to be replaced by electrical methods.

A commonly used method of producing a pointer deflection which is proportional to speed is the magnetic *drag-cup*, used extensively in hand

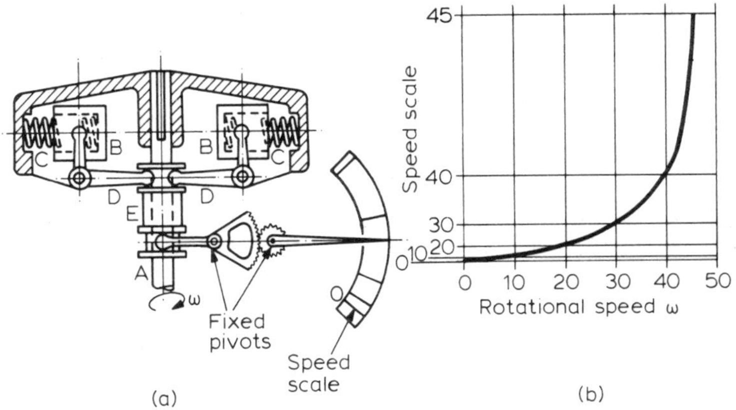

Fig. 6.1 (a) Centrifugal tachometer.
(b) Relationship between ω and x.

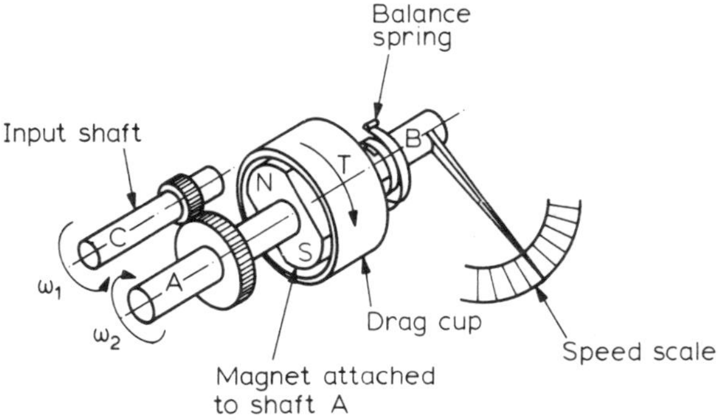

Fig. 6.2 Drag-cup tachometer.

held tachometers, motor vehicle tachometers and speedometers, and in similar speed measuring applications. The main features of the device are shown in Fig. 6.2. The shaft A rotates at a speed ω_2 which is proportional to the speed to be measured. A permanent magnet rotates with shaft A, positioned inside a drag-cup attached to shaft B. The drag-cup is made from an electrically conducting material, in which eddy currents are induced by the magnetic field. Interaction of the eddy currents with the magnetic field causes a torque T on the cup, in the direction of rotation of the shaft A. The shaft B turns until the balance-spring torque T' equals the eddy current torque T. The pointer movement is proportional to the torque, which in turn is proportional to the speed of shaft A, and hence proportional to the speed of the shaft C which is to be measured. In hand held tachometers, variable-ratio gears connect the input shaft C to shaft A so that a suitable range may be selected.

6.1.2 Electrical instruments for speed and frequency measurement

Electrical methods of speed measurement are now commonly used. The stroboscope is a useful and versatile instrument in this category, and a typical model is illustrated in Fig. 6.3(a). This particular instrument has three ranges of flashing, up to 1500, 5000 and 15 000 flashes per minute,

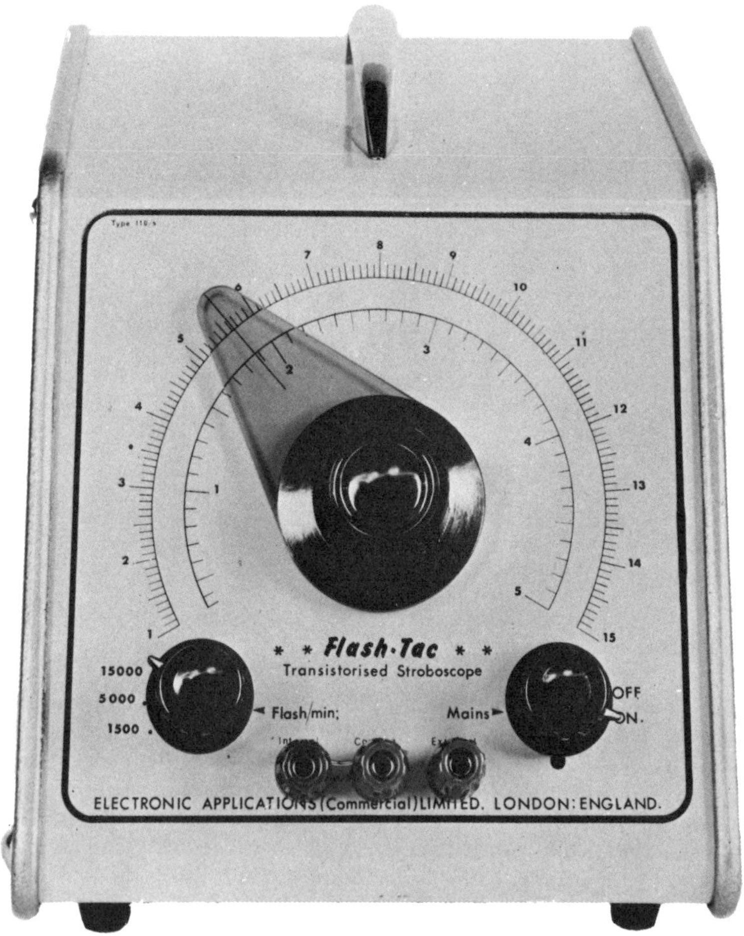

(c)

Fig. 6.3 (a) Xenon stroboscope

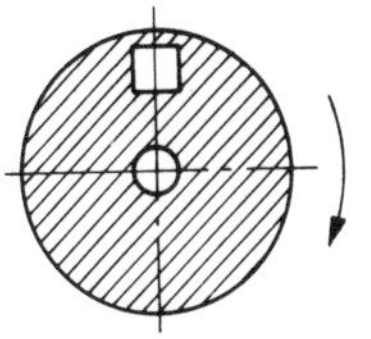

Fig. 6.3 (b) Image at stroboscope flashing frequency *f*.

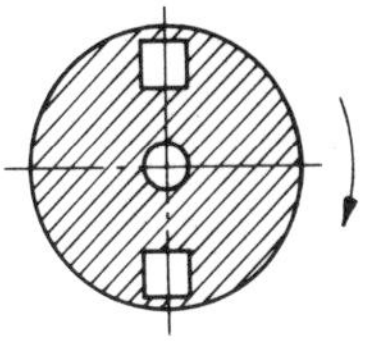

Fig. 6.3 (c) Image at stroboscope flashing frequency 2*f*.

but instruments with higher flashing rates are available. In measuring rotational speed, a reflective mark is made in a suitable position on a rotating part. The stroboscopic light is directed onto it, and the flashing rate adjusted until a single stationary image of the mark is obtained as shown in Fig. 6.3(b). The light is then either flashing at the same rate as the shaft is rotating, or is flashing once every *n*th revolution, where *n* is a whole number. To check that the stroboscope rate is the same as the rotational speed, the flashing rate is increased until two images appear, since the spot is being illuminated twice each revolution as shown in Fig. 6.3(c). The frequency on the scale is halved, then one stationary image should be obtained, and the frequency read from the scale. If the instrument does not have a range extending to twice the rotational speed, then the speed may be checked at a lower value and the single image maintained whilst the rotational speed is gradually increased to the required condition. The use of the stroboscope is illustrated in Example 6.5.1.

The stroboscope may also be used to measure the frequency of vibration of machinery, by setting the stroboscope to give one flash per oscillation. If set *near* to this frequency, a slow motion image of the oscillation may be observed. This method is also useful in observing the operation of rapidly moving mechanisms such as the valve motion or the contact breaker of an internal combustion engine. Approximate timing and other measurements such as that of amplitude may be carried out using these slow motion images.

A convenient device for either built in or portable shaft-speed measurement is the tachogenerator. This is a very small d.c. generator or alternator (a.c.) driven by the shaft. The output voltage or voltage amplitude is proportional to the rotational speed, and may be used with

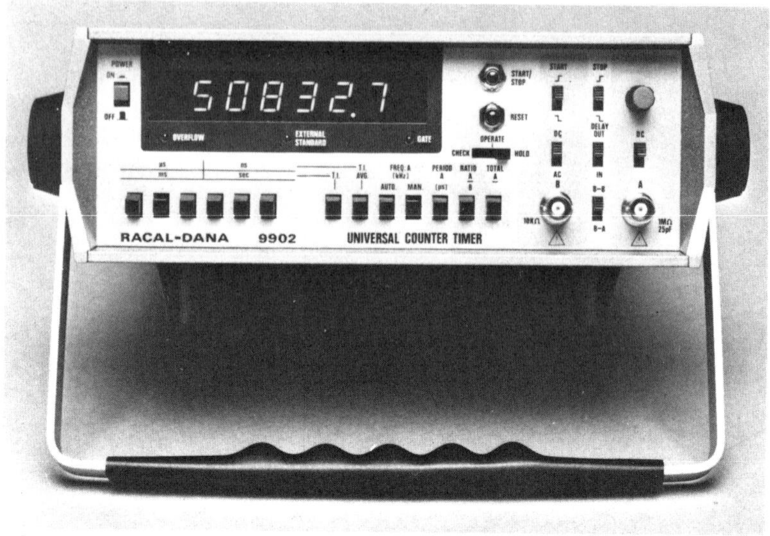

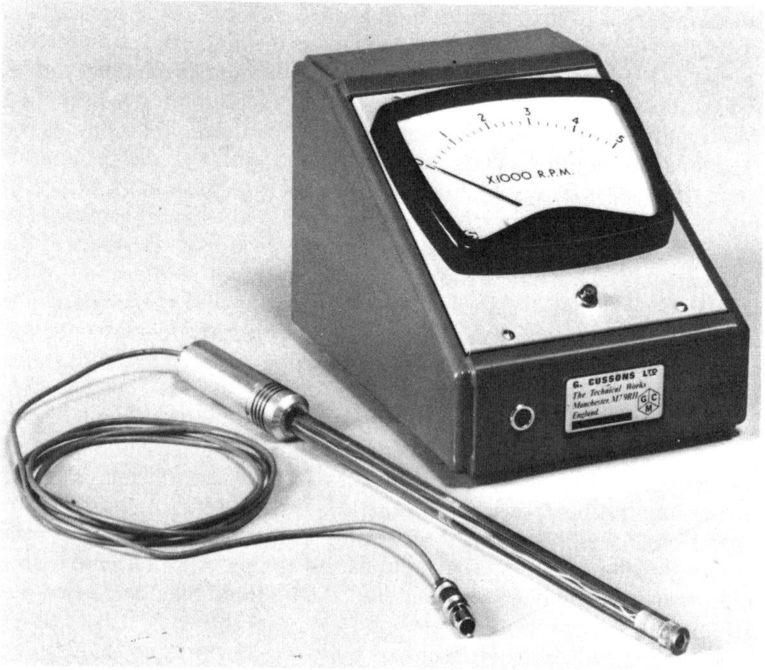

Fig. 6.4 (a) Timer/counter/frequency meter.
(b) Optical tachometer.

a d.c. or a.c. voltmeter calibrated directly in speed units, (see Example 6.5.4). For shaft speed control, the output voltage may be used as a speed feedback signal.

The timer/counter/frequency meter is a versatile instrument which, as its name implies, can carry out such measurements as the timing between events, the counting of a number of events, and the measurement of frequency. For timing, the start and stop may be by a manual setting of a switch on the instrument, or by an external applied voltage or by make/break of the circuit. These may be from micro-switches, or transducers such as the light-beam and photo-diode. For counting a number of events, the input signal is usually a series of voltage pulses. An input sensitivity control is usually provided, so that pulses of different strength may be accepted. For frequency measurement, the number of pulses in one second is counted. Two or more signal input channels may be available, and there may be facilities for the continuous updating of frequency measurement, the determining of the difference or ratio of two frequencies, and dividing the count by 10^n etc. The display is usually a four or more digit light-emitting diode (l.e.d.) type. A typical instrument of this type is illustrated in Fig. 6.4(a).

To provide pulses, magnetic pickups and photo-diodes etc. as described in Chapter 3 are commonly used, together with moving components with suitable teeth, slots or similar features, although capacitive pickups may be used in some applications. The principle of operation of a magnetic pickup is illustrated in Fig. 6.5(a). A coil of conducting wire is wound around a permanent magnet. When a ferrous material moves through the magnetic field, the magnetic flux changes. An e.m.f. is induced in the coil, proportional to the rate of change of flux. The ferrous material must have sufficient velocity, and be near to the end of the probe, to produce sufficient induced e.m.f. The pulses may be fed directly to a counter/timer/frequency meter, or if required for accurate timing measurements, may be conditioned by a shaper/amplifier unit to give a more suitable shape of pulse. Fig. 6.5(b) shows a system for the simultaneous display of the pressure in an engine cylinder on one channel of a c.r.o., together with timing marks initiated by a magnetic pickup sensing a number of *slots* in a disc on the engine shaft. The shaper/amplifier sharpens the pulses, giving a more definite peak. The traces enable the pressure to be related to the outer dead centre position.

If a 60-tooth ferrous wheel is mounted on a rotating shaft the frequency in hertz of the pulses from a single magnetic pick-up will indicate the shaft speed in rev/min. The same effect may also be obtained by a single light-source and photo-diode sensor, as shown in Fig. 3.18, with a disc having 60 slots. Examples 6.5.2, 3 and 4 illustrate speed measurements by these methods.

Self-contained portable instruments containing a light source, a light-sensitive pickup and frequency meter are also available. In use, the light is directed at some suitable reflective rotating part. The reflected light

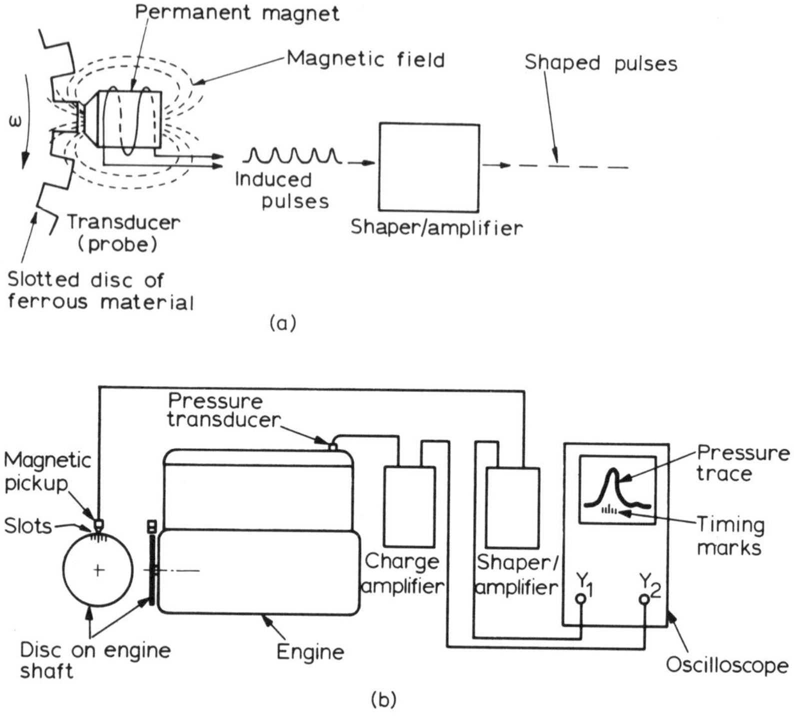

Fig. 6.5 (a) Magnetic pickup.
(b) Cylinder-pressure measurement and timing.

pulses are detected by a sensor which gives out electrical pulses. The frequency of the pulses is measured by a built-in frequency meter, and the output display shows the shaft speed indicated by a pointer on a scale, or a digital value. Fig. 6.4(b) shows an instrument of this type.

6.1.3 Calibration of frequency-measuring devices

The accuracy of frequency measurement depends on counting and timing. If care is taken in mounting and using the magnetic or photo-sensitive pickups, then each 'event' should give a pulse, and if the meter input sensitivity is set to a suitable value, the count should be correct. However, a pulse part-way developed at either end of a time period may or may not be included in a count, and hence an error of ± 1 should be allowed for.

The timing part of the measurement is usually provided by an electronic oscillator. The frequency of oscillation of this may be calibrated against a frequency standard, and a very convenient one to use is the electrical mains supply frequency of 50 Hz, which by statute should be accurate within ± 1 %, and in practice is maintained well within these limits. Hence many frequency meters and stroboscopes have built in facility for this calibration, either automatically or by the operator, with either automatic or manual correction. However, a better arrangement uses a quartz crystal. This has a very stable natural frequency of mechanical vibration which depends on the crystal shape and size. It is caused to vibrate by an alternating current and the forces in the crystal cause piezoelectric charges across its faces. These charges correct any small differences between the applied frequency and the crystal frequency and hence maintain a very constant output frequency. Fig. 6.6 shows the schematic arrangement. Many instruments contain such a crystal oscillator standard.

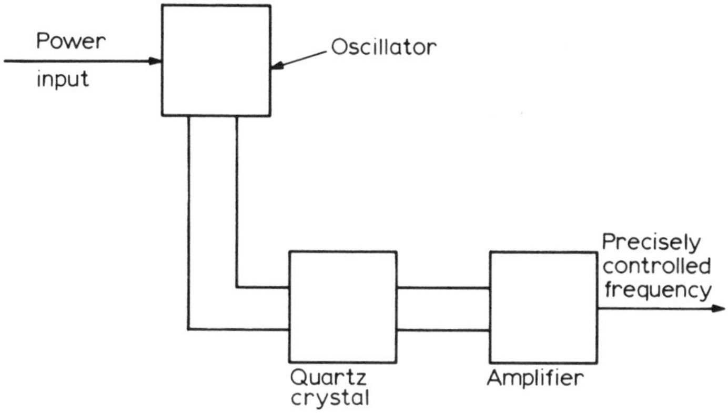

Fig. 6.6 Crystal-controlled oscillator.

Application error may be caused by some of the speed-measuring transducers. The drag exerted on the moving body by the mechanical tachometer may be considerable, causing slowing down of the shaft speed in some cases. The tachogenerator and the magnetic pick-up both cause a small drag force, but the drag of the light-sensitive pick-up is negligible. In carrying out calibration of speed-measuring devices, the light-sensitive pick-up connected to a quartz-crystal controlled timer/counter provides a good standard. Example 6.5.4 illustrates the calibration of speed-measuring instruments.

6.2 Displacement-measuring devices and systems

6.2.1 The dial indicator

The dial indicator and its built-in amplification system are illustrated in Figs. 6.7 and 4.4. The plunger is spring-loaded, and its travel (x) is

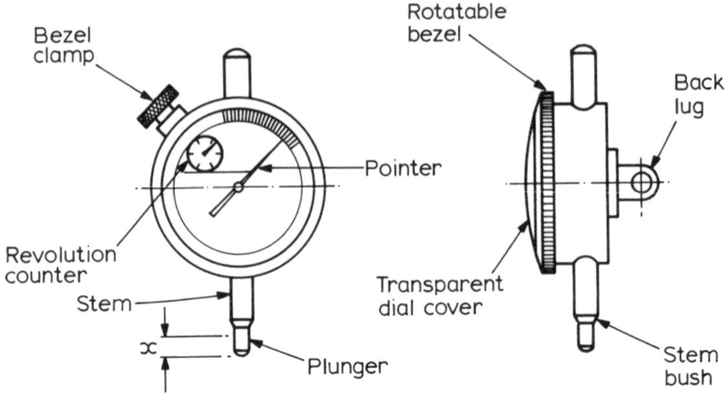

Fig. 6.7 Dial indicator.

typically 1 mm for one revolution of the pointer. If the dial is divided into 100 equal parts, each division will represent a 0.01 mm movement of the plunger. The smaller dial indicates the number of revolutions of the pointer, and the total travel is about 5 mm. The spring force increases as the plunger is raised. The scale may be rotated to zero with the pointer at any angular position. It is a common instrument in workshops and inspection sections, and is robust and reliable in these situations.

6.2.2 The linear variable differential transformer

The linear variable differential transformer (l.v.d.t.) described in Section 3.4 is available in many different stroke lengths from about $\pm$ 0.5 mm upwards. With electrical amplification it may have a much higher sensitivity than the dial indicator. Its discrimination depends only on the output side of the measuring system, since minute movements of the core may cause a change of output voltage. The indicator may be remote from the primary transducer, which gives an advantage when compared with the dial indicator. The spindle of the l.v.d.t. may be built into the transducer housing, and spring-loaded if required. Alternatively, a model may be chosen with a free 'slug' of magnetic material, as shown in Fig. 6.8, which may be mounted on a non-magnetic rod built in to the moving part of a machine. With this type, the friction of the spindle in the transducer is eliminated. The l.v.d.t. is a more expensive instrument than the dial gauge, but is potentially much more versatile. It may, for example, be built into automatic measuring or sorting equipment, and is the primary or secondary sensing element in many electronic measuring devices.

An application of the l.v.d.t. in liquid level measurement is shown in Fig. 6.9. The float is shown attached directly onto the spindle of the

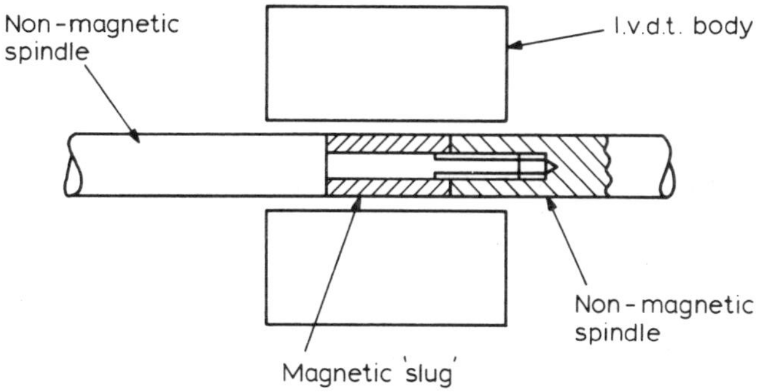

Fig. 6.8 L.V.D.T with free slug.

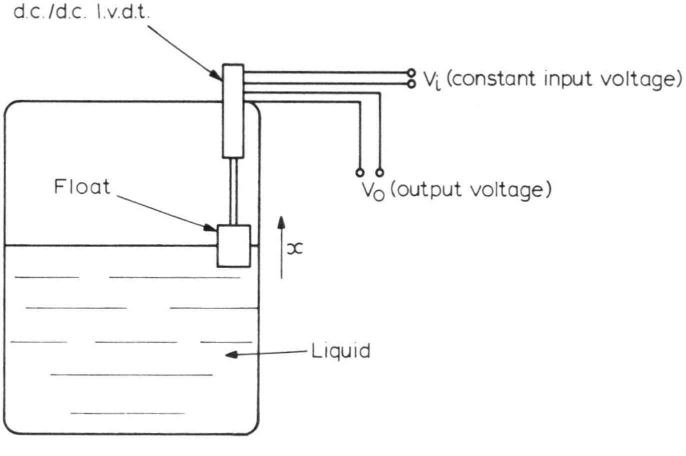

Fig. 6.9 Liquid-level measurement with an l.v.d.t.

transducer. Here the l.v.d.t. is a primary transducer. If the float was on the surface of the liquid in a U-tube manometer, it would then function as a secondary transducer, since the liquid height is proportional to pressure.

Most of the functions of an l.v.d.t. may be performed at less cost by a resistance-type displacement transducer, but with less discrimination and more friction and wear. Fig. 4.15 shows typical resistance-type displacement transducers.

6.2.3 Calibration of displacement-measuring instruments

Calibration of dial gauges, l.v.d.t.s and other displacement-measuring instruments should be carried out against the best length standard available. This is usually a set of reference-quality slip gauges with a calibration chart, and the method is basically the same as described in Example 2.8.1 for the calibration of a micrometer.

6.3 Force-measuring devices and systems

6.3.1. Force-measurement with elastic elements

Some force-measuring transducers using elastic deflection were described in Section 3.1. Force-measuring equipment may incorporate elastic elements for force measurement, together with levers or beams etc. which amplify or attenuate the measured force. Fig. 6.10 shows a spring balance and lever system used to measure the force exerted on a flat plate by the impact of a liquid jet. Before the jet is applied, the beam is balanced horizontally using the movable mass (m), and the spring balance is zeroed. When the jet is applied, the screw S is adjusted so that the spring-balance force (F_s) maintains the beam in the horizontal position, as indicated by the pointer. Then, taking moments about the pivot P:

$$F_s \times b = F \times a$$

$$F = \frac{b}{a} \times F_s \qquad (6.1)$$

With a little ingenuity, a knife-edge pivot may be used instead of the conical pivot, thus reducing friction.

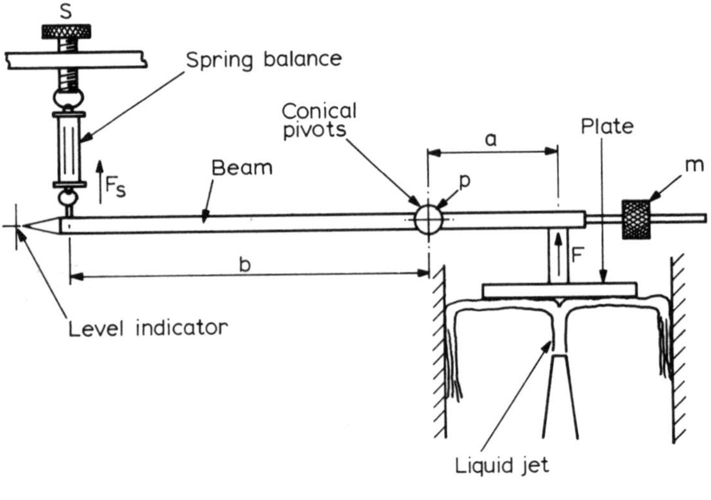

Fig. 6.10 Measurement of jet impact force.

Force measurement and calibration may be carried out using *load cells* and proving rings. The proving ring in its basic form is a simple device, as shown in Fig. 6.11. It is made usually of alloy steel heat-treated to give high strength, and machined accurately to size. The diametral deflection (x) in the direction of a tensile or compressive force F applied across a diameter is given by the equation in Fig. 6.11(a). The force may be applied by steel balls, either to a clamped abutment as in Fig. 6.11(b) or to a solid abutment as in Fig. 6.12(a), but it must be across a diameter.

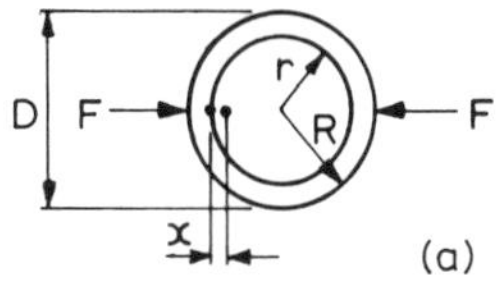

Ring

F = tensile or compressive force (radial)
x = change of radius in direction of F
E = modulus of elasticity
I = second moment of area of the section about the neutral axis.

$$= \frac{k}{16}\left(\frac{\pi}{2} - \frac{4}{\pi}\right)\frac{FD^3}{EI}$$

R/r	1·3	1·4	1·5	1·6
k	1·030	1·055	1·090	1·114

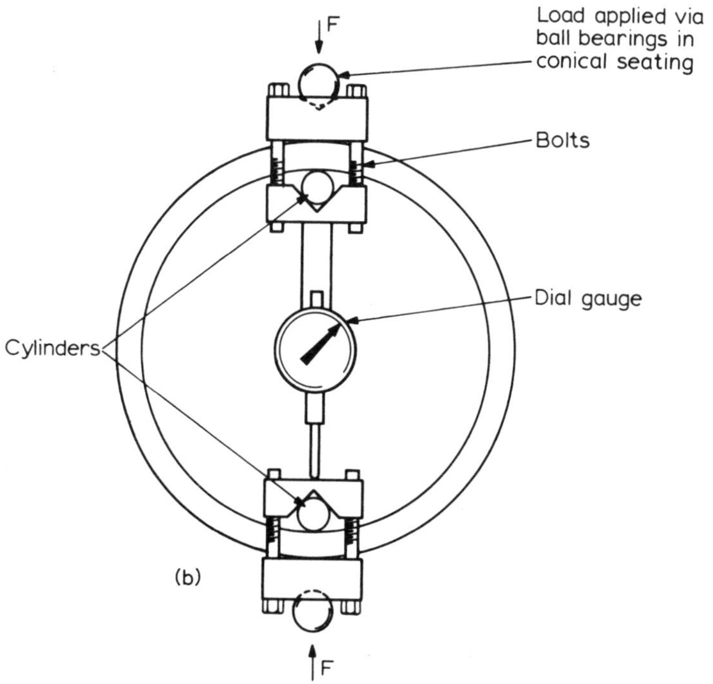

Fig. 6.11 (a) Proving ring.
(b) Proving ring with dial guage.

The deflection must be measured to a suitable standard of accuracy and precision. An internal micrometer is used in some rings, with a vibrating reed touch sensor. This changes tone when the ring inner surface is touched, providing a *fiducial indicator* more sensitive than a spring ratchet. The l.v.d.t. is a very convenient deflection-measuring instrument which may be used, and may be arranged so that very little force is applied to the ring. In less precise instruments a dial indicator may be used to measure the ring deflection, as in Fig. 6.11(b).

A further method of force measurement with a ring is illustrated in Fig. 6.12(a). Electrical-resistance strain gauges are bonded to the surfaces of the ring at 90° to the points of application of the force. They are arranged so that the compressive forces do not unbalance the bridge, since all four gauges carry the same direct tensile strain. But the bridge *is* unbalanced by the bending strain as the ring deflects. Bridge unbalance is a function of the applied force (F). The ring may also be used in tension.

The term load cell is used to describe a variety of force transducers which may utilise the deflection or strain of elastic elements, or the increase in pressure of enclosed fluids. A typical arrangement of a strain-gauge load cell is shown in Fig. 6.12(b). In this, four electrical-resistance strain gauges P, R, T, V are bonded longitudinally to a precisely-machined hardened alloy steel bar. A further four gauges Q, S, U, W are bonded circumferentially between the longitudinal ones. The longitudinal gauges measure the direct strain (ε) due to F. The circumferential gauges measure the lateral (Poisson) strain ($-\nu\varepsilon$), where ν is Poisson's ratio, about 0.3 for metals. The number of gauges used averages out the differences due to the load forces being slightly misaligned with the true axis of the bar. The circumferential gauges, as well as increasing the output of the bridge, also provide temperature compensation. The output of the bridge is $2\ (1 + \nu)$ times that of a single active arm bridge with longitudinal gauges (see Example 6.5.5). A load cell such as this is generally very stable and accurate. Similar cells may be used for measuring tensile forces. Load cells find use in industry in applications such as draw-bar and tool-force dynamometers, crane load monitoring, road vehicle weighing devices etc.

6.3.2. Calibration of force measuring instruments

Calibration of testing machines, all types of load cell, and weighing and other similar machines which utilise them, must be carried out at suitable intervals. Proving rings and load cells may be obtained which are calibrated by the supplier to NPL and BCS standards to within a specified percentage accuracy. These may be preserved as reference standards and used only to calibrate other rings, load cells and similar instruments. Calibration using these standards may be done with the standard and the device being calibrated arranged to carry the force in series with each other (see Fig. 6.13(b)). For calibration of lower

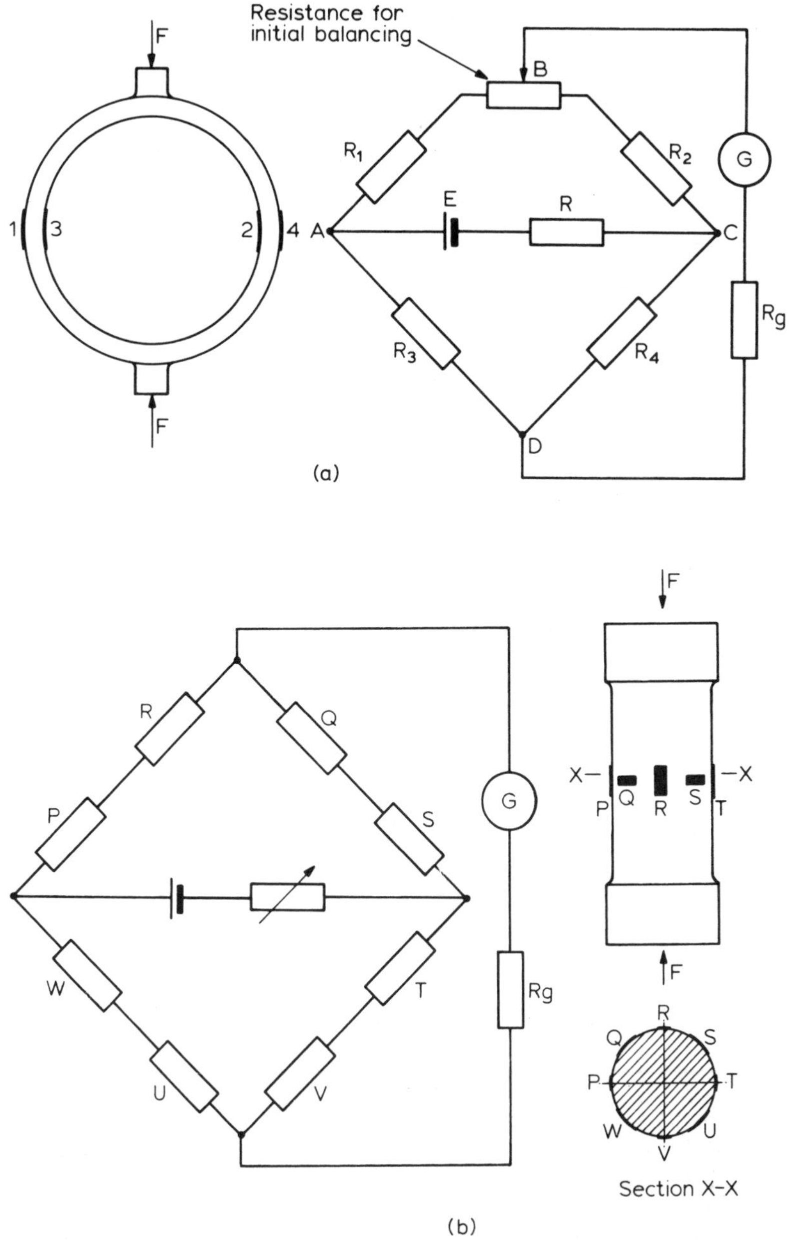

Fig. 6.12 (a) Strain-gauged proving ring.
(b) Strain-gauge load cell.

capacity devices, a Hounsfield tensometer with a set of calibrated beams provides a useful standard (see 3.8.2.). Piezoelectric force-measuring systems such as that described in Section 3.1.2 can provide a precise force standard. Force transducers of this type are available in a large range of sizes and force capacities, as large as 10^9 N. A portable weighbridge is illustrated in Fig. 6.13(a) and its calibration in Fig. 6.13(b).

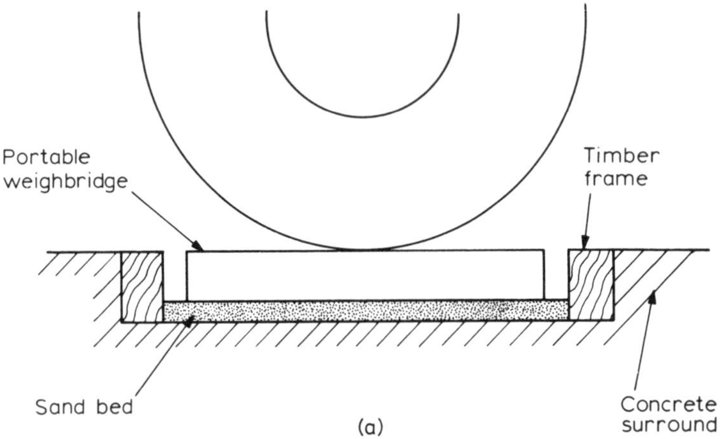

(a)

Fig. 6.13 (a) Installation of a portable weighbridge designed by the Transport and Road Research Laboratory.
(b) Calibration of load-cell for the weighbridge.

In many cases, calibration using the weight of standard masses is a suitable method. However, the accuracy of the masses must be known, care must be taken that moment-arm lengths are measured accurately and that pivots are virtually friction free, if they are incorporated.

6.4 Pressure measuring devices and systems

6.4.1 Bourdon-tube pressure gauges

The Bourdon-tube pressure gauge will already be familiar to many technicians. However, it is important enough to warrant inclusion again here, and Fig. 6.14 illustrates the simple C type. The applied pressure p_1 acts inside the tube and p_2, usually atmospheric pressure, acts on the outside. These apply a bending moment to the tube which tends to straighten it. The deflection x of the end C is a function of $p_1 - p_2$, and is amplified by the lever, quadrant, pinion and pointer arrangement. A flat spiral spring is commonly used to take up the backlash between the quadrant gear and the pinion. Bourdon-tube gauges are available to measure pressures up to the equivalent of a few centimetres of water, or pressures up to a thousand or more bar. Other Bourdon-tube con-

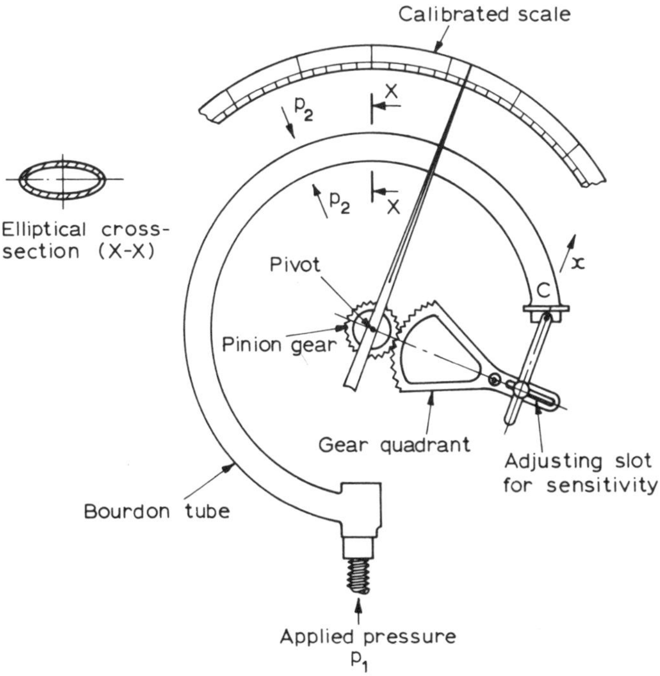

Fig. 6.14 Bourdon Tube with mechanical amplification.

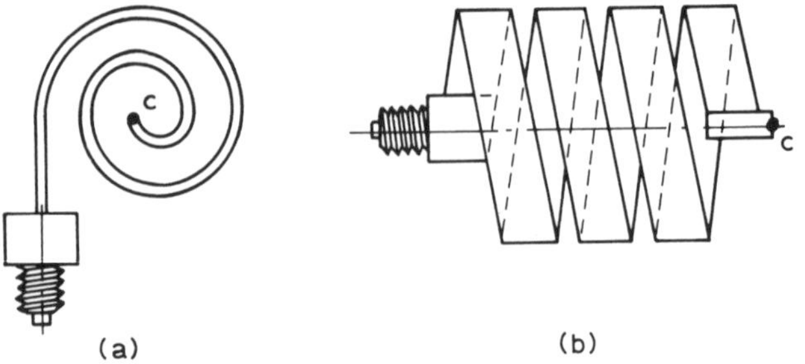

Fig. 6.15

figurations are shown in Fig. 6.15. That in (a) is a flat spiral, the one in (b) a helix. Both give increased sensitivity compared with the C-tube type.

6.4.2 Piezoelectric pressure transducers

Piezoelectric pressure transducers work in exactly the same way as the piezoelectric force transducers described in Section 3.1.2. The only difference is the arrangement for the fluid pressure to apply the force to the face of the crystal. A piezoelectric pressure transducer is shown in Fig. 6.16(a), whilst (b) shows a miniature version mounted in a special sparking-plug adaptor so that the pressure in an engine cylinder may be measured without the need for a special pressure tapping. The pressure range of such transducers may be up to several thousand bar if required.

6.4.3 Piezometer tubes and manometers

For measuring low pressures, piezometers and manometers provide a cheap and effective method. Fig. 6.17 illustrates two piezometer tubes measuring the pressure head loss due to fluid friction between points 1 and 2. Example 6.5.6 shows the method of calculating the pressure difference.

Care must be taken that the tappings for the tubes are at 90° to the pipe, and do not protrude into the pipe, or some of the dynamic pressure head, i.e., that due to velocity, may be included. If the pipes are of different diameter, giving different velocities at points 1 and 2, then this must be taken into account in the calculation of pressure difference due to friction, using Bernoulli's equation. If the static pressure in the pipe is too large, the tubes may be too long for convenience. To maintain them short, the tops of the tubes may be connected by a tube which is pressurised with air (e.g., by a bicycle pump). Since this pressure is applied to both piezometer tubes, the head difference (δh) is unchanged, although both liquid levels become lower. Example 6.5.6 illustrates this.

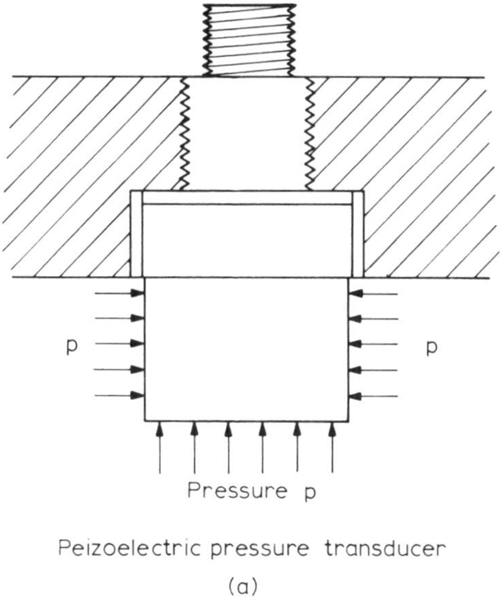

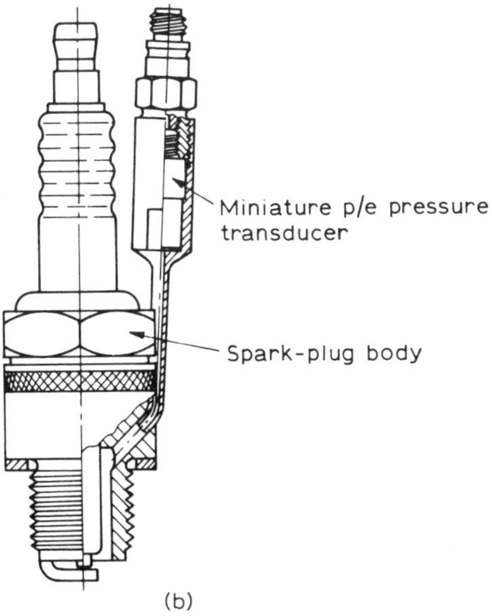

Fig. 6.16 (a) Piezoelectric pressure transducer.
(b) Miniature piezoelectric pressure transducer.

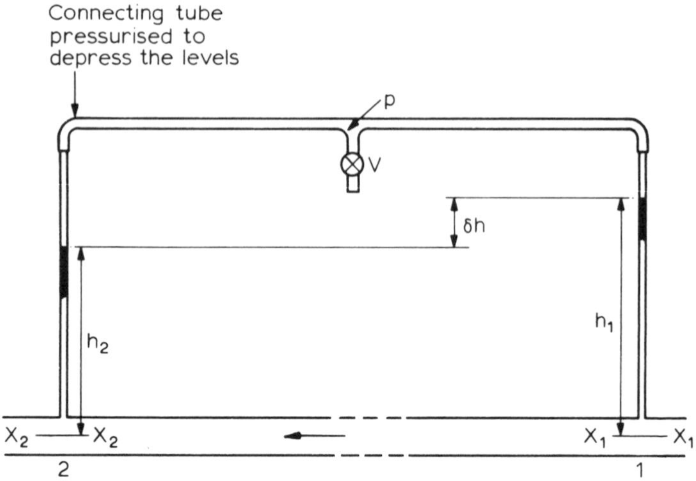

Fig. 6.17

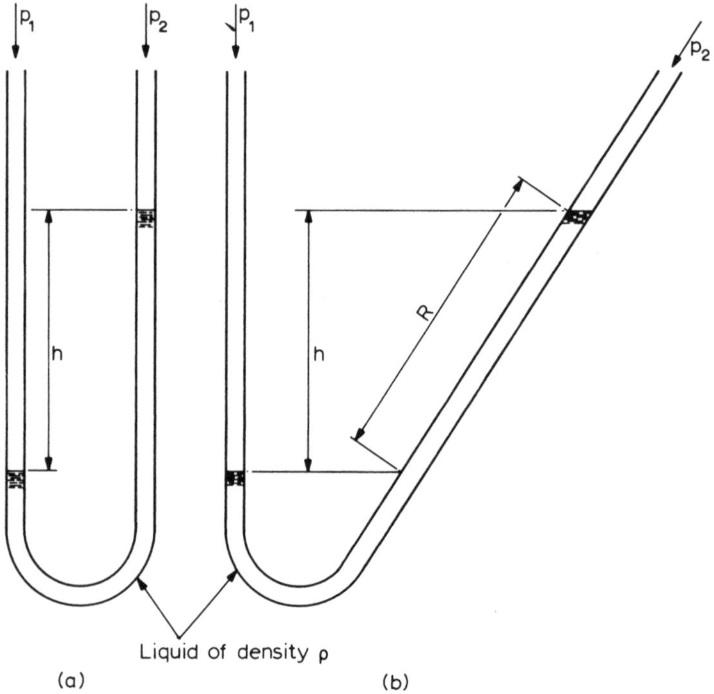

Fig. 6.18 U-tube manometers.

Piezometer tubes are only suitable for liquids. If gas pressures are to be measured, or liquid pressures at higher values, then a U-tube manometer is more suitable. Fig. 6.18(a) shows a simple U-tube, and in (b) an inclined leg U-tube is illustrated. The latter has increased sensitivity since for a given pressure difference p_1–p_2, the change of reading (R) is greater than h. The pressure difference is given by:

$$p_1 - p_2 = \rho g h \text{ for both types} \tag{6.2}$$

since $h = R \sin\theta$, then:

$$p_1 - p_2 = \rho g\, R \sin\theta \text{ for the inclined-tube manometer} \tag{6.3}$$

If p_2 is atmospheric pressure, then $p_1 - p_2$ is *gauge pressure*. Variations in the diameter of the tubes do not affect the accuracy of either manometer, but h must be measured vertically and R at angle θ, or error will ensue.

The main difficulty in reading the simple U-tube manometers is due to both levels varying. A fixed datum from which to measure is obtained by using a well-type manometer, as shown in Fig. 6.19(a). The volume of liquid displaced from the well by the pressure difference causes its level to drop by d. The level in the tube side increases by h', and hence the head difference is $h' + d$. Let the well cross-section area be A, and that of the

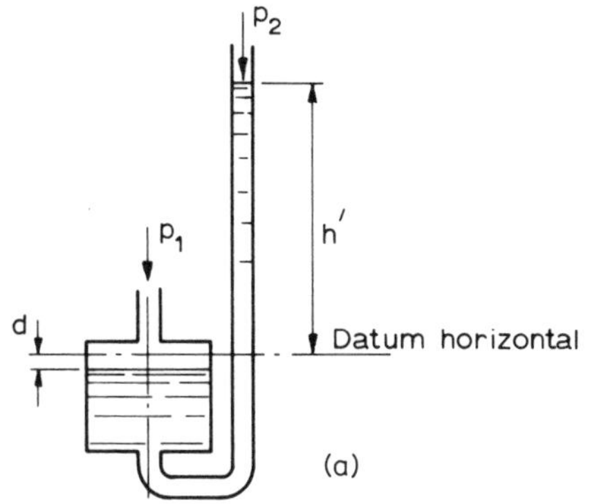

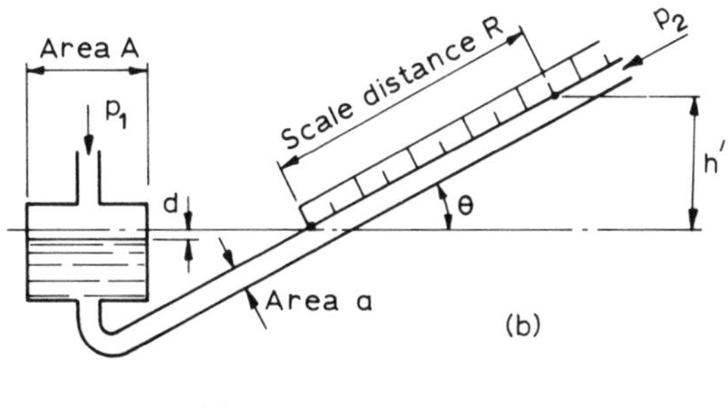

Fig. 6.19 (a) and (b) Well-type manometers.

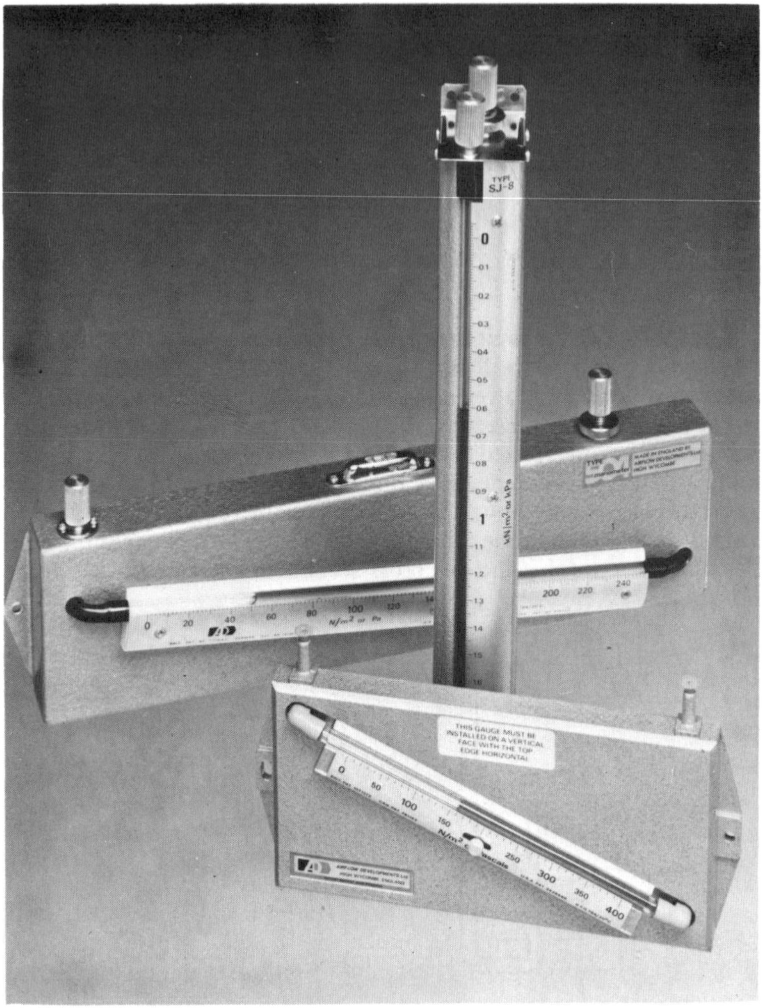

Fig. 6.19 (c) Well-type manometers.

tube a, both uniform over the range of movement of the levels. The volume displaced from the well enters the tube.

Thus $$A \times d = a \times h'$$

$$d = \frac{a}{A} \times h' \qquad \text{eqn. (i)}$$

Equating pressures at the lower surface level,

$$p_1 = p_2 + \rho g(h' + d) \qquad \text{eqn. (ii)}$$

Combining eqns. (i) and (ii) gives:

$$p_1 - p_2 = \rho g(h' + ah'/A)$$
$$= \rho g h'(1 + a/A) \tag{6.4}$$

According to the degree of accuracy required, the a/A term may be neglected, or corrected for by calculation, or the scale divided so that true distance along the scale multiplied by $(1 + a/A)$ gives the marked value. It may be shown that for the inclined-tube well-type manometer of Fig. 6.19(b), the pressure difference is given by:

$$p_1 - p_2 = gR\,(\sin\theta + a/A) \tag{6.5}$$

Hence the scale should be divided so that true distance along the scale multiplied by $(\sin\theta + a/A)$ gives the marked value. Fig. 6.19(c) illustrates well-type manometers. Example 6.5.8 illustrates an application of this type of manometer.

For the remote indication, recording or control application of the pressure signal from a piezometer or U-tube manometer, a secondary transducer may be used to provide a voltage, which is convenient for transmission. One method is to use a float connected to a resistance or l.v.d.t. type displacement transducer, as in Fig. 6.9.

6.4.4 Calibration of pressure measuring instruments

Calibration of pressure gauges and transducers may be carried out against other gauges or devices of higher standard by supplying the same fluid pressure to both and comparing readings. However, a more direct and accurate method is to use a dead-weight tester as shown in Fig. 6.20(a) and (b).

With this type of tester, the calibration pressure is provided by the gravity force on calibrated masses, each mass on the spindle S giving an accurately known pressure. The gauge or transducer is connected as shown, and air is bled from the system. Handle H is wound to move the piston T to pressurise the hydraulic fluid. When the spindle S is lifted by the fluid pressure, the pressure force under the spindle is balanced against the gravity force on mass M, consisting of the spindle platform and added masses; and a friction force. The friction drag is minimised by good surface finish and fit between the spindle S and its bore, and by rotating the table so that kinetic friction applies rather than static friction, the latter introducing the probability of stick-slip conditions. Many kinds of pressure measuring devices may be calibrated, such as industrial pressure gauges, piezoelectric or potentiometric pressure transducers, engine pressure-indicators, high-standard pressure switches etc. The tester is calibrated initially by the manufacturer for a given g value, usually the standard 9.80665 m/s^2, and local variations may be corrected for if significant.

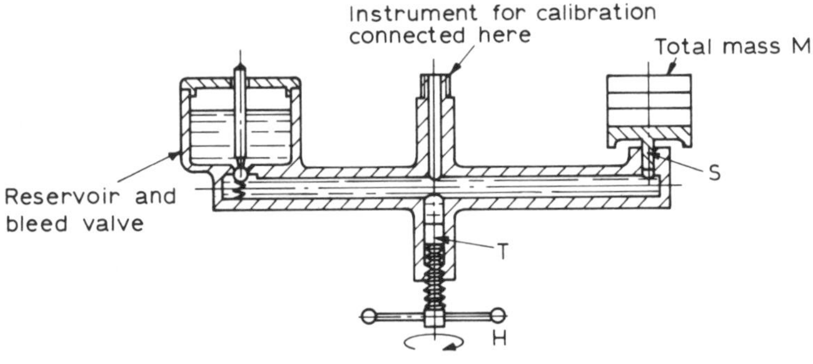

(b)

Fig. 6.20 (a) Smiths Industries' deadweight pressure-calibration unit.
(b) Deadweight pressure-calibration unit.

Well-type manometers and similar fixed-scale devices depend on accurate well and tube sizes, and should be calibrated against simple U-tube manometers or other accurate standards. An accurate standard instrument available uses a helical Bourdon-tube made of fused quartz, and is extremely stable. The deflection is measured optically and the accuracy may be within 0.015% of the reading. The instrument has a wide range. Vacuum gauges may be calibrated using U-tube manometers, as shown in Example 6.5.9.

6.5 Worked examples

6.5.1 A stroboscope flashing on the end of a rotating shaft carrying one reflective mark gave the images shown in Fig. 6.21. State the speed of the shaft, and explain each of the images.

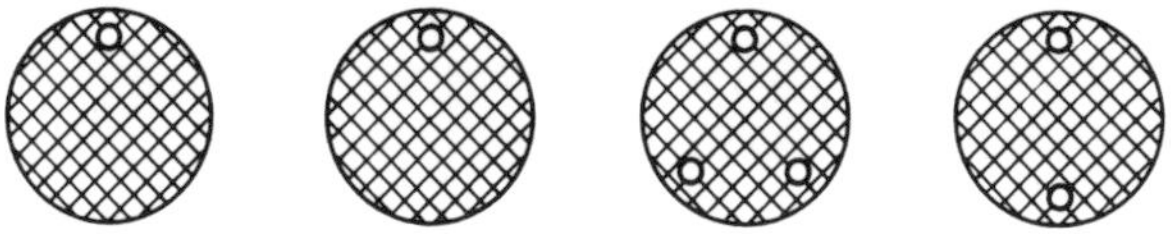

Fig. 6.21 Stroboscope images.

Image D must show illumination of the single spot twice each revolution, hence B must show illumination once each revolution, and A once every second revolution. A possible explanation of C is that the spot is illuminated once in two-thirds of a revolution. To check this, assuming that 3000 rev/min is the shaft speed, then the time taken to rotate 2/3 rev is $\frac{2}{3} \times \frac{1}{3000}$ min

Hence $$\text{flashing rate} = \frac{9000}{2} = 4500 \text{ flashes/min.}$$

It is not necessary to check multiple images as above in practice. Only images D and B with flashing frequency ratios 2:1 need be obtained, to ensure reading the correct value with one image.

6.5.2 A 20-tooth ferrous gear wheel was used with a magnetic pickup, connected to a frequency meter, for shaft speed measurement. The frequency meter was checked against the mains frequency standard and found to give a count within ± 1 Hz.

(a) If the measured frequency was 720 Hz calculate the shaft speed.

(b) Calculate the discrimination and the repeatability in rev/min.

(a) $$\text{Shaft speed}\left(\frac{\text{rev}}{\text{min}}\right) = \text{pulse rate}\left(\frac{\text{pulse}}{\text{s}}\right) \times 60\left(\frac{\text{s}}{\text{min}}\right) \times \frac{1}{20}\left(\frac{\text{rev}}{\text{pulse}}\right)$$

$$= 720 \times \frac{60}{20} = 2160 \text{ rev/min.}$$

(b) Discrimination, the smallest speed change that may be detected, is that which causes ± 1 Hz change of frequency. In this case, the repeatability will also be the same value, provided the time base of the meter is stable. The value is:

$$1\left(\frac{\cancel{\text{pulse}}}{\cancel{\text{s}}}\right) \times \frac{1}{20}\left(\frac{\text{rev}}{\cancel{\text{pulse}}}\right) \times 60\left(\frac{\cancel{\text{s}}}{\text{min}}\right) = 3\ \text{rev/min}.$$

The accuracy of the measurement cannot be better than the repeatability, and hence is no better than $\left(\frac{\pm 3}{2260}\right) \times 100\,\% = \pm 0.13\,\%$ of the point value.

6.5.3 The rotational speed ω rad/s of a disc of diameter 200 mm is to be continuously measured by using a light source with pickup unit as shown in Fig. 6.22 together with a number of slots (x) around the periphery. The frequency (f) of the pulses from the pickup is to be measured in hertz using a frequency meter which continuously updates its reading. Calculate a convenient number of slots so that the frequency reading multiplied by 10^n gives the angular velocity of the table, and state n. Calculate the percentage error in the measurement when the speed is 10 rad/s, if the frequency reading is accurate to ± 1 Hz.

$$\text{Angular velocity } \omega\left(\frac{\text{rad}}{s}\right) = f\left(\frac{\cancel{\text{pulse}}}{s}\right) \times \frac{1}{x}\left(\frac{\cancel{\text{rev}}}{\cancel{\text{pulse}}}\right) \times 2\pi\left(\frac{\text{rad}}{\cancel{\text{rev}}}\right) \times 10^n$$

$$\therefore \qquad x = \frac{f}{\omega} \times 2\pi \times 10^n$$

(a) Try $f = \omega$, and $n = 0$ then $x = 6.28$ or 6 slots—unsuitable.
(b) Try $f = 10\omega$ and $n = -1$, $x = 62.8$ or 63 slots
(c) Try $f = 100\omega$ and $n = -2$, $x = 628$ slots.

$$\text{Slot spacing for (b) is } \frac{\pi \times 200}{63} = 9.97\ \text{mm}.$$

$$\text{Slot spacing for (c) is } \frac{\pi \times 200}{628} = 1.00\ \text{mm—unsuitable}$$

Hence, $x = 63$ and $n = -1$ i.e. $f/10 = \omega$ approximately.
At a disc speed of $\omega = 2\pi$ rad/s (1 rev/s) the *measured* speed ω' is given by:

$$\omega' = \frac{f \pm 1}{10} \quad \text{where f is the measured frequency}$$

$$= \frac{63 \pm 1}{10} = 6.3 \pm 0.1\ \text{rad/s}.$$

Error, percentage of point value:

$$= \left(\frac{\omega' - \omega}{\omega}\right) \times 100\,\%$$

$$= \left(\frac{6.3 \pm 0.1 - 2\pi}{2\pi}\right) \times 100\,\%$$

$$= \left\{\left(\frac{6.3 - 2\pi}{2\pi}\right) \pm \left(\frac{0.1}{2\pi}\right)\right\} \times 100\,\%$$

$= +0.27\,\%$ due to inexact number of slots, $\pm 1.6\,\%$ due to ± 1 frequency error.

6.5.4 The rig of Fig. 6.22 was devised to check the calibration of a number of rotational-speed measuring systems. It comprises a motor, whose speed is variable, driving the following:

(a) a d.c. tachogenerator with a stated sensitivity of 1 mV per rev/s,

(b) a disc with ten radial slots at the periphery, with a light source plus photodiode sensor connected to a frequency meter,

(c) a 60-tooth ferrous gearwheel with a magnetic pickup connected to a frequency meter,

(d) a disc with one reflective spot on its face, on which a stroboscopic flash is directed.

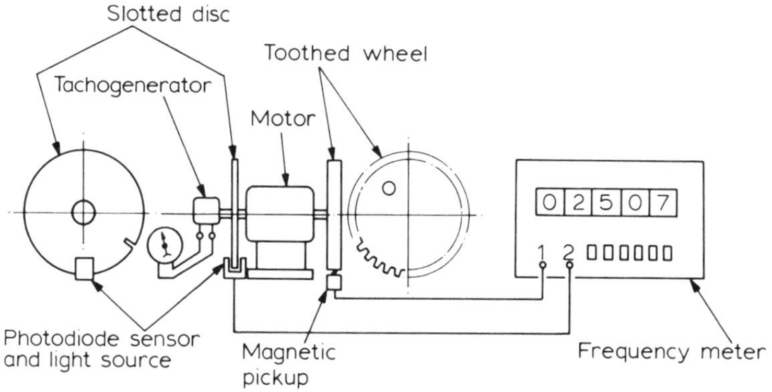

Fig. 6.22 Shaft speed measurement.

The following readings were taken during a test, the values in brackets being the readings converted to rev/min units:

	Tachometer output (V)	*Frequency from light pick-up* (Hz)	*Frequency from magnetic pickup* (Hz)	*Stroboscope reading (flashes/min)*
1	0.5 (500)	84 (504)	504	495
2	1.0 (1000)	166 (996)	998	1000
3	1.5 (1500)	249 (1494)	1492	1505
4	2.0 (2000)	333 (1998)	1998	2015
5	2.5 (2500)	418 (2508)	2505	2520
6	3.0 (3000)	502 (3012)	3011	3030
7	3.5 (3500)	587 (3522)	3520	3545
8	4.0 (4000)	671 (4026)	4031	4060

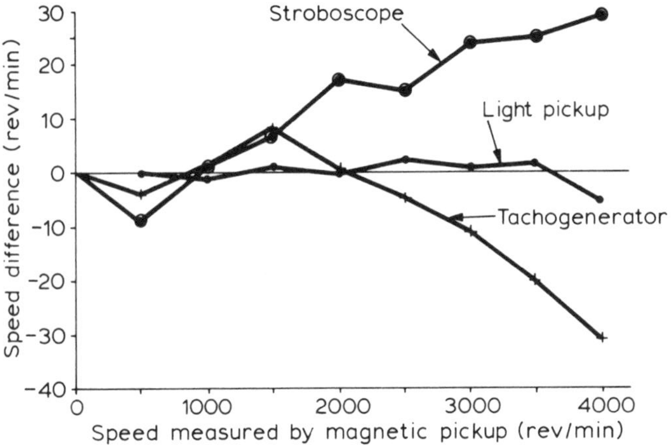

Fig. 6.23

One of the systems has to be taken as a standard, against which the others will be compared. The crystal-controlled frequency meter is itself an accurate frequency standard. The magnetic pick-up, receiving 60 pulses/rev, has better discrimination than the light-sensitive pick-up, which receives only 10 pulses/rev. The differences between the speed values from the light-sensitive and magnetic pick-ups is obviously due to this lesser discrimination. Hence the magnetic pick-up speed will be taken as the standard. The differences between the values are tabulated in rev/min:

	Tachometer	Light pickup	Stroboscope
1	−4	0	−9
2	+2	−2	+2
3	+8	+2	+7
4	+2	0	+17
5	−5	+3	+15
6	−11	+1	+19
7	−20	+2	+25
8	−31	−5	+29

The above values are plotted against the speed measured by the magnetic pickup in Fig. 6.23.

6.5.5 A strain-gauge load cell and bridge as shown in Fig. 6.12(b) has the following details:

modulus of elasticity of steel	$= 200\,\text{GN/m}^2$
limit of proportionality stress of steel	$= 200\,\text{MN/m}^2$
Poisson's ratio for steel	$= 0.30$
resistance of each strain gauge	$= 100\,\Omega$
gauge factor of each strain gauge	$= 2.0$

If the bridge is of voltage-sensitive type, supplied with a constant 4.0 V, calculate the bridge output voltage when the applied compressive force produces the limit of proportionality stress in compression.

Compressive stress $\theta = 200\,\text{MN/m}^2$
Tensile stress in circumferential direction $= \nu \times \varepsilon$

$$\text{Compressive strain } \varepsilon = \frac{\theta}{E} = \frac{200 \times 10^6}{200 \times 10^9} = 10^{-3}$$

Tensile strain in circumferential direction $= \nu \times \varepsilon$
For a single-active-arm bridge, the output is, by eqn. 4.7:

$$V_{BD} = \frac{\delta R}{R} \times \frac{V_{AC}}{4}$$

In this bridge, the two compressive gauge arms *each* give the above output, and each tensile arm gives ν times the above output

$$\therefore \qquad V_{BD} = \frac{\delta R}{R} \times \frac{V_{AC}}{4}(1 + 1 + 0.3 + 0.3)$$

and

$$V_{BD} = \frac{\delta R}{R} \times \frac{V_{AC}}{4} \times 2.6$$

also, $$\frac{\delta R}{R} = \varepsilon F \text{ from equation 3.2.}$$

$\therefore$ $$V_{BD} = \varepsilon F \times \frac{2.6}{4} \times V_{AC}$$

$$= 10^{-3} \times 2.0 \times \frac{2.6}{4} \times 4.0\,\text{V}$$

$$= 5.2\,\text{mV}$$

6.5.6 Two piezometer tubes are used to measure the pressure loss due to friction, between points 1 and 2 in a pipe in which water flows. To reduce the heads h_1 and h_2, the tops of the tubes are connected by a tube as shown in Fig. 6.17, which is pressurised by air to a pressure p through the valve V. Calculate the difference in the static pressures at 1 and 2, when the head difference is $\delta h = 255$ mm.

At X_1X_1 the static pressure is $p_1 = \rho g h_1 + p$
At X_2X_2 the static pressure is $p_2 = \rho g h_2 + p$
Static pressure difference is $p_1 - p_2 = (\rho g h_1 + p) - (\rho g h_2 + p)$

$$= \rho g h_1 - \rho g h_2$$
$$= \rho g (h_1 - h_2)$$
$$= \rho g \delta h$$
$$= 1000 \times 9.81 \times 0.255$$
$$= 2500\,\text{N/m}^2$$

Note that the air pressure p cancels out.

6.5.7 A well-type U-tube manometer using mercury as the measuring fluid has a well 30 mm diameter and a tube of 1 mm bore. If a scale graduated correctly in millimetres is used, and the datum level is at 0 mm, calculate the reading on the scale when a pressure difference equivalent to 1.00 m of mercury head is applied across the instrument, and the percentage error if the reading is not corrected.

$$\frac{p_1 - p_2}{\rho g} = h' + d = h'\left(1 + \frac{a}{A}\right) \quad \text{by eqn. 6.4}$$

$$1000 = h'\left(1 + \frac{\pi d^2/4}{\pi D^2/4}\right)$$

$$= h'\left\{1 + \left(\frac{1}{30}\right)^2\right\}$$

$$= h'\left(\frac{900+1}{900}\right)$$

$$h' = 1000 \times \frac{900}{901} = 998.9\,\text{mm}$$

$$\text{Percentage error} = \left(\frac{998.9-1000}{1000}\right) \times 100\,\%$$

$$= \frac{-1.1}{1000} = -0.11\,\%$$

6.5.8 A well-type, inclined tube manometer with a well 80 mm diameter and a tube 5 mm diameter is to be used to measure the pressure difference across the orifice in an airbox, used to measure the air flowrate into a reciprocating engine. Calculate:

(a) the angle (θ) at which the tube should be inclined to give a sensitivity of R/(true head difference of water) = 2 (see Fig. 6.24).

(b) the air flow rate into the engine when $R = 150$ mm, if the orifice has an area A_o of 1000 mm^2 and a co-efficient of discharge (C_D) of 0.60. Take the density of air as 1.2 kg/m^3.

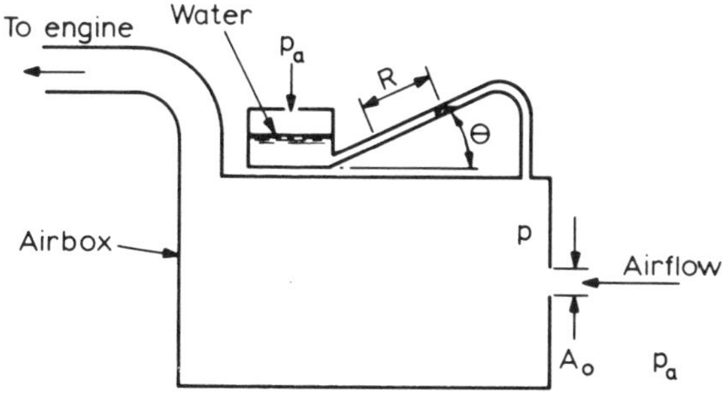

Fig. 6.24 Airbox for measuring pulsating air flowrate.

(a) By eqn. 6.5: $p_a - p = \rho g R(\sin\theta + a/A)$

or $$\frac{p_a - p}{\rho g} = R\left(\sin\theta + \frac{a}{A}\right) = h_w, \text{ the true head of water}$$

$\therefore$ $$h_w = R\left(\sin\theta + \frac{a}{A}\right)$$

$$\frac{h_w}{R} = \sin\theta + \frac{a}{A}, \text{ but } \frac{R}{h_w} = 2$$

$\therefore$ $$\frac{1}{2} = \sin\theta + \frac{\pi d^2/4}{\pi D^2/4}$$

$$\sin\theta = 0.5 - (5/80)^2$$
$$\theta = 29.7^\circ$$

(b) The flow rate is given by

$$\dot{V} = C_D \times A_o \times \sqrt{2gh_a} \text{ where } h_a \text{ is the 'head' of air.}$$

$$= C_D \times A_o \times \sqrt{2gh_w \times \rho_w/\rho_a} \text{ where } \rho_w = \text{density of water,}$$

and ρ_a = density of air

$$= 0.60 \times \frac{10^3}{10^6} \times \sqrt{\left(2 \times 9.81 \times \frac{0.150}{2} \times \frac{10^3}{1.2}\right)}$$

$\therefore$ $\dot{V} = 0.021\ \text{m}^3/\text{s}$

6.5.9 A vacuum gauge whose scale is graduated in 5 mm of mercury increments was calibrated using a mercury U-tube manometer and

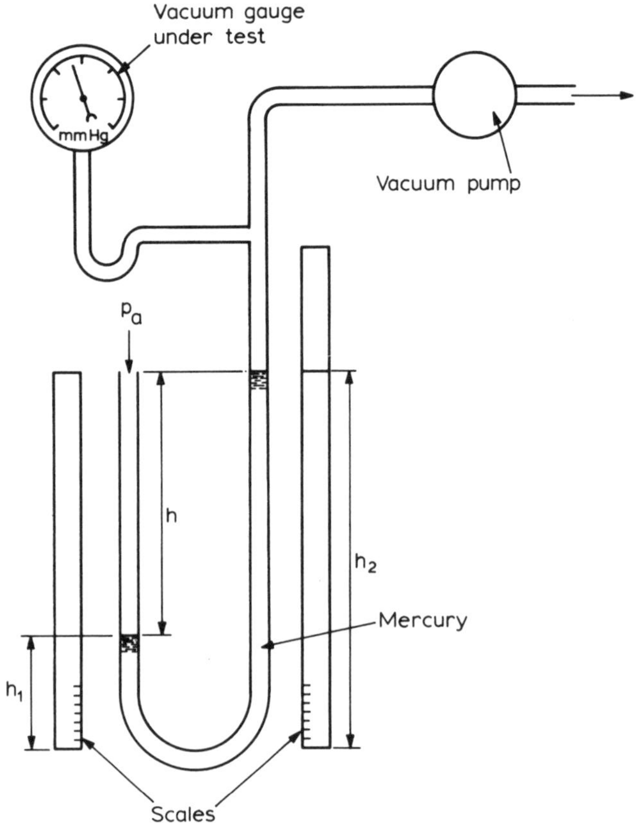

Fig. 6.25 Calibration of a vacuum guage.

vacuum pump as shown in Fig. 6.25. The following readings were taken:

Gauge reading (mm Hg)	100	200	300	400	500	600	700
h_1 (mm)	450	400	350	298	251	201	150
h_2 (mm)	549	598	655	700	753	802	852

Check that the accuracy of the gauge is within the discrimination of the gauge scale graduations.

Gauge reading (mm Hg)	100	200	300	400	500	600	700
$h_2 - h_1$ (mm Hg)	99	198	305	402	502	601	702

From these values it is seen that the maximum difference between the calibration pressure head $(h_2 - h_1)$ does not exceed the discrimination of the gauge graduations.

6.6 Practical and tutorial work

6.6.1 Use a stroboscope to observe the oscillations of cam followers, ignition contact-breaker mechanisms or similar devices.

6.6.2 From the manufacturers literature for stroboscopes and timer/counter/frequency meters compare their range, discrimination and timebase accuracy.

6.6.3 Investigate the effect of varying the distance from a magnetic pick-up to a rotating toothed wheel, and the effect of the speed of the wheel on the reliability of output voltage pulses.

6.6.4 Devise a method of measuring the discrimination of an l.v.d.t. system.

6.6.5 It is proposed to use a float and l.v.d.t. to measure the liquid level in a U-tube manometer, the voltage output to be a function of the pressure difference applied to the manometer. Will the presence of the float alter the pressure/liquid-level equations?

6.7 Exercises

6.7.1 Using a stroboscope with a flashing rate of 10 000/min maximum, a single stationary image was obtained of a single spot on a rotating disc when the flashing rate was set at 8000/min. If the speed of rotation of the disc *is* 8000 rev/min show, as a check, that at a setting of 10 000 flashes/min, five stationary images should be visible.

6.7.2 Fig. 6.26 shows the number of stationary images of a reflective spot on a rotating disc, when illuminated by a stroboscope flashing at the frequencies indicated. Determine the rotational speed in revolutions per second and explain why the number of images of the spot occur in each case.

6.7.3 A single-start leadscrew of 4 mm pitch drives a machine table. On the end of the leadscrew is an 80 mm diameter disc which is to be slotted radially around the periphery, and used with a light source and

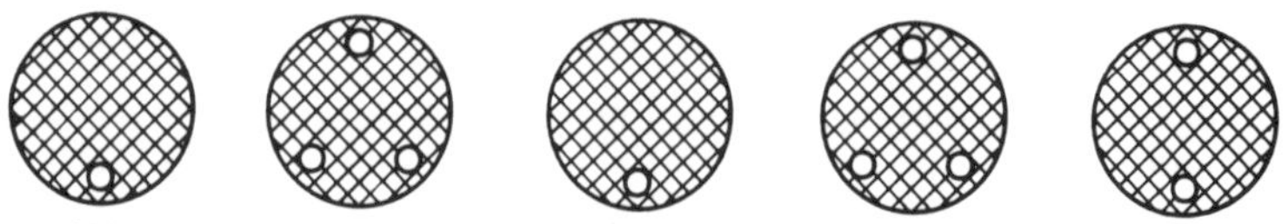

Fig. 6.26 Stroboscope images.

photodiode, coupled to a frequency meter. Determine the number (x) of equally-spaced slots so that the frequency indicated by the meter $\times 10^{-1}$ gives the table speed in mm/s.

6.7.4 The speed of vehicles, up to 80 km/h, is to be measured using two sensing strips on the road surface. The first strip starts a timer and the second one stops it, as the leading wheels pass over them. If the minimum time (t) which may be measured to sufficient accuracy is 0.30 s, calculate the required distance (x) between the strips, and the value of K so that the speed in km/h is given by K/t.

6.7.5 In a gearbox, the only gear accessible for mounting a magnetic pickup for speed measurement has 85 teeth. This meshes with a 37 tooth gear on the shaft whose speed is to be measured. Calculate (a) the constant to be multiplied by the measured frequency from the pickup to give the required shaft speed in rev/min, (b) the discrimination of this measurement system if the frequency is measured within ± 1Hz.

6.7.6 The speed of a railway locomotive is to be measured using a magnetic pickup receiving impulses from a toothed disc attached to a wheel 0.920 m diameter. The frequency of the voltage pulses are to be measured by a meter in the driver's cab which reads 100.0 km/h when it receives pulses at a frequency of 1000 Hz. Calculate the nearest whole number of pulses the pick-up must receive each revolution of the wheel to give this indicated speed, and the percentage error in the speed measurement due to rounding off the number. State whether this error will increase or decrease due to wear of the wheel.

6.7.7 A miniature piezoelectric pressure transducer was connected to a deadweight tester, and the electrical output was connected through a charge amplifier to a valve voltmeter. For various deadweight pressures on the tester, the voltmeter readings were noted immediately after each pressure value was applied, giving the following data:

Deadweight pressure (lbf/in^2)	200	400	600	800	1000
Valve voltmeter reading (V)	1.20	2.20	3.60	4.90	6.00

(see appendix re-units)

Plot the values and from the "best straight line" through the points calculate the sensitivity of the system. Using this value, determine the maximum error in N/m^2 and hence the accuracy % f.s.d. of the system.

6.7.8 A manometer has a well 20 mm diameter and the inclined tube of the other leg is 4 mm diameter bore. It is proposed to use a scale graduated accurately in millimetres to measure the pressure head directly, i.e. a 1 mm scale division indicates a 1 mm pressure-head change. Calculate the angle at which the tube must be inclined to the vertical.

6.7.9 A mercury manometer is to use a well of 30 mm diameter bore and a vertical tube of 5 mm diameter bore. Calculate the distance between the zero and 1 bar scale marks. The density of mercury is 13 600 kg/m^3.

6.7.10 Magnetic pick-ups are available which give out a voltage pulse when ferrous material moves through their magnetic field.

(a) Using a simple sketch, describe the principle of operation of this type of transducer.

(b) Sketch and describe the application of this type of transducer to the measurement of the rotational speed of a shaft, noting any precautions which must be taken to ensure accuracy and precision of the measurement.

(c) Sketch and describe the application of two such transducers to the measurement of the torque in a rotating shaft, and suggest a method of calibrating the system against some other standard.

6.7.11 A linear-displacement transducer is to be used for controlling the position of a gate valve in a heating and ventilating system, sited where the temperature is variable, and where vibration and dust may be present. The transducer consists of a helical coil of conductor, with a wiper, forming a voltage-balancing potentiometer. It is tested by applying a constant voltage over the coil, and reading the potential difference at the wiper using a high-impedance digital voltmeter, at displacements set by slip gauges.

The following readings were taken:

displacement x (mm)	*p.d. over wiper* (V)	*minimum change of x to produce a change of voltmeter reading* (mm)
0	0	0.11
10	1.02	0.20
20	2.03	0.19
30	3.03	0.09
40	4.02	0.20
50	5.04	0.11
60	6.03	0.09
70	7.02	0.18
80	7.99	0.19
90	9.01	0.12
100	10.01	0.11

(a) Sketch the electrical circuit of the transducer and equipment for the test, and state why a high-impedance voltmeter is necessary.

(b) From the tabulated values determine:
(i) the transducer accuracy as percentage f.s.d.
(ii) the transducer accuracy as percentage of point value.
(iii) the discrimination of the transducer.
(c) Discuss briefly:
(i) why the readings of the third column of the table vary in the way they do.
(ii) how the environmental conditions in the proposed use of the transducer may affect its accuracy and life.
(iii) the advantages and disadvantages of using an l.v.d.t. transducer in place of the one above.

6.8 Measurement projects

Students of the unit 'Engineering Instrumentation and Control' are required to carry out a project on a measurement system. The objectives are to:
(a) analyse the system requirements,
(b) specify a suitable system,
(c) test the system and analyse the results,
(d) write a report.

The particular projects which students may attempt will depend on the instruments and technician aid available. It is suggested that many of the following projects may be carried out with the instruments and equipment found in the laboratories and workshops of many colleges. Some of the projects require simple parts to be made, and it is assumed that these will be attempted only if technician assistance is available for this purpose.

Not all of the projects are of equal difficulty. Some of them may be suitable for two or more students to attempt together; some of the projects may be put together to form a group project as suggested in 6.8.8. In these cases, responsibility must be accepted by each student for a particular area of the investigation.

It is suggested that it may be appropriate to select project work related to areas of study in other units of the combination being followed. Thus students studying 'Mechanical Science IV' could carry out a project in the area of strength of materials or dynamics, whilst a student taking 'Manufacturing Technology IV' or 'Properties of Materials IV' could carry out measurements on machine tools or materials testing respectively. The project suggestions are classified in sections for clarity.

6.8.1 Measurement of size and displacement

(a) Devise and test a system to record the displacement-time relationship for a pneumatic ram from the moment of operation of the solenoid-controlled valve supplying the air. Hence find the delay time and the maximum velocity.

(b) Devise and test a system for measuring the diameter and ovality of a large component, the values to be displayed on voltmeters.

(c) Devise and test a system for measuring the extension *of the specimen* during tensile testing with a Hounsfield Tensometer.

(d) Devise and calibrate a float-l.v.d.t.-voltmeter system for:

(i) the measurement of liquid level in a tank, calibrating the voltmeter in height units,

(ii) the measurement of level in a manometer, calibrating the voltmeter in pressure units.

(e) Devise and test a height comparator using strain gauges on a thin steel strip.

(f) Devise and test a system for rapidly testing a length, diameter or angle of a mass-produced component from a machine, and giving a signal if the component is inside the required limits.

(g) Devise and test a liquid-level indicating system consisting of a 'float' fixed to a strain-gauged cantilever beam, the indicator being a voltmeter calibrated in height units.

(h) Devise and test a system using the pressure at the bottom of a tank of liquid to measure the height to the surface.

(i) Devise and test a force transducer or strain-gauge system to measure the quantity of liquid or solid in a tank or hopper.

(j) Study the specification and measurement of surface finish, and the sensing, conditioning, display and recording elements of a surface-finish measuring system.

(k) Study the operation of a back-pressure type air-jet sensing system, and determine its pressure against displacement sensitivity. Select a suitable pressure to voltage secondary transducer and devise a system for the non-contacting measurement of component size, giving an output on a voltmeter, suitably calibrated in size units.

6.8.2 Timing, and the measurement of frequency, velocity and acceleration

(a) Devise and test a system to measure, and if possible to record against time, the shaft speed of an engine, air-compressor, electric motor or similar machine.

(b) Devise and test a system for measuring electrically the instantaneous velocity of a Fletcher's trolley, an air-track vehicle, or the moving table of a machine.

(c) Device and test a timing-mark system for an internal-combustion engine to display on an oscilloscope marks corresponding to $-15°$, $-10°$, $-5°$, outer dead centre, $+5°$, $+10°$ and $+15°$ of the crank. (The system will probably use a slotted disc on the crankshaft, with a suitable pickup and conditioning elements.)

(d) Devise and test a method of measuring and recording the acceleration of an electric motor after being switched on, with different inertia loads on the shaft.

(e) Devise and test an accelerometer which may be placed in a motor vehicle and used to test its braking efficiency.

(f) Study the action of the mechanical ignition-advance mechanism of a petrol engine, noting the advance angle at differing speeds, and recording these photographically if possible.

(g) Devise and test a system to measure and indicate the crank angle to outer-dead centre at which the spark occurs in a petrol engine, under different load conditions.

(h) Devise and use a method of calibrating an accelerometer.

6.8.3 Measurement of force, torque and pressure

(a) Select an l.v.d.t. of suitable range to measure the deflection of a proving ring, and design a suitable mounting for it. Calibrate the system against the best available force standard.

(b) Select an l.v.d.t. to measure the deflection of the free end of a Bourdon-tube or bellows, and design a suitable mounting for it. Calibrate the system against the best available pressure standard.

(c) Select suitable conditioning items for a piezoelectric or strain-gauge type force-transducer and calibrate the system against the best available standard. Use the system to measure one of the following, recording the results by suitable means:
(i) the force due to the impact of a dropping mass
(ii) the force during a punching or blanking operation
(iii) the force in a moving link in a mechanism
(iv) the load on the lifting hook of a hoist.

(d) Devise and test a system to provide a voltage signal which is a function of the force applied to a test piece in the Hounsfield Tensometer.

(e) Devise and test a method of measuring, and recording continuously if possible, the torque:
(i) delivered by an electric motor, hydraulic motor or engine
(ii) delivered to a generator, hydraulic pump or air compressor
(iii) transmitted by a rotating shaft.

(f) Devise and test a method of measuring, and recording if possible, the force or torque in the machining operations:
(i) turning
(ii) shaping
(iii) drilling
(iv) milling.

(g) Devise, test, and calibrate, a system to measure and record the pressure in an engine cylinder under operating conditions.

(h) Devise a compression load-cell from a length of ground steel bar, bonding strain gauges to it axially and circumferentially. Calibrate the cell against the best force standard available.

(i) Devise and test a system to give a voltage which is proportional to the small *pressure difference* between two relatively high pressures.

(j) Apply strain gauges to a proving ring and calibrate the output from the Wheatstone bridge against force applied to the ring, using the best force standard available.

6.8.4 Strength of materials

(a) Devise and carry out an experiment to measure Poisson's ratio for a material either in compression or tension.

(b) Devise and carry out an experiment to measure the torque in a circular rod, using torsion strain-gauges. Oscillate the rod with one end fixed and a heavy disc firmly attached to the other, and record the torque at different amplitudes of oscillation.

(c) Measure the change of longitudinal and circumferential strain at the surface of the cylindrical part of the air receiver of an air compressor, (N.B.—due to Poisson's ratio effect, the *measured* strains have to be modified) (Ref. 4) and hence find the longitudinal and hoop stresses.

(d) Measure the modulus of rigidity (G) of a metal by measuring the frequency of torsional oscillation of a thin rod fixed at one end and having a disc mass attached at the other.

(e) Measure the twist of a rotating shaft (i) using magnetic or light-sensitive pickups and a c.r.o., (ii) a stroboscope.

6.8.5 Measurement of temperature

Temperature-measuring methods have been studied previously in the TEC unit 'Engineering Science III'. However, it may be appropriate to study the application of these methods in measurement systems, as a project.

(a) Devise and assemble a Wheatstone bridge of current- or voltage-sensitive type using a thermistor or platinum-resistance temperature sensor to measure a specified temperature range. Calibrate the output of the instrument in temperature units against a suitable standard.

(b) Devise and calibrate a bridge circuit similar to the previous one, but suitable for measuring the small *difference* between two temperatures.

(c) Devise and test a method of measuring the temperature of a tensile test specimen whilst under test in the miniature cylindrical furnace of the Hounsfield Tensometer.

(d) Apply a multichannel temperature recorder with thermistor, thermocouple or resistance sensors to measure the temperature at different points in a system, e.g., a refrigeration circuit, a heat exchanger, or a central heating system. Calibrate each channel against the best temperature standard available.

(e) Arrange an l.v.d.t. to measure the displacement of the free end of a bimetal strip, and calibrate the voltage output of the l.v.d.t. against the temperature of the strip.

6.8.6 Measurement of flow

Flow-measuring methods have been studied previously in the TEC unit 'Engineering Science III'. However, it may be appropriate to study the application of these methods in measurement systems, as a project.

(a) Select a suitable instrument to measure the instantaneous or the average flow rate of:
(i) fuel into an engine
(ii) cooling water through an engine jacket
(iii) airflow into an engine or compressor
(iv) hydraulic oil in a power hydraulic system
(v) flow rate of gas through a burner.

(b) Select a suitable secondary transducer for one of the items in (a) so that the flowrate may be recorded against time over the period of a test. Assemble and test the system.

(c) Devise a measurement system to sense small items coming off automatic machines and count them over a given time period. If possible, arrange for a record of the count to be made automatically, at the end of each count period.

6.8.7 Measurement of vibration and noise

(a) Select a vibration meter with suitable pick-ups and recording devices, and record the frequency and amplitude of the vibration of:
(i) machine tool structures during machining
(ii) reciprocating engines and compressors
(iii) building installations such as air extraction fans and systems.

(b) Devise and test a method of determining the positions of the nodes (i.e. the points of zero oscillation) and the anti-nodes (i.e. the points of maximum oscillation) of a vibrating beam.

(c) Devise and use a method of measuring the amplitude of vibration at different frequencies of:
(i) the main frame or base of a machine and
(ii) an instrument panel mounted on anti-vibration mountings.

(d) Study the measurement of noise. Select a suitable instrument system (e.g., microphone plus c.r.o. or recorder, or a noise level meter) and measure the frequencies and relative noise levels at different parts of a workshop.

6.8.8 Combined measurement projects

(a) Performance tests on a reciprocating engine
(i) Measure and record engine shaft speed (6.8.2(a)).
(ii) Measure and record output shaft torque (6.8.3(e)).
(iii) Measure and record fuel flowrate (6.8.6(a)).
(iv) Measure and record cooling-water flowrate (6.8.6(a)).
(v) Measure and record temperatures at significant points, such as the

cooling-water inlet and outlet, the exhaust pipe, and the inlet manifold. (6.8.5(d)).

(vi) Observe the operation of the ignition-advance mechanism, noting the advance angle at different speeds. (6.8.2(f)).

(vii) Measure the ignition advance angle of the engine when in operation and display or record the value (6.8.2(g)).

(viii) Measure and record the cylinder pressure under operating conditions. (6.8.3(g)).

(ix) Display crank-angle position markings on an oscilloscope trace or the recording in (viii). (6.8.2(c)).

Using recordings and observed values from the above, the following may be determined as required:

(i) shaft speed, torque and power

(ii) mechanical and thermal efficiencies

(iii) brake specific fuel consumption

(vi) brake and indicated mean effective pressures (vii) effectiveness of ignition-advance mechanism.

Other items may be added to the above, depending on the type of engine being studied.

(b) Performance test on an air compressor set.

(i) Measure and record the shaft speed (6.8.2(a)).

(ii) Measure and record the shaft torque (if possible) (6.8.3(e)).

(iii) Measure the electrical input power to the motor (For this item, safety precautions are particularly important, and it is recommended that students *observe* the test being carried out by an experienced person).

(iv) Measure and record the pressure in the cylinder(s), against stroke or time. (6.8.3(g)).

(v) Measure and record the air flowrate. (6.8.6(a)).

(vi) Measure and record the receiver air pressure (6.8.3(b)).

(vii) Measure the stresses in the air receiver under different pressure conditions (6.8.4(c)).

(viii) Measure and record the relevant temperatures of the system during operation. (6.8.5(d)).

Hence determine the power output and the efficiencies of the unit.

(c) Measurement of work done during the stroke of a shaping tool, or a hydraulic or pneumatic ram.

(i) Record the force/time relationship (6.8.3(f)).

(ii) Record the stroke/time relationship (6.8.1(a)).

(iii) Record the force/stroke relationship (6.8.3(c)(f)).

Hence determine the work done from $\int F\,ds$.

(d) Performance test on a machine tool.

(i) Measure the cutting force or torque under different conditions (6.8.3(f)).

(ii) Measure the vibration of the structure (6.8.7(a) (b)).

(iii) Measure the noise level. (6.8.7(d)).

(iv) Measure the surface finish produced. (6.8.1(j)).
(v) Measure the cutting speed. (6.8.2).
(vi) Measure the electrical power absorbed by the machine
(For this item, safety precautions are particularly important, and it is recommended that students *observe* the test being carried out by an experienced person).

Hence determine:
(i) the cutting power and efficiency,
(ii) the relationships between variables such as the depth of cut, the surface speed, the feed rate, and power.
(iii) any correlation between variables such as vibration, noise, and surface finish.

(e) Performance test on a heat exchanger

(i) Measure and record the flow rates of both fluids against time (6.8.6(a)).
(ii) Measure and record the temperatures at inlet and outlet of both fluids, against time. (6.8.5(d)).

Hence determine the heat transfer rate and losses under operating conditions.

2 CONTROL

7 Automatic control systems

Automatic control systems are part of our daily life. We have them in our body – one controls our body temperature within close limits, another controls our balance so that we can stay upright, and so on. The temperature of a house, its oven, refrigerator, hot-water tank etc., may all be controlled by automatic systems. In engineering workshops, laboratories and plant, automatic systems may be found controlling such variables as the following:

Controlled variable	Example
displacement	i) position of a machine-tool table,
	ii) position of a valve spindle,
velocity	i) speed of a machine-tool table,
	ii) rotational speed of rollers,
force	i) tension in strip being rolled,
	ii) during materials testing,
pressure	i) in a compressor air-receiver,
	ii) in a chemical reactor vessel,
temperature	i) in a heat-treatment furnace,
	ii) of heated rollers for plastic processing.

7.1 'Open-loop' and 'closed-loop' systems

Consider the control system, shown in Fig. 7.1, for positioning the table of a machine tool. If it was required to move the table by a distance s to a new position, this could be done by sending n electrical pulses to the *stepping motor* mounted on the table. In this type of motor, the spindle rotates through a particular angle (α) for each pulse it receives. If the motor spindle carries a gear-wheel which meshes with a rack attached to the machine bed, the table will move through a distance directly proportional to the number of pulses received. Hence a given number of pulses will cause a known displacement, as shown in Example 7.6.1. The

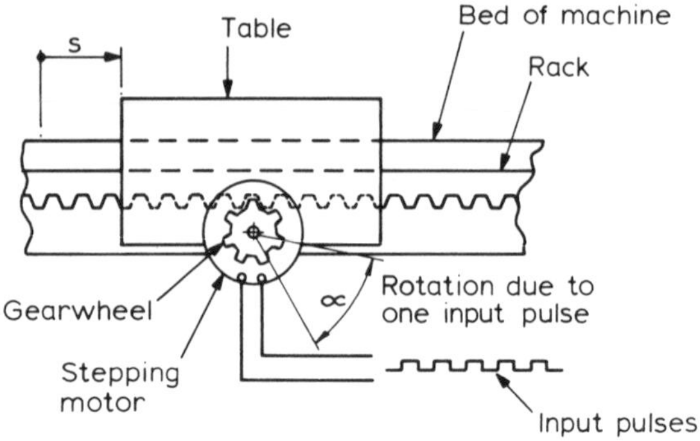

Fig. 7.1 Open-loop displacement-control system.

rate at which pulses are supplied controls the velocity, and the rate of change of pulse frequency controls acceleration. With this type of system there is no feedback of information on how far the table has moved after the pulses have been supplied. This absence of feedback leads to the system being referred to as an *open-loop* system, contrasting with the closed-loop system referred to in the next paragraph.

Many other open-loop systems are less satisfactory in operation than the previous example. Consider an electric fire switched on in a room.

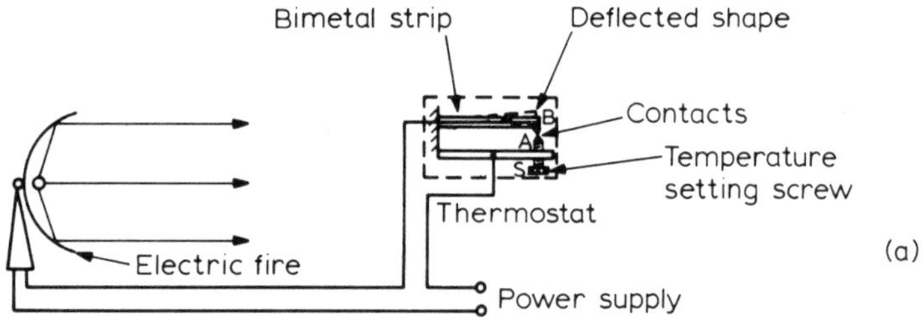

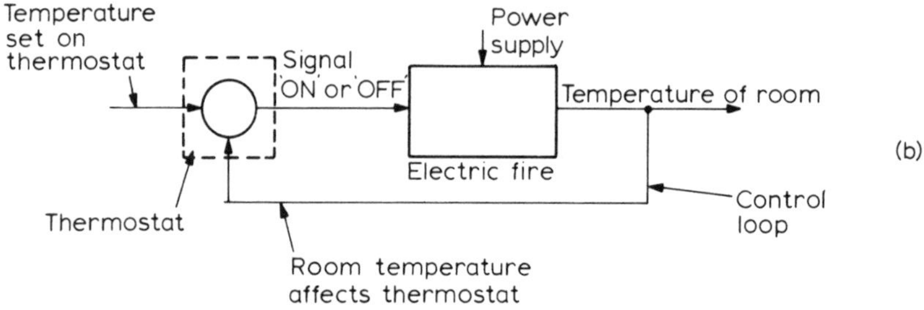

Fig. 7.2 Closed-loop control system.

The temperature of the room will become stable when the heat energy being supplied by the fire equals that lost through the walls, windows, floor and ceiling. This stable temperature may or may not be that desired by the occupants of the room. As the temperature becomes too high, a person sensing this will turn off the fire or, conversely, switch it on as the room becomes too cold. To control the temperature automatically a thermostat is used to sense the temperature and switch off or switch on the fire at a preset level. Both the thermostat and the person operating the switch are providing *feedback* of the *controlled variable*, the room temperature. The system is shown in Fig. 7.2 (a), and may be represented by a block diagram as shown in Fig. 7.2 (b). The controlled quantity, the room temperature, is sensed by the bimetal strip of the thermostat which changes its curvature with changing temperature. When the temperature of the strip is rising, and the temperature of the strip equals the preset temperature, set by the screw S, the contacts open and the fire is switched off. The path of the signal is seen to form a complete loop, and hence the system is classified as of *closed-loop* type.

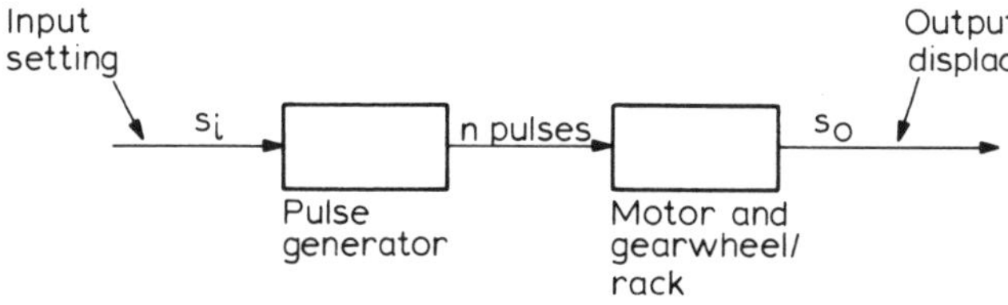

Fig. 7.3 System diagram for open-loop displacement-control system.

The machine-tool table position in the previous example was not sensed, i.e., there was no position feedback. Hence its system diagram is as shown in Fig. 7.3. It does not form a closed loop, hence is referred to as of open-loop type.

7.2 Terms used in feedback-control systems

Feedback-control systems using different working media, e.g. electrical, mechanical, hydraulic, or pneumatic, or combinations of these media, will have a number of features in common. Each will have an output quantity which is to be controlled, i.e. the *controlled variable*, denoted θ_o, and an input point where the required value of this output is set. This input is called the *demand* or *reference signal*, denoted θ_i. These signals are shown in the system block diagram, Fig. 7.4. The actual value of the controlled variable at any instant is sensed by a *feedback transducer*, and the signal from this is fed to a *comparator*, where it is subtracted from the demand signal. The difference, demand signal minus feedback signal, is the *error* or *deviation signal*, denoted θ_e. This signal goes forward in the system to change the controlled variable, by operating the *regulating unit*. This may be an electric motor, a hydraulic or pneumatic ram, a heater, or a flow control valve etc, each of these items requiring power. To supply this power, the error signal usually has to be amplified by some means, hence an amplifier is a typical control system component.

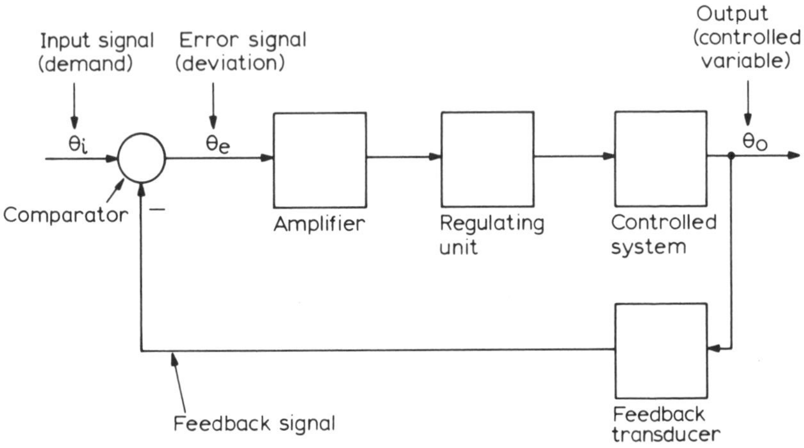

Fig. 7.4 Control-system elements.

The type of feedback discussed in the previous paragraph is referred to as *negative feedback*, since it is subtracted from the input or demand signal, and this is the type usually met in control systems. However, in electronic amplifier systems, positive feedback is used in some circum-

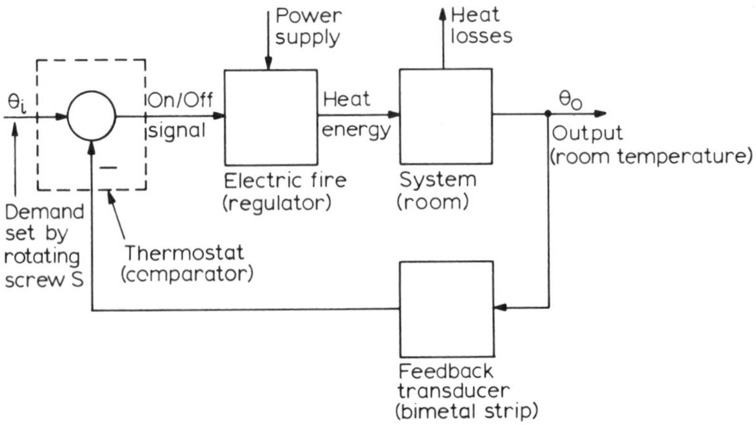

Fig. 7.5 Control-system diagram for thermostat-controlled electric fire.

stances, i.e. the feedback signal is added to the input signal. The effects of this are discussed in Section 8. Relating these terms to the thermostat controlled electric fire of Fig. 7.2, it is seen that the demand signal is the required room temperature, which is set by rotating the screw S to place the contact A in a particular position. The output signal is the temperature of the room (*not* the output of the fire.) The room temperature affects the bimetal strip of the thermostat, causing it to bend. As the room temperature reaches the set value B breaks contact with A, and the fire is switched off. Hence the bimetal strip senses the temperature, i.e., it is the feedback transducer, converting the change of room temperature to a displacement (x). The thermostat also compares the room temperature with the demand temperature, i.e., it functions as a comparator by the movements of the contacts. The error signal in this case has only two values, *on* when the room temperature is less than the set temperature, and *off*, when it is higher, thus controlling the fire. In this example, the fire is the regulating unit, since its action directly affects the controlled variable, the room temperature. The system block diagram is shown in more detail in Fig. 7.5.

7.3 On-off control systems

The output signal from this system, i.e. the room temperature, will vary with time as shown in Fig. 7.6. When the room temperature reaches the set temperature, the power supply to the elecric fire is switched off. But the heating elements are at a high temperature, and they continue to give off heat for a while as they cool. The room loses heat gradually, and hence it takes some time for the room temperature to come down again to the value set on the thermostat, at which point the fire is switched on again. However, it now takes some time for the heating elements to warm up and start to increase the room temperature. Hence the oscillation shown occurs, and the amplitude and frequency of this will depend on the heat lag in the fire elements, the rate of heat output (the power) of the fire, and the rate of heat loss from the room.

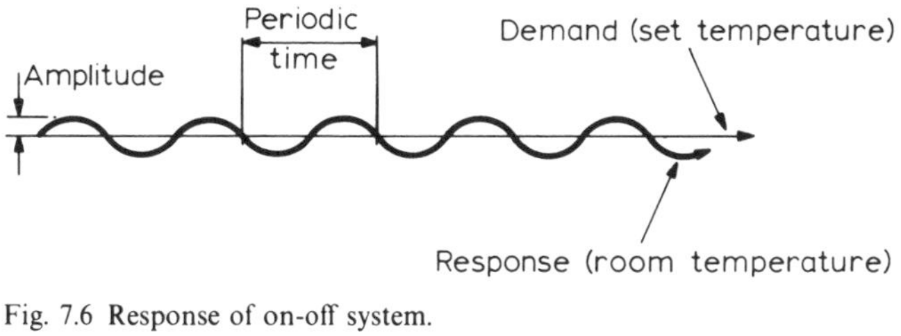

Fig. 7.6 Response of on-off system.

To avoid the rapid switching and resulting deterioration of contacts and other components, the control in on-off systems may be arranged so that the regulator is switched on at a lower value of the controlled variable, and switched off at a higher value, the desired output being midway between these two. This modified type of on-off control system may be illustrated by the system controlling the level of liquid in a tank, as in Fig. 7.7. In this system each of the sensors A and B gives a signal such as by closing contacts, or by applying voltage or pneumatic pressure, when the liquid is at or above their level. This may be regarded as a logic 1. When the liquid is below the sensor level, the contacts open, or the voltage or pressure is absent, giving a logic 0. The problem in this kind of control is to ensure that pump (P) is not switched on when the level is falling between A and B, but only when it goes below B, and that when it is switched on, it does not stop with a rising level until the level is at A. The logic system for doing this is shown in Fig. 7.8. From the truth table of the required function, table (a), it is seen that different functions are required for the same inputs from the sensors for rising and falling levels between A and B. The *memory* circuit (also called a *flip-flop*), shown in (c) will provide these. It must be noted that, irrespective of the states of A and B, Q and $\overline{Q}$ (not Q) are *always* the complement of each other.

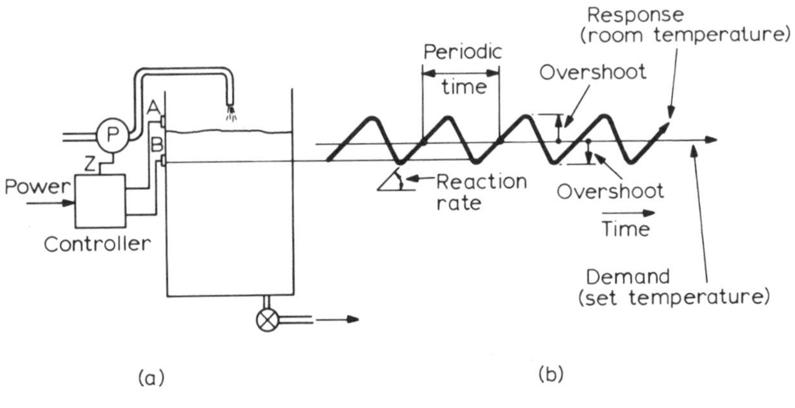

Fig. 7.7 Level-control system.

(a) Level below B: A = 0, B = 0, assume $Q = 1$, then $\overline{Q} = 0$, and the states of the gates may be verified.

(b) Level between A and B, rising: A = 0, B = 1. Although B has changed, this does not alter the output of gate M, and both outputs remain the same.

(c) The level is at A, A = 1, B = 1, the output of gate L becomes $Q = 0$, and hence the output of gate M becomes $\overline{Q} = 1$.

(d) Level between A and B, falling: A = 0, B = 1, the output of gate L remains $Q = 0$, held in this state by its input $\overline{Q} = 1$. The next operation is (a) again. The states in the system are shown in truth table (b). The output Q is seen to be indentical with the output Z of the required function.

	Required	Truth table		Gate L Inputs		Gate L Output	Gate M Inputs		Gate M Output
	A	B	Z	A	$\bar{Q}$	Q	Q	$\bar{B}$	$\bar{Q}$
(I) Lower level	0	0	1	0	0	1	1	1	0
(II) Rising level	0	1	1	0	0	1	1	0	0
(III) Top level	1	1	0	1	1	0	0	0	1
(IV) Falling level	0	1	0	0	1	0	0	0	1
	(a)			(b)					

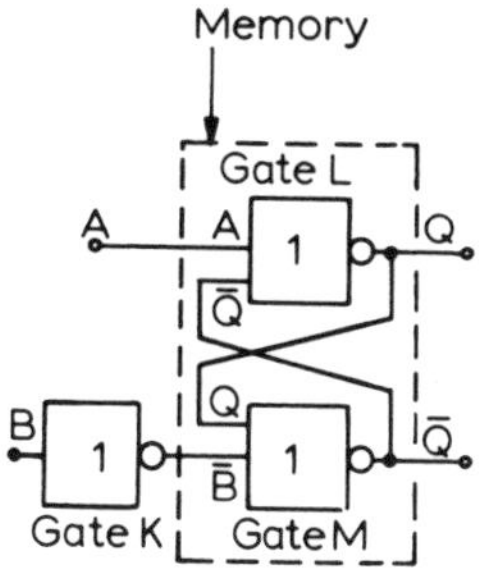

(c)

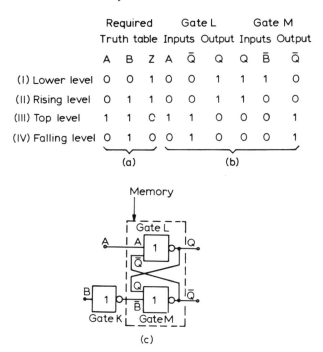

Fig. 7.8 Memory system for on-off (two-step) control.

Hence if Q controls the starting and stopping of the pump motor, we have the required system.

The effect of using two sensors is shown in Fig. 7.7(b). The rate at which the level rises, the *reaction rate*, depends on the flowrate from the pump, the flowrate from the tank outlet, and the cross-sectional area of the tank. The rate at which it falls depends on the latter two only. The rate of switching is slower than with a single sensor, but the fluctuation about the set level is greater. Example 7.6.2 illustrates this.

7.4 Sequence-control systems

In many practical control systems, a number of events are controlled in a sequence, which may (i) follow a set pattern or (ii) follow a variable pattern. Either of these may be conditional upon circumstances. In many of these, fail-safe features are incorporated, or the operations may only be carried out if adequate safety precautions are provided, such as guards being in position.

Consider the operation of feeding a circular blank of metal into a press, forming this with a stroke of the punch, and finally ejecting it. The

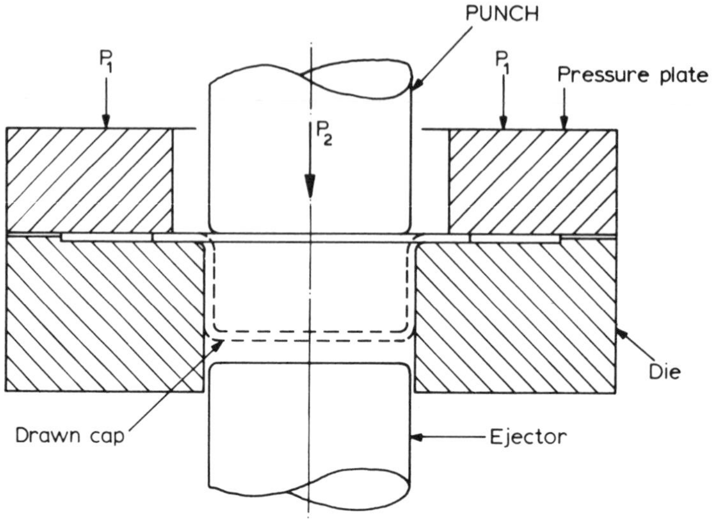

Fig. 7.9

components are shown in Fig. 7.9. The operations to be carried out automatically are:

(a) load blank into position – logic $Z_1 = 1$
(b) operate punch – logic $Z_2 = 1$
(c) operate ejector – logic $Z_3 = 1$

Considering operation (a), the blank may only be loaded if:

(i) the die is clear, indicated by a sensor giving A = 1, and
(ii) the punch is raised, indicated by B = 1, and
(iii) the guard is in position, indicated by C = 1, and
(iv) the operating switch is on, indicated by D = 1, and
(v) the stop button has not been pressed. Pressing the stop button causes and retains a signal E = 1, and
(vi) the pressure plate is raised, indicated by G = 0.

The system logic diagram is shown in Fig. 7.10(a).

Considering operation (b), the punch may operate if:

(i) the blank is in position, indicated by F = 1, and
(ii) the pressure plate is completely down, indicated by G = 1, and
(iii) the ejector is withdrawn, indicated by H = 1, and
(iv) the guard is in position, indicated by C = 1, and
(v) the stop button has not been pressed.

The system logic diagram is shown in Fig. 7.10(b).

The reader should have no difficulty in devising the logic system to obtain the function Z_3. The type of sensor used to determine the logic level (1 or 0) of the functions A to H may be electrical, such as a micro switch or proximity sensor, or it may be pneumatic. The logic diagram is

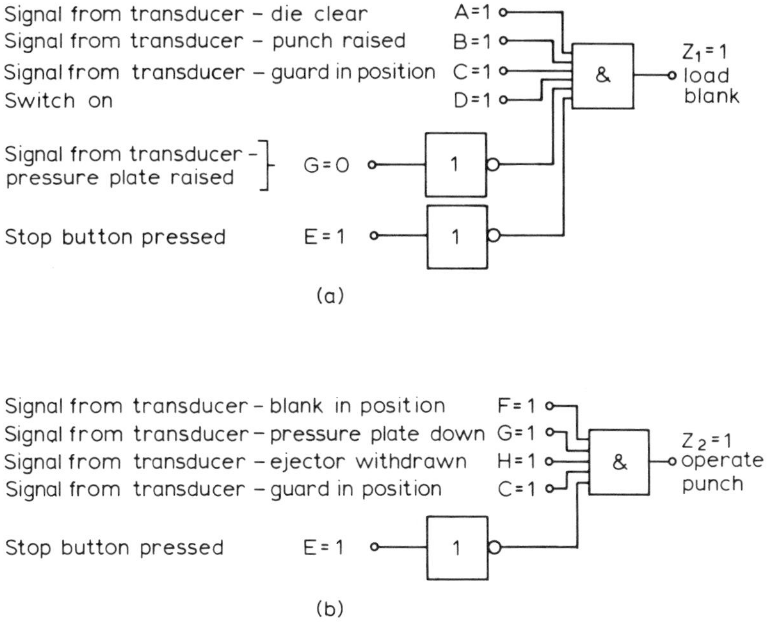

Fig. 7.10 (a) Logic system for loading of blanks.
(b) Logic system for operation of punch.

independent of the type of sensor or the type of gate used. However, particular types of gate may be preferred in systems using a particular media, e.g., NOR or NAND gates may be preferred in electrical systems. In such cases the logic system may be rearranged, using the preferred gates, to give the same overall function. Further conditional and sequential logic systems are shown in examples 7.6.3 to 7.6.5.

7.5 Components used in on-off and sequence-control systems

7.5.1 Components forming logic gates

Logic gates have been studied previously in Engineering Science III, when it will have been noted that electrical switches connected in parallel give an OR function, and when connected in series give an AND function. Other electrical devices and fluid valves may also provide OR and AND functions, and also the inverse of these, the NOR (not or) and NAND (not and) functions. Gates may be interconnected to give a memory function such as the *bistable* (or *flip-flop* or *latch*), as shown in Fig. 7.8. Alternatively these memory functions may be provided in a single electronic or fluid unit.

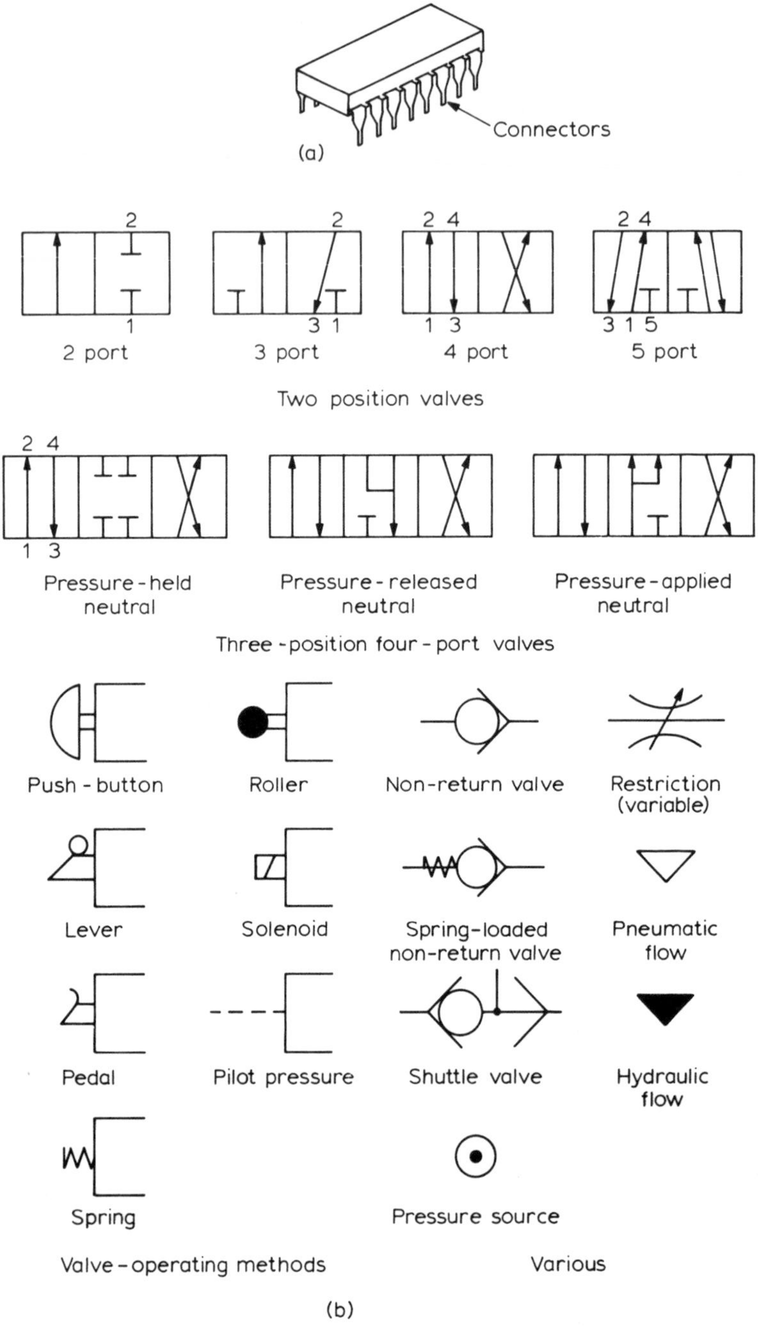

Fig. 7.11 Components used in logic circuits.
(a) Integrated-circuit transistor logic "chip".
(b) Symbols for fluid system components.

Integrated circuit (i.c.) logic elements consist of miniature transistor circuits deposited on a semiconductor base, the external appearance of the units being similar to Fig. 7.11(a). Large-scale integrated circuits capable of carrying out arithmetic processes such as addition, subtraction, multiplication and integration, in addition to the basic logic functions, when suitably programmed, are referred to as microprocessors. The separate gates OR, AND, NOR, NAND and memory are used in fixed systems (referred to as *hard-wired* in electronics), whilst the microprocessor may be programmed at will, to control the system in different ways, enabling more complex control functions to be carried out. The use of these i.c. units may reduce the cost of control systems by replacing fluid valves and other items.

Hydraulic and pneumatic valves of different types may be incorporated into systems to perform logic functions. The standard symbols (BS 2917:1977) for two- and three-position valves are shown in Fig. 7.11(b), together with some common valve-operating-device symbols, etc. The convention for valves is that each square represents one position of the valve. Fig. 7.12 shows some common logic functions, with their truth tables, and some switching and valve methods of obtaining

Truth table

Or function

A	B	Z
0	0	0
1	0	1
0	1	1
1	1	1

And function

A	B	Z
0	0	0
1	0	0
0	1	0
1	1	1

Nor function

A	B	Z
0	0	1
1	0	0
0	1	0
1	1	0

Nand function

A	B	Z
0	0	1
1	0	1
0	1	1
1	1	0

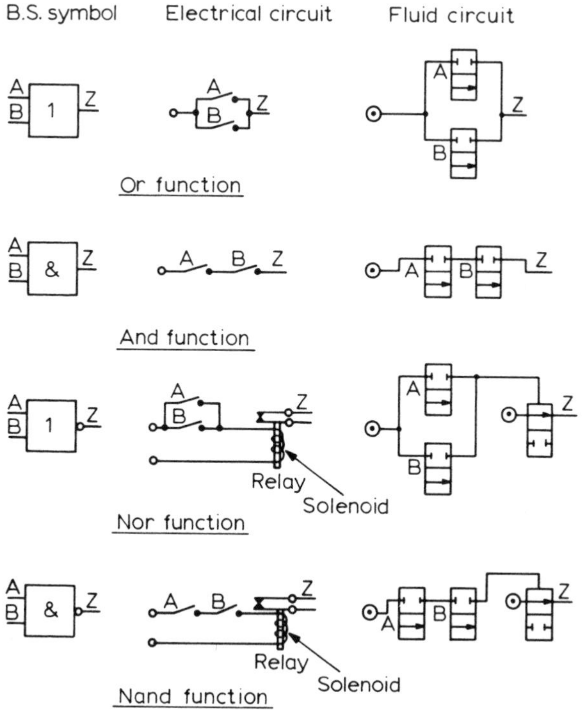

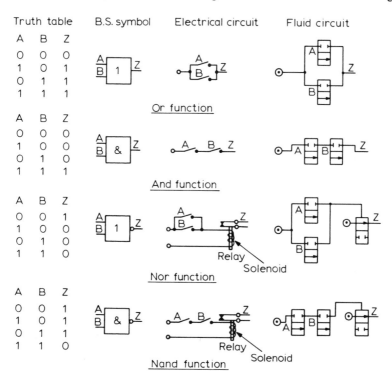

Fig. 7.12 Truth tables and logic functions.

them. The valves may be of the common spool type, of rotary type, or be more specialised types such as the Schrader Bellows Transistair components shown in Fig. 7.13. Fluidic gates are also available, these having no moving parts, but they appear to offer little advantage over moving-part valves for industrial applications. Several manufacturers offer manifolds which are designed for the easy mounting of, air supply to and interconnection of the miniature logic valves. At least one manufacturer supplies a pneumatic sequencer, such that a programmed function cannot operate until the previous function has been completed, and a signal is received that this has occurred.

Unit	Function	IEC Symbol	Mechanism
 n°. 9701101 Colour-grey	AND $S = X.Y$	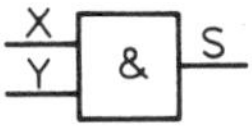	 X S Y
 n°. 9701103 Colour-black	OR $S = X + Y$	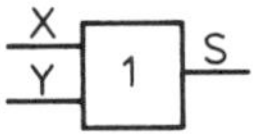	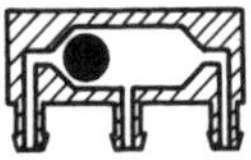 X S Y
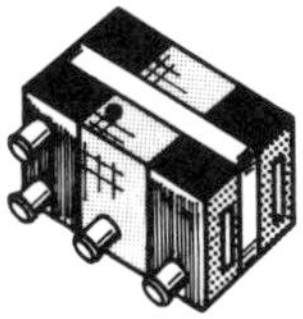 n°. 9701004 Centre section blue	NOR $S = \overline{X+Y}$ $= \overline{X}.\overline{Y}$	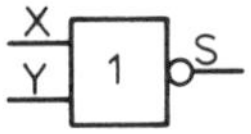	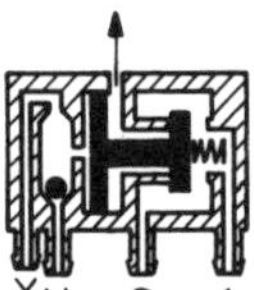 XY S 1
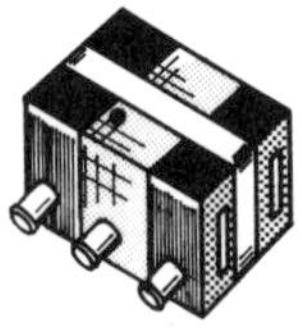 n°. 9701001 Centre section red	BUFFER X is low pressure signal, Y is high pressure supply. Thus X becomes higher pressure signal at S.		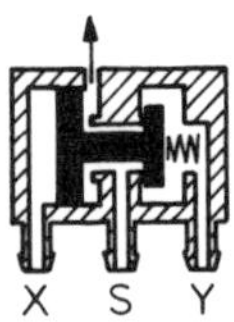 X S Y

Fig. 7.13 Schrader Bellows Transistair moving-part logic units.

Buffers or amplifiers (signal conditioners) are sometimes necessary for both electrical and fluid circuits, where the voltage or pressure levels, or the current or fluid flow values from a unit are insufficient to power the next unit. Transducers are common circuit components converting, for example, pressure to voltage, as also are electric-solenoid-operated valves.

7.5.2 Sensing devices for on-off and sequence-control

Micro-switches are commonly used as 'limit' switches in machine tools and other machines to provide a signal indicating that a moving part has reached a particular point and thus providing a feedback signal. Micro-switches may have both normally-open and normally-closed contacts, either of which may be used. A typical example is shown in Fig. 7.14. Such switches may also be incorporated into units operated by floats for liquid-level sensing, and in many other applications.

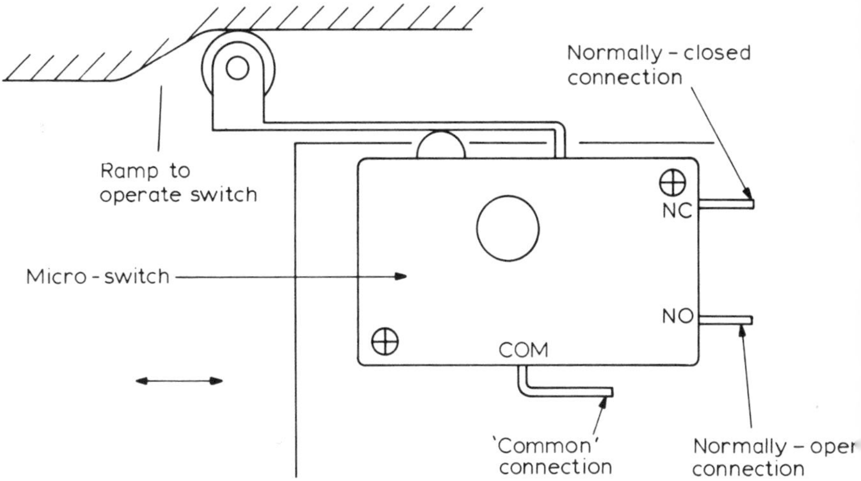

Fig. 7.14 Microswitch.

A further switching method incorporates the *reed switch*. This consists of two small nickel-iron blades sealed in a glass capsule, typically about 40 mm long by 5 mm diameter. The blades overlap, but normally have a small gap between them. The presence of a magnetic field causes them to attract each other and complete a circuit. They are reliable, are capable of operating for millions of operations, and have a very low contact resistance. Operation may be 'mechanically' by a permanant magnet, as shown in the float-operated switch of Fig. 7.15, or by producing an

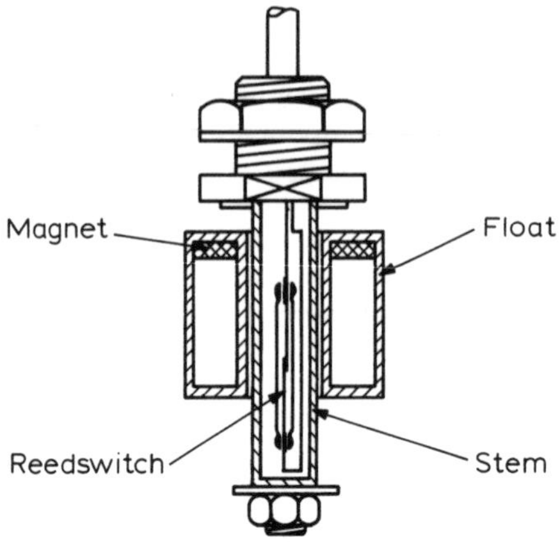

Fig. 7.15 Float-operated reed switch.

electromagnetic field by means of a coil. They also find many applications in limit switches in machine tools.

The air-jet sensing device shown in Fig. 7.16 provides a back pressure directly proportional to the gap x, for a very small range of x, up to about 1 mm. It may be used purely as a two-level switch between levels 1 and 2, or it may be used with an adjustable pressure switch to open or close contacts at any intermediate level (Ref. 4).

Fig. 7. 17 shows air jets used for sensing the presence or absence of objects. An air jet from A passes to a receiver B and maintains a pressure there (p_B) which may be used as a logic signal. An object R intruding into the jet in the space x_1 breaks the jet and the pressure p_B is reduced. If a larger gap x_2 is required, an air jet 2 may normally be directed at jet 1 to break it. An object breaking jet 2, such as a drill bit as shown, allows jet 1 to re-establish the pressure. The arrangement could be used, for example, to detect drill breakage and give a warning or stop the machine etc.

Pressure switches such as that shown in Fig. 7.18 are designed to open or close electrical contacts at a given pressure. The pressure is adjustable within a range to the required value. With a different transducer, switching may be caused by temperature changes.

Similarly, temperature switches using mercury thermometers are available which use the wire contact arrangement shown in Fig. 7.19. A thin wire is adjustable in height to correspond to any temperature value. When the mercury meniscus touches the wire, a circuit is completed as shown. Alternatively a bimetal thermostat may be used, but its action is much less precise.

The outputs from pressure transducers such as the potentiometric Bourdon-tube type shown in Fig. 8.4, or from platinum resistance or thermocouple temperature sensors, are continuous analogue signals.

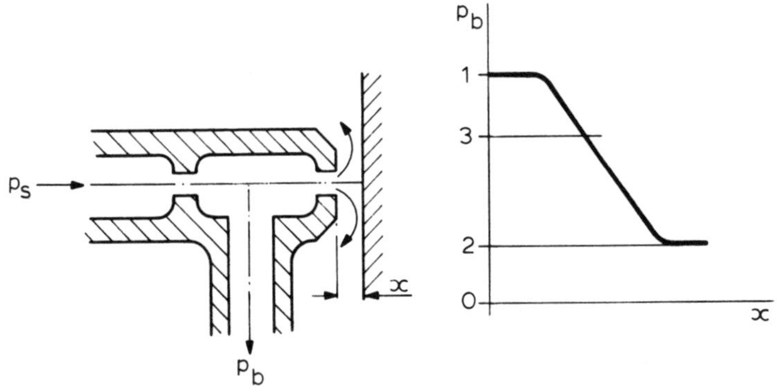

Fig. 7.16 Air-jet sensor.

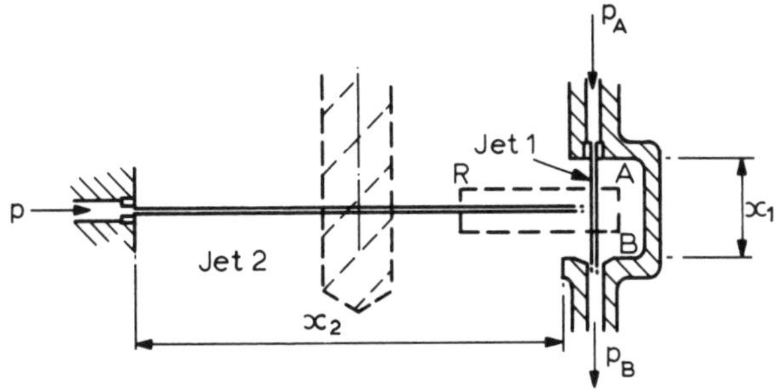

Fig. 7.17 Interruptible-jet sensors.

These may be the input to a trip amplifier, and the trips set so that electrical contacts are opened or closed at predetermined values. However this method, though versatile, is more expensive to use than the switches described in the previous paragraph.

The selection of the type of working media for a particular control system, e.g., electrical, electronic, hydraulic or pneumatic, or combinations of these, will depend on a number of factors. The basic requirements of a system will usually determine the type of regulating or operating units used. For example, where considerable force is involved an electric or hydraulic motor (rotational or linear arrangement) may be used. If the force required is lower, electric solenoids or pneumatic operation may be suitable. In difficult environments, such as mines and chemical factories it may be preferred that electrics be excluded. If a control system is complex, it may be essential to use electronics, with units responding within a few microseconds, rather than pneumatics, with units responding within several milliseconds. Fluid valve units have long been available with electric solenoids to activate them, usually

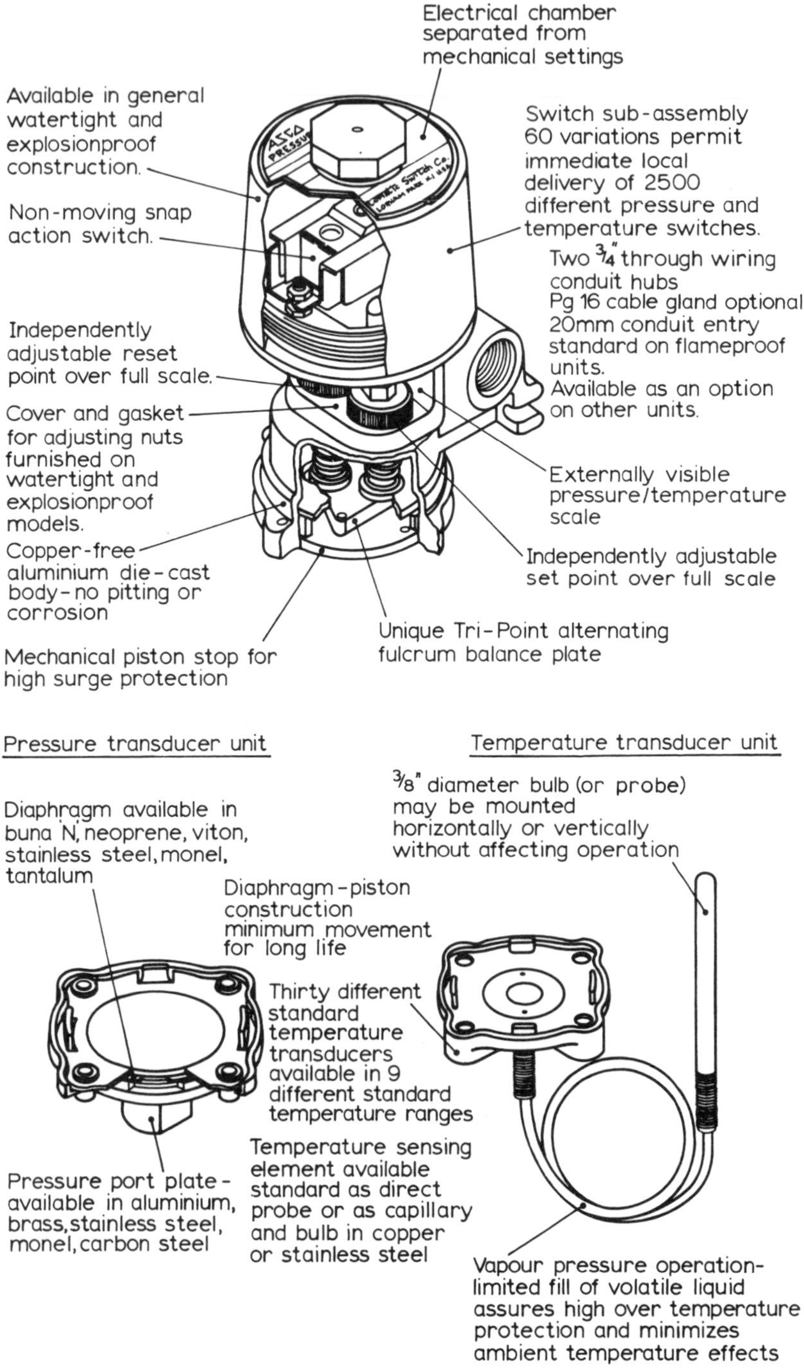
Electrical chamber separated from mechanical settings
Available in general watertight and explosionproof construction.
Switch sub-assembly 60 variations permit immediate local delivery of 2500 different pressure and temperature switches.
Non-moving snap action switch.
Two ¾" through wiring conduit hubs
Pg 16 cable gland optional
20mm conduit entry standard on flameproof units.
Available as an option on other units.
Independently adjustable reset point over full scale.
Cover and gasket for adjusting nuts furnished on watertight and explosionproof models.
Externally visible pressure/temperature scale
Copper-free aluminium die-cast body-no pitting or corrosion
Independently adjustable set point over full scale
Unique Tri-Point alternating fulcrum balance plate
Mechanical piston stop for high surge protection
Pressure transducer unit
Temperature transducer unit
⅜" diameter bulb (or probe) may be mounted horizontally or vertically without affecting operation
Diaphragm available in buna N, neoprene, viton, stainless steel, monel, tantalum
Diaphragm-piston construction minimum movement for long life
Thirty different standard temperature transducers available in 9 different standard temperature ranges
Temperature sensing element available standard as direct probe or as capillary and bulb in copper or stainless steel
Pressure port plate-available in aluminium, brass, stainless steel, monel, carbon steel
Vapour pressure operation-limited fill of volatile liquid assures high over temperature protection and minimizes ambient temperature effects

Fig. 7.18 Dewraswitch pressure or temperature switch.

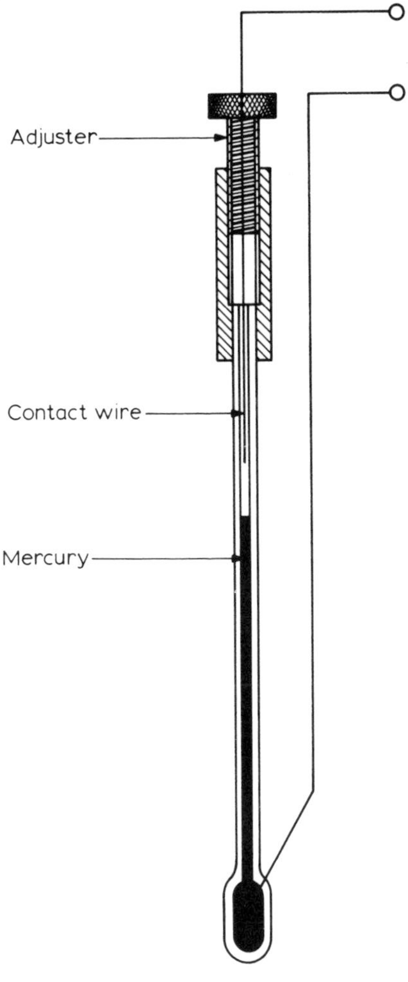

Fig. 7.19 Thermometer switch.

supplied at 12 V, 24 V or mains voltage. A recent innovation is a series of fluid valves which can be directly connected to electronic logic and micro-processor chips, giving lower cost systems by eliminating electrical relays. In the next section, several examples of on-off and sequence-control systems are shown.

7.6 Worked examples

7.6.1 An open-loop control-system controls the displacement, velocity and acceleration of a machine-tool table. It utilises a stepping-motor, mounted on the table, and a 60 tooth gearwheel on the motor shaft

engages with a rack of 3 mm pitch on the bed of the machine. If one electrical pulse supplied to the motor causes its shaft to rotate through 0.5° calculate:
(a) the displacement of the table due to one pulse
(b) the frequency of pulses required to produce a table velocity of 1 mm/s
(c) the rate of change of the frequency of the pulses necessary to accelerate the table uniformly from rest to a velocity of 10 mm/s in a distance of 10 mm.

(a) One pulse causes a rotation of $\frac{0.5}{360} \times 60 = \frac{0.5}{6}$ tooth pitches

The corresponding displacement of the table is $\frac{0.5}{6} \times 3 = 0.25$ mm

(b) Pulses at 1 Hz will cause a velocity of:

$$1\left(\frac{\text{pulse}}{\text{s}}\right) \times 0.25\left(\frac{\text{mm}}{\text{pulse}}\right) = 0.25 \text{ mm/s}$$

To produce a velocity of 1 mm/s, pulses at 4 Hz are required.
(c) $v^2 = u^2 + 2as$ where v is the velocity when the displacement(s) $= 10$ mm
a is the acceleration
and u is the initial velocity $= 0$

$\therefore$ $10^2 = 0 + 2a \times 10$
and $a = 5.0 \text{ mm/s}^2$

Using $v = u + at$, $t = 2s$.
Hence the rate of change of pulse frequency is 20 Hz/s. The acceleration is limited by the rate at which the motor shaft can slew against a given torque resistance, when a pulse is applied. The rotation due to a pulse should be completed before the next pulse is received, otherwise pulses may be missed, causing error in the displacement, velocity and acceleration values.

7.6.2 In a level-control system similar to that of Fig. 7.7 the height between the sensors A and B is 100 mm. The tank is cylindrical with inside diameter 1.00 m. The pump delivers water at the rate of 10 l/s, and the time lag of the water flow after switching on and off is small enough to be neglected.
Calculate the periodic time of the switching:
(a) when the out flow rate is constant at 4 l/s
(b) when the out flowrate is constant at 8 l/s.
(a) The net flowrate of water = area of tank cross-section × rate of change of height

i.e. $\dot{V} = A \times \delta h/\delta t$

For rising level, pump off, $\dot{V} = 10 - 4$
$= 6$ l/s

$$\therefore \quad \frac{6}{1000} = \frac{\pi}{4} \times 1.00^2 \times \frac{\delta h}{\delta t}$$

and

$$\frac{\delta h}{\delta t} = \frac{6 \times 10^{-3}}{0.7854}$$

$$= 7.64 \times 10^{-3} \text{ m/s} = 7.64 \text{ mm/s}$$

$$\text{Time to rise 100 mm} = \frac{100}{7.64} = 13.1 \text{ s}$$

For falling level, pump off, $\dot{V} = 4$ l/s

$$\therefore \quad \frac{4}{1000} = 0.7854 \frac{\delta h}{\delta t}$$

and

$$\frac{\delta h}{\delta t} = 5.1 \times 10^{-3} \text{ m/s} = 5.1 \text{ mm/s}$$

$$\text{Time to fall 100 mm} = \frac{100}{5.1} = 19.6 \text{ s}$$

Periodic time of switching = 13.1 + 19.6 = 32.7 s

(b) For rising level, pump on, $\dot{V} = 10 - 8$
$= 2$ l/s

$$\therefore \quad \frac{2}{1000} = 0.7854 \frac{\delta h}{\delta t}$$

and

$$\frac{\delta h}{\delta t} = \frac{2 \times 10^{-3}}{0.7854}$$

$$= 2.55 \times 10^{-3} \text{ m/s} = 2.55 \text{ mm/s}$$

$$\text{Time to rise 100 mm} = \frac{100}{2.55} = 39.3 \text{ s}$$

For falling level, pump off, V = 8 l/s

$$\therefore \quad \frac{\delta h}{\delta t} = \frac{\dot{V}}{A}$$

$$= \frac{8 \times 10^{-3}}{0.7854}$$

$$= 10.2 \times 10^{-3} \text{ m/s} = 10.2 \text{ mm/s.}$$

$$\text{Time to fall 100 s} = \frac{100}{10.2} = 9.8 \text{ s}$$

Periodic time of switching = 39.3 + 9.8 = 49.1 s

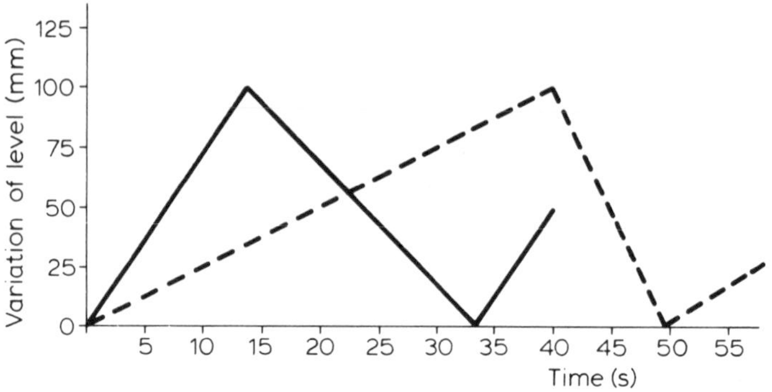

Fig. 7.20

The height/time graphs are shown in Fig. 7.20.

7.6.3 A vending machine is to offer the choice of three items, W, X and Y, each costing 10p. It must accept either two 5p pieces, or one 10p piece. The sequence of operation is to be:

(A) The coins are inserted into a single slot, a 10p piece then rolling into channel A, or two 5p pieces one into each of channels B and C. Faulty coins are rejected.

(B) The appropriate item is selected by pressing one only of three buttons. If the item is not sold out, it is delivered down the chute; if it is sold out the coins are returned.

(a) Devise a logic circuit for each of the following, in connection with this:

(i) *Coin acceptance*—an output signal 1 is to be given if either one 10p coin is retained, or two 5p coins are retained.

(ii) *Item selection*—an output signal 1 is to be given on one only of the three vending channels if its selection button is pressed, and 0 on all three channels if two or more buttons are pressed.

(iii) *Item despatch and coin acceptance*—an output signal 1 is to be given on the appropriate channel of the three, if a signal 1 is received from the coin-acceptance sub-system, and a signal 1 is received that the hopper for that item is not empty, and a signal 1 is received from the appropriate selector button. The coins are to be accepted into the coin box.

(iv) *Coin return*—if the hopper is empty, the coins are rejected.

Show how these parts of the system are connected to each other.

(b) If the function of the coin-acceptance sub-system is given by the Boolean function $G = A + B.C$, construct a truth table which will cover every combination of input together with the appropriate output. Discuss any undesirable feature of the vending machine which becomes apparent on examination of the truth table.

This problem has features which are common to many logic control

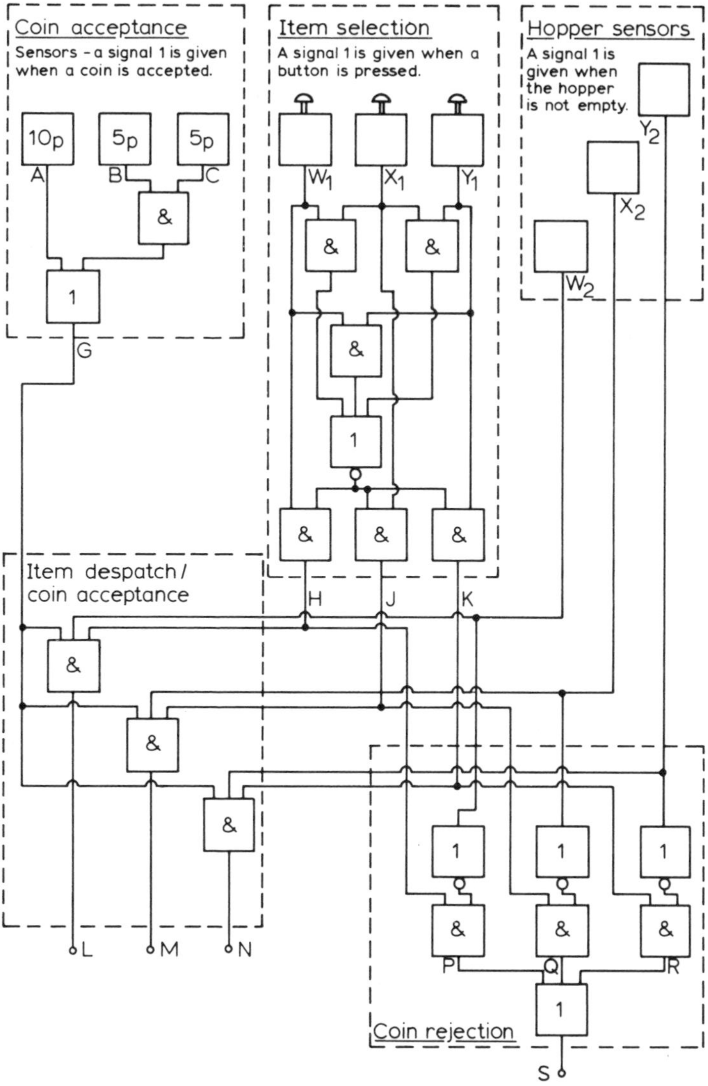

Fig. 7.21 Logical-control circuit for a vending machine.

systems. Fig. 7.21 shows a solution of the problem, but several other versions are possible.

(i) *Coin acceptance* $G = A + B . C$ gives a logic 1 when a 10p coin is put in A, or a 5p coin is put into B *and* a 5p in C.

(ii) *Item selection* $H = W_1 . \overline{(W_1 . X_1 + W_1 . Y_1 + X_1 . Y_1)}$, i.e. W_1 and not (W_1 and X_1 or W_1 and Y_1 or X_1 and Y_1). Similar expressions apply for J and K. The result is that a logic 1 will occur for H or J or K but not for two or three of these together.

(iii) *Item despatch and coin acceptance*—a signal L or M or N equals logic 1 is given from a channel which has had the correct coins accepted, the appropriate selector button has been pressed, and which has the required items present in the hopper. This signal activates the despatch mechanism, and the coins are accepted into the collecting box.

(iv) *Coin return*—if a hopper is empty, the NOT gate gives a logic 1, which combines with the signal from the item selection to give a logic 1 output for P or Q or R, which will give an output S = 1 to activate the coin rejection device.

The truth table is shown below for the coin acceptance section.

A	B	C	G	
0	0	0	0	
1	0	0	1	
0	1	0	0	
0	0	1	0	
0	1	1	1	
1	1	1	1	The machine will accept 15p or 20p combinations of input, which is undesirable to a user.
1	0	1	1	
1	1	0	1	

7.6.4. A conveyor belt 1 feeds to either of the conveyor belts 2 or 3, the delivery chute from 1 being switched by an air-operated cylinder, as shown in Fig. 7.22. The required conditions are:

(a) If belt 2 is full, its motor M switches off, i.e., M = 0
(b) If belt 3 is full, its motor N switches off, i.e., N = 0
(c) If both 2 and 3 are full, motor L of conveyor 1 switches off, i.e., L = 0.
(d) If belt 2 is full, but 3 is not, the components from 1 are delivered to 3,

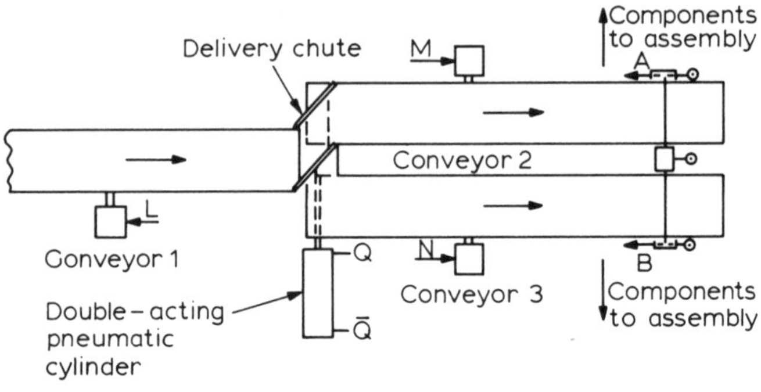

Fig. 7.22 Conveyor system.

i.e., Q = 1, and if 3 is full but 2 is not, then components are delivered to 2, i.e., $\overline{Q} = 1$.

(i) Draw a logic diagram and write down its truth table.
(ii) Devise a pneumatic circuit to carry out the control.

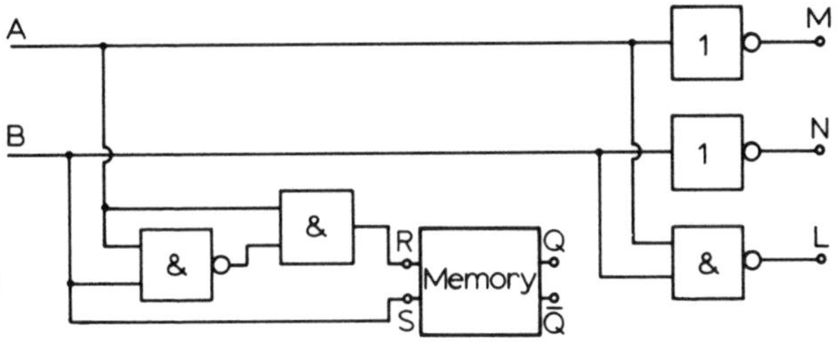

(a)

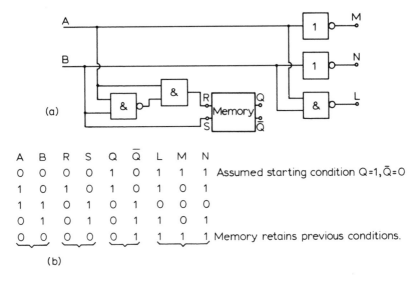

A	B	R	S	Q	$\overline{Q}$	L	M	N	
0	0	0	0	1	0	1	1	1	Assumed starting condition Q=1, $\bar{Q}$=0
1	0	1	0	1	0	1	0	1	
1	1	0	1	0	1	0	0	0	
0	1	0	1	0	1	1	0	1	
0	0	0	0	0	1	1	1	1	Memory retains previous conditions.

(b)

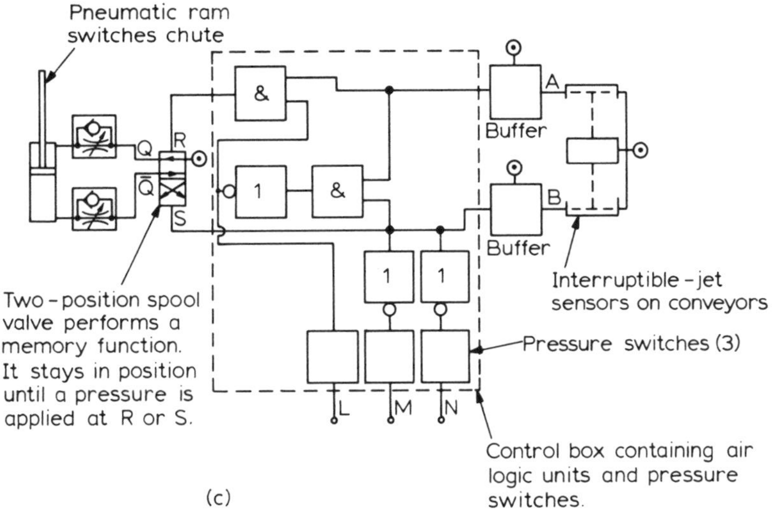

(c)

Fig. 7.23 Conveyor control system.
(a) Logic diagram
(b) Truth table
(c) Pneumatic system.

The logic system is shown in Fig. 7.23(a). Assuming that the components on the belts 2 and 3 may be detected by an interruptible jet sensor as shown in Fig. 7.17, then a signal A = 1 indicates conveyor 2 is full, and B = 1 indicates conveyor 3 is full. The NOT gates give a signal 1 to each motor when the respective conveyor is not full. A NAND gate gives a signal 1 to the motor of conveyor 1 when either 2 or 3 is not full, and a signal 0 when both are full. A memory (bistable) is used to give signals Q = 1 for feed to belt 3, and $\overline{Q}$ = 1 for feed to belt 2. The truth table for this arrangement is shown in Fig. 7.23(b). It should be noted that when the inputs A and B both become zero, the outputs Q and $\overline{Q}$ retain their previous state. When A and B are both 1, the AND and NAND gates feeding to R and S give R = 0, S = 1.

The circuit design using pneumatic components is shown in Fig. 7.23(c). The memory function is provided by a two-way four-part spool valve, operated by pilot pressure from pneumatic logic gates (e.g., Schrader Bellows Transistair). The start and stop signals to the motors are provided by pressure switches. The speed of the switching operation of the chute in each direction is controlled to a suitable value by the variable restrictors. Many of the units may be housed in a control box as shown. Further circuitry needs to be incorporated for start-up control and emergency stop of each conveyor.

7.6.5. Fig. 7.24 shows a pneumatic circuit where cylinder A is used to clamp a work piece in position, and then cylinder B is operated to punch a hole in the component. The required sequence of operations, starting with both cylinders retracted is:
advance ram A to clamp component, and then
advance ram B to punch component, and then,
retract ram B, and then,
retract ram A.

Describe the sequence of operations in the pneumatic circuit to obtain this.

Valve P is operated by the push-button and remains in its new position, allowing air under pressure to flow to the LH side of cylinder A, and air to exhaust from the RH side. The ram advances, clamping the component and operating the trip valve Q, allowing air under pressure to the top of valve R, moving it to its second position. This allows air under pressure to flow to the top of cylinder B, and air to exhaust from the bottom. The ram B advances, does not affect valve S on the way down, punches the workpiece and then trips valve T, which allows pressurised air to flow to the bottom of valve R, moving this to its original position. This connects pressurised air to the lower part of cylinder B, and air to exhaust from the top. The ram B retracts, and operates valve S momentarily, allowing air to flow to valve P, returning it to its original position. This allows pressurised air to flow to the RH side of cylinder A, and air to exhaust from the LH side, returning ram A to its starting position, unclamping the workpiece. It may be seen that all rams and

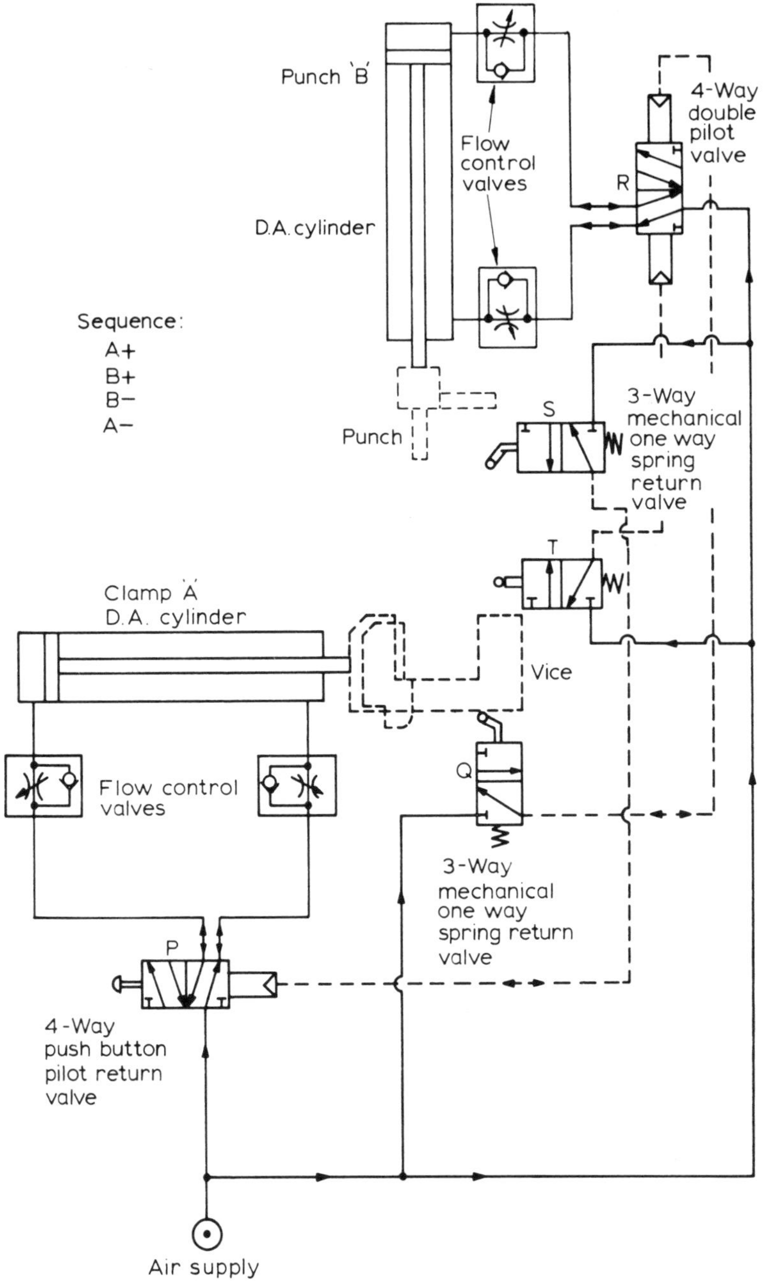

Fig. 7.24 Pneumatic circuit for clamp and punch operation.

valves are returned to the original position. The variable restrictor/non-return valve units in the flow lines to and from each cylinder allow for adjustment of the velocity of each ram stroke. Hence one operation and release of the push-button has given the required sequence, and the system has returned to its original state.

7.7 Exercises

7.7.1 The stepping motor used in Example 7.6.1 is connected directly to the leadscrew of a lathe. If the leadscrew has a single-start thread of 4 mm pitch, calculate for the lathe carriage the items of 7.6.1, (a) (b) and (c).
7.7.2 In a level-control system using a pump with a delivery rate of 10 l/s discharging into a cylindrical tank, calculate the periodic time of switching, (a) when the height between the sensors is 60 mm and the inside diameter of the tank is 1.00 m and, (b) when the height between the sensors is 100 mm and the inside diameter of the tank is 0.50 m. In each case ignore the dead time and assume a constant outflow rate of 4 l/s. Compare the values obtained with those of 7.6.2.
7.8.3 A conveyor as in Fig. 7.25 carrying components through a normalising furnace, can only be set in motion when:
(a) there are no components in the volume A, and
(b) there are components in volume D, and
(c) the temperatures at both B and C are within the specified range, and
(d) either control E or control F has been switched on.

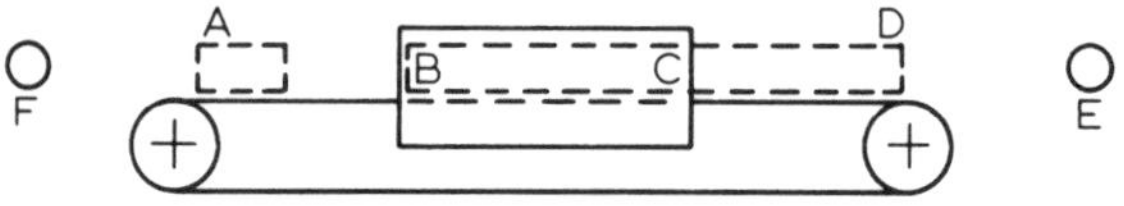

Fig. 7.25 Conveyor.

The sensors in spaces A and D give a signal when there are components in the respective volumes, sensors at B and C each gives a signal when its temperature is within the required range, and an output is to be given from the control system when conditions (a) to (c) are met.

Devise a logic circuit to give the required functions.
7.8.4 To prevent the power supply to three machines becoming overloaded, it is essential that not more than one of the machines may *start* at any instant, although one may start when others are *running*. Devise a logic system to provide the necessary function.
7.8.5 In the system of Fig. 7.26, the motor may only be started and

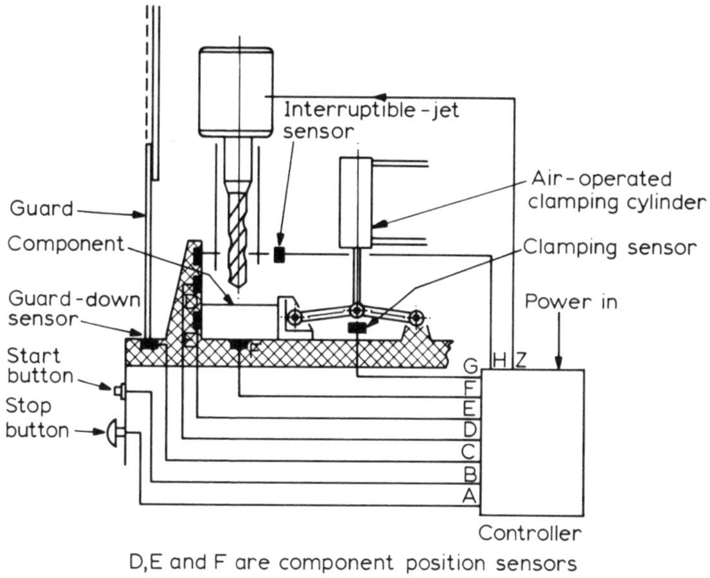

Fig. 7.26 Safeguarded operation of a drilling machine.

continue to operate if the following conditions are met:

(a) a component is correctly in position, and clamped, and
(b) a drill is present, and
(c) the guard is down, and
(d) the start button has been pressed, and
(e) the stop button has *not* been pressed.

(i) Devise a suitable logic system for the controller to meet the above requirements, using a memory for the start-stop function, and basic gates as required for the remainder.

(ii) Select suitable sensors, outlining their operation, and show by means of sketches how they are arranged.

7.8.6 Explain step-by-step the operation of the semi-automatic loading circuits of Figs. 7.27(a) and (b). Explain the difference in operation of circuit (b) compared with circuit (a), due to its extra circuitry.

7.8.7 Consider the safe operation of the conveyor system of 7.6.4. Devise additional circuitry to ensure that the system cannot be started or continue to operate, when conditions are unsafe.

7.8.8 Devise a system to be added to the clamp and punch system of 7.6.5 to allow continuous automatic operation. The components are to be fed in by a third ram, C, ejecting the workpiece previously punched. The system is to run continuously on operation of push-button P, but

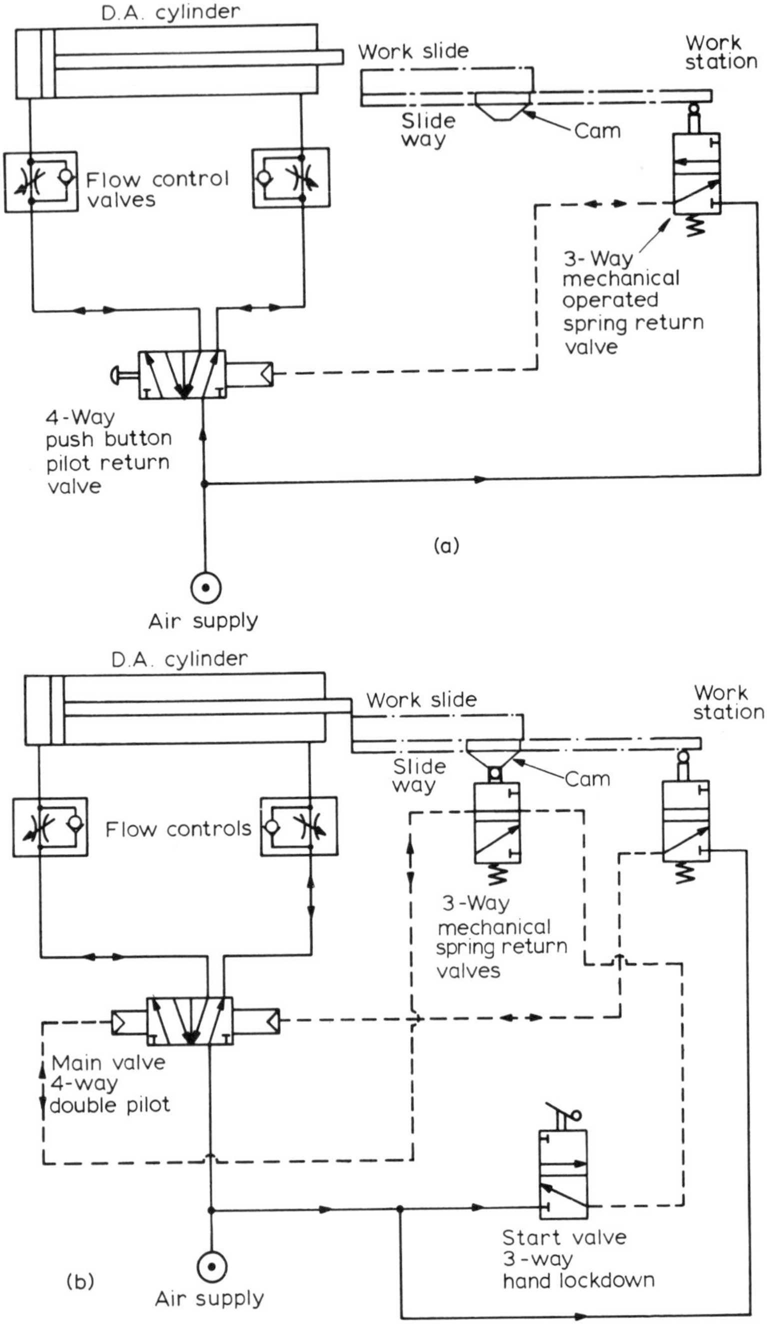

Fig. 7.27 (a) Pneumatic semi-automatic loading system.
(b) Pneumatic automatic loading system.

retracts all rams if the guard is raised, and stops at the end of the cycle if the stop button is pressed.

7.8.9 A machine-tool ram (e.g. for a shaping machine) has to:

(a) have variable stroke length,
(b) have variable speeds on both out and retract strokes,
(c) retract immediately if excessive force has to be applied.

Devise suitable systems to meet these requirements using:

(i) a hydraulic ram and valves
(ii) a geared stepper motor drive
(iii) a d.c. motor drive.

State the types of valve, sensors etc. which you would require for each type of system.

7.8.10 Devise a system of NAND gates to give the same memory function as the NOR gate arrangement of Fig. 7.8(c).

8 Continuous-control systems

In industry there are many variables which have to be controlled on a continuous basis. Quantities such as pressure, temperature, flowrate, chemical composition, and liquid level are referred to as *process-control* variables. Quantities such as linear or angular displacement, velocity and acceleration are referred to as *servo-control* variables. Similar basic control theory is used in both of these types of control, but in servo-control the effects of inertia in the acceleration of masses are considerable, whereas in many process-control systems the inertia effects are minor.

8.1 Input elements

Theoretically, the input signal θ_i may be a *step*, i.e., a sudden change from one level to another, or it may be a *ramp*, i.e. a steadily increasing or reducing quantity, or it may be of sinusoidal form. However, in practical control systems, the input may be none of these. For example, it may follow the complex profile of a template for the machining of a die-block, and is then known as a *random* input. These types of input are shown in Fig. 8.1. Frequently, the input is a linear displacement applied, for example, by the manual operation of a slider, or by the linear displacement of a follower in contact with a cam profile. The cam may rotate, as in Fig. 8.2(a), or move in a straight line as in Fig. 8.2(b). Fig. 8.2(c) illustrates the air-jet sensing principle shown in Fig. 7.16 applied in an input device which converts an input displacement θ_i to a change of back-pressure. Fig. 8.2(d) shows a joystick potentiometer input device, giving output voltages proportional to the x and y displacements of the joystick.

8.2 Output elements

Transducers are used at the output of a system to provide a feedback signal for comparison with the input signal. Typical output quantities

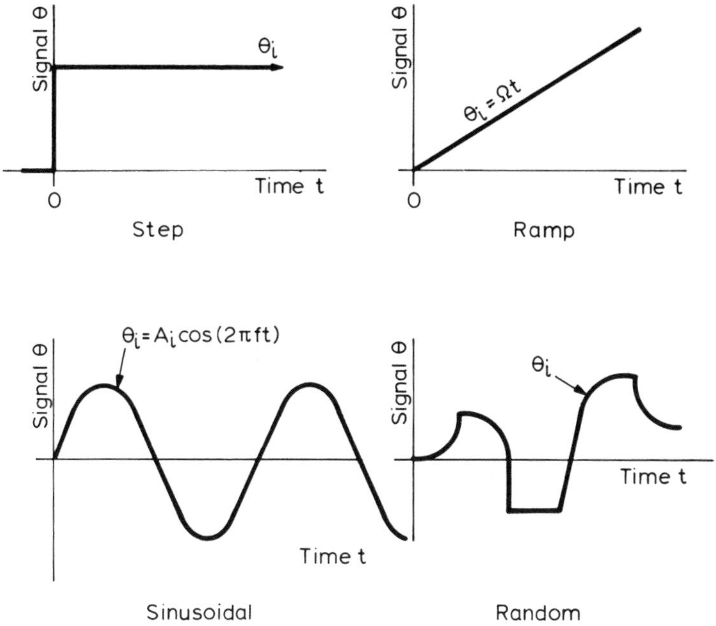

Fig. 8.1 Types of input (demand or reference) signal.

are displacement and velocity (either linear or rotational), pressure, force, temperature and volume or mass flowrate. Linear-displacement transducers were discussed in Sections 3.4 and 6.2. A typical potentiometric angular-displacement transducer is illustrated in Fig. 8.3. Pressure and force transducers were discussed in Section 6.4, and a potentiometric pressure transducer is illustrated in Fig. 8.4. This may be arranged to measure gauge pressure, vacuum, absolute or differential pressure values (in this range, lower-pressure models use a diaphragm, higher-pressure models a Bourdon tube). Temperature transducers may be of thermocouple type, whose output is a small e.m.f., measured by a voltage-balancing potentiometer; or by a platinum resistance or thermistor sensor incorporated in a Wheatstone bridge circuit. If a bi-metal strip is used, the output is displacement.

8.3 Comparison element

A comparison element is an essential requirement in a feedback control system, as discussed in Section 7.2. Some common devices carrying out this function are now discussed.

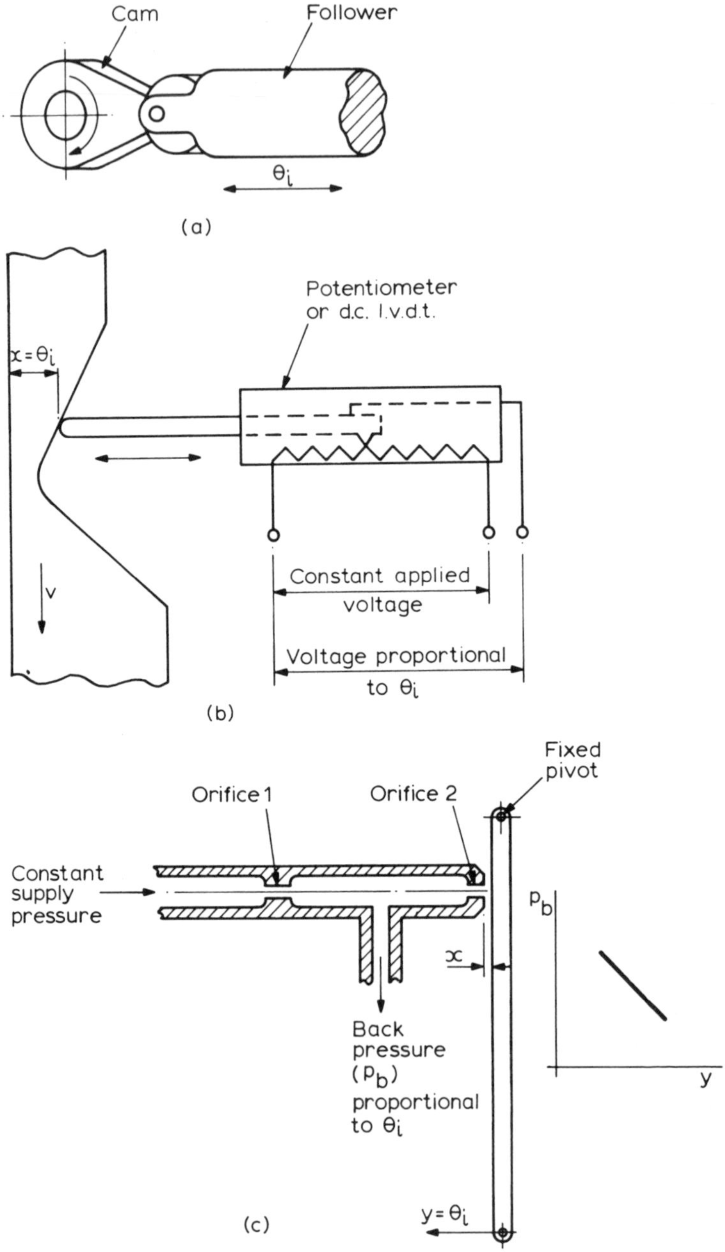

Fig. 8.2 (a) Linear input from rotational cam.
(b) Input cam with linear motion (template).
(c) Air-jet back-pressure input device.

1, 2 & 3 axis heavy duty controllers

The heavy duty potentiometric controllers are designed for operation in adverse industrial environments. The lever is intended for hand operation and the wide operating angle of the lever provides sensitive control even when the instrument is activated by a gloved hand. The controllers are rugged and capable of withstanding both their operating environment and rough handling by operators. The X and Y axes are controlled by movement of the lever; the Z axis by rotation of the lever. Dual output is available on each axis. Models HDC1 and HDC2 are available ex-stock with self-centring mechanisms.

Performance specification

Controller model number	HDC1	HDC2	HDC3
axis control	single X or Y	X and Y	X, Y & Z
lever operating angle nominal	60 degrees	60 degrees	X & Y 60 degrees Z – knob rotation ±30 degrees
resistance	2kΩ±10% on each axis		
power dissipation at 20°C	0·75 watt on each axis		
insulation resistance	greater than 50MΩ at 500V d.c.		
centre tap width	2·5% to 4% of travel		
centre tap position	50% of applied voltage ±3%		
lever self-centring capability	lever self-centres such that voltage between wiper and centre tap is less than 0·5% of applied voltage		
lever operating force	1000gm		
operational temperature range	−20°C to +70°C		

Options

dual output	dual output can be provided on each axis
resistance range	the instruments can be specified with resistance from 250Ω to 5kΩ per section
switches	end of travel and dead mans handle switches can be fitted
gate profiles	special purpose gate profiles are available
operating lever	removable, retractable and custom built handles available
non self-centring	pre-set mechanism can be specified
lever locks and detents	lever locks and detents can be provided in almost any configuration

Dimensional specification

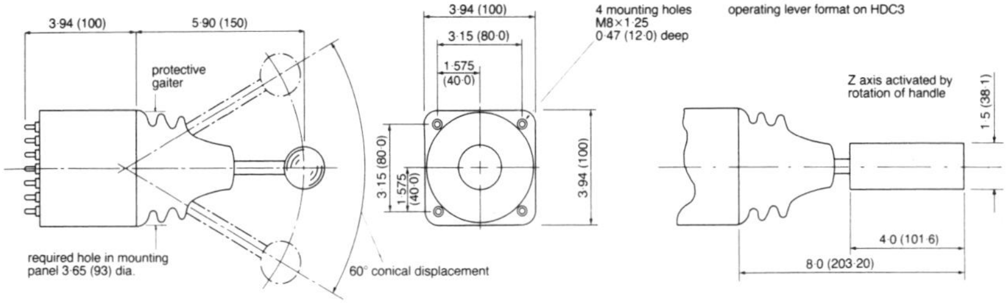

Electrical connections

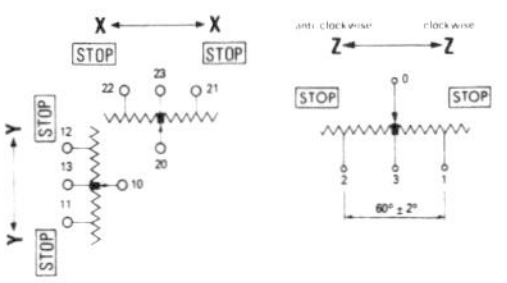

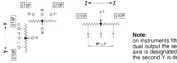

Note:
on instruments fitted with dual output the second X axis is designated 40, and the second Y is designated 30.

Ordering information

To order, or to obtain a quotation please quote the controller model number, the quantity required and specify any of the options.

Fig. 8.2 (d) Joystick controller.

heavy duty rotary potentiometer

The heavy duty potentiometer is designed to provide a reliable precision potentiometer for operation in rugged industrial situations.

performance specification

model number	HDP
Resistance range ± 10%	70Ω to 30kΩ
Electrical angle ±2° up to	357° maximum
Independent linearity	±0.5%
Resolution – turns per degree	2.2 to 7.4
Power dissipation at 20°C	2.0 watt
Contact resistance maximum	0.25Ω ENR in accordance with DEF 5123
Additional tappings permissible	1
Starting torque maximum	35gm cm without seal 200gm cm with seal
Wiper velocity maximum	1360°/sec
Mechanical angle	360° continuous
Operational temperature range	−20°C to +70°C
Insulation resistance at 500Vdc	greater than 50MΩ
Typical life at 3Hz over ±30°	10 × 10^6 cycles for a 3kΩ potentiometer

dimensional specification

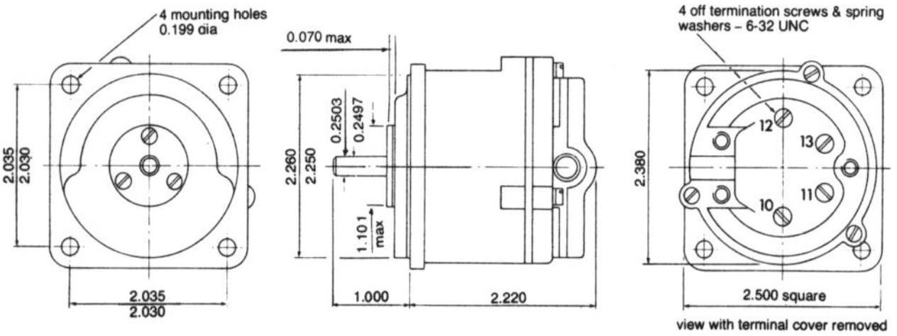

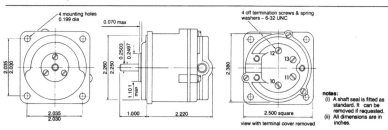

notes:
(i) A shaft seal is fitted as standard. It can be removed if requested.
(ii) All dimensions are in inches.

terminal pin identification

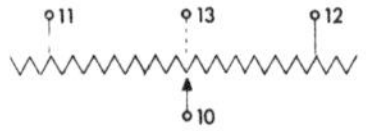

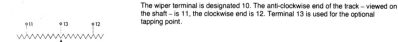

The wiper terminal is designated 10. The anti-clockwise end of the track – viewed on the shaft – is 11, the clockwise end is 12. Terminal 13 is used for the optional tapping point.

ordering information

When ordering, or if you wish to obtain a quotation, please state model number, resistance value, electrical angle and quantity required.

Fig. 8.3 Rotary potentiometer.

PRESSURE TRANSDUCERS FROM PENNY&GILES

type 70 & 71

general purpose pressure transducers

high level output signals
pressure ranges from 0-1 to 0-10000psi
gauge, absolute, vacuum and differential pressure inputs
absolute accuracy ±1.0% ±1.5% ±2.0%
designed to operate in industrial environment
wirewound or conductive plastic electrical elements

Dimensional & Installation Data

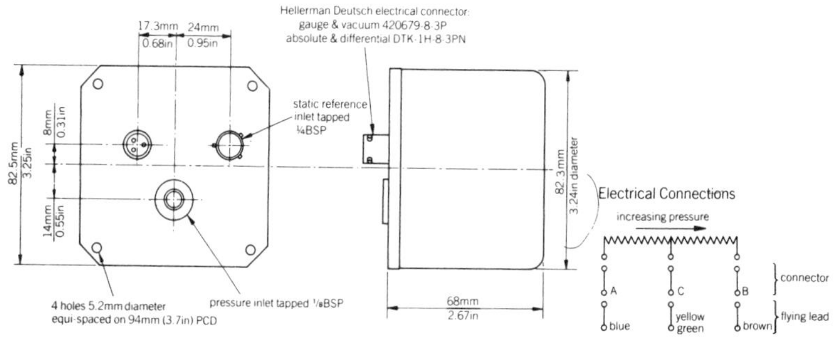

Ordering Information

When you wish to order, or to obtain a quotation please advise the following information:

the transducer reference number
the pressure format
the pressure range
any of the options required
and the quantity

Penny & Giles Transducers Limited Christchurch Dorset United Kingdom

Fig. 8.4 (a) Penny and Giles potentiometric pressure transducer.

transducer reference number	TP70/100	TP70/150	TP70/200	TP71/100
Electrical Element	wirewound potentiometer	wirewound potentiometer	wirewound potentiometer	conductive plastic element
Performance				
absolute accuracy – including all accumulative errors due to non-linearity, hysteresis and repeatability at 18°C ±2°C	±1.0%	±1.5%	±2.0%	±1.0%
temperature coefficient	0.03% per°C	0.03% per°C	0.03% per°C	0.03% per°C
resolution	0.25%	0.5%	1.0%	infinite
repeatability	0.25%	0.5%	1.0%	0.25%
response time – less than	200mS	200mS	200mS	200mS
life	10×10^6 cycles	10×10^6 cycles	10×10^6 cycles	70×10^6 cycles
Electrical Data				
potentiometer resistance	5kΩ ±10%	5kΩ ±10%	2kΩ ±10%	1kΩ ±20%
coefficient of resistance	200ppm	200ppm	200ppm	±200ppm
supply voltage – maximum	45V	60V	30V	10V
power rating at 50°C – maximum	0.4watt	0.72watt	0.45watt	0.1watt
output signal	0 to 100% supply voltage	0 to 100% supply voltage	0 to 100% supply voltage	5 to 95% supply voltage
insulation resistance at 500V d.c.	10MΩ	10MΩ	10MΩ	10MΩ
Environment				
temperature range – operational	−40°C to +70°C	−40°C to +70°C	−40°C to +70°C	−40°C to +70°C
temperature range – non operational without derangement	−55°C to +85°C	−55°C to +85°C	−55°C to +85°C	−55°C to +85°C

Pressure Input Data	
pressure ranges	gauge – psig 3-15 and 0-1 0-3 0-6 0-10 0-15 0-30 0-60 0-100 0-160 0-200 0-300 0-400 0-600 0-1000 0-2000 0-3000 0-6000 0-10000 vacuum – psivac 0-1 0-3 0-6 0-10 0-15 absolute – psiA pressure media dry air or inert gas only 0-1 0-3 0-6 0-10 0-15 0-30 0-60 0-100 differential – psi diff 0-1 0-3 0-6 0-10 0-15 0-30 0-60 0-100 media into case dry air or inert gas only to a maximum pressure of 75psi
overload pressure – maximum	125% range
materials in contact with pressure media	beryllium copper, brass and solder
Options	
potentiometer resistance	from 500Ω to 10kΩ on TP70 only
overload protection	gauge – protection in all ranges up to 100psi to 125psi vacuum – protection in all ranges up to 15psi absolute – protection in all ranges to 125psi differential – protection in all ranges on high pressure side to 125psi
temperature compensation	accuracy maintained within temperature band 0 to 40°C
flying lead	2 metres long PVC covered 16/002

Penny & Giles Transducers Limited

Christchurch Dorset United Kingdom
Telephone: Highcliffe (04252) 71511 Telex: 41266

Issue July 80

Fig. 8.4 (b) Potentiometric pressure transducer data sheet.

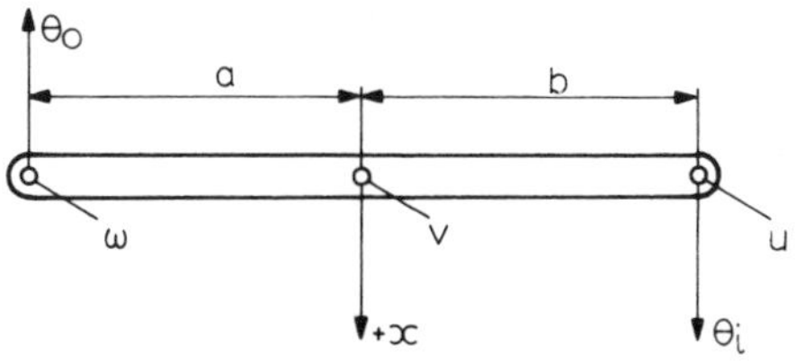

Fig. 8.5 Differential lever comparison element.

Fig. 8.5 illustrates a *differential lever*, a common component in mechanical, hydraulic and pneumatic systems. The lever has three possible pivot points. However, none of these is *permanently* fixed, and hence it is sometimes referred to as a 'floating' lever. Let θ_i and θ_o be inputs to the lever, and the resulting displacement x an output, each of these positive in the direction shown. Consider a displacement $+\theta_i$ with point w fixed. The resulting displacement of point v is $x_1 = \left(\dfrac{a}{a+b}\right)\theta_i$. Now let point u be fixed, and an input $+\theta_o$ applied.The resulting displacement of point v due to this is $x_2 = -\left(\dfrac{b}{a+b}\right)\theta_o$. With both inputs applied, the movement of v is:

$$x = x_1 + x_2$$

or

$$x = \left(\frac{a}{a+b}\right)\theta_i - \left(\frac{b}{a+b}\right)\theta_o \tag{8.1}$$

If $a = b$, then:

$$x = \tfrac{1}{2}\theta_i - \tfrac{1}{2}\theta_o$$

or

$$x = \tfrac{1}{2}(\theta_i - \theta_o) \tag{8.2}$$

Fig. 8.6 shows a potentiometer used to set an input (demand) voltage V_i by moving the slider through a distance x. A feedback voltage V_o is

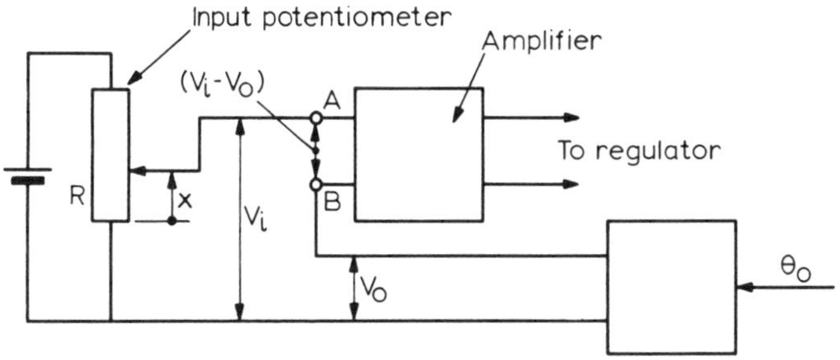

Fig. 8.6 Potentiometric comparison element.

received from a feedback transducer, which may be an item such as another potentiometer, a d.c. l.v.d.t., a tachogenerator, or a potentiometric pressure transducer. The difference between the input and output signal voltages, $V_i - V_o$, is available at the terminals AB. This is the error signal. No appreciable current may be taken from the input potentiometer or the output transducer. Hence the error signal is usually amplified by a high input-impedance power amplifier, which in turn drives the regulating element to correct the output. The arrangement

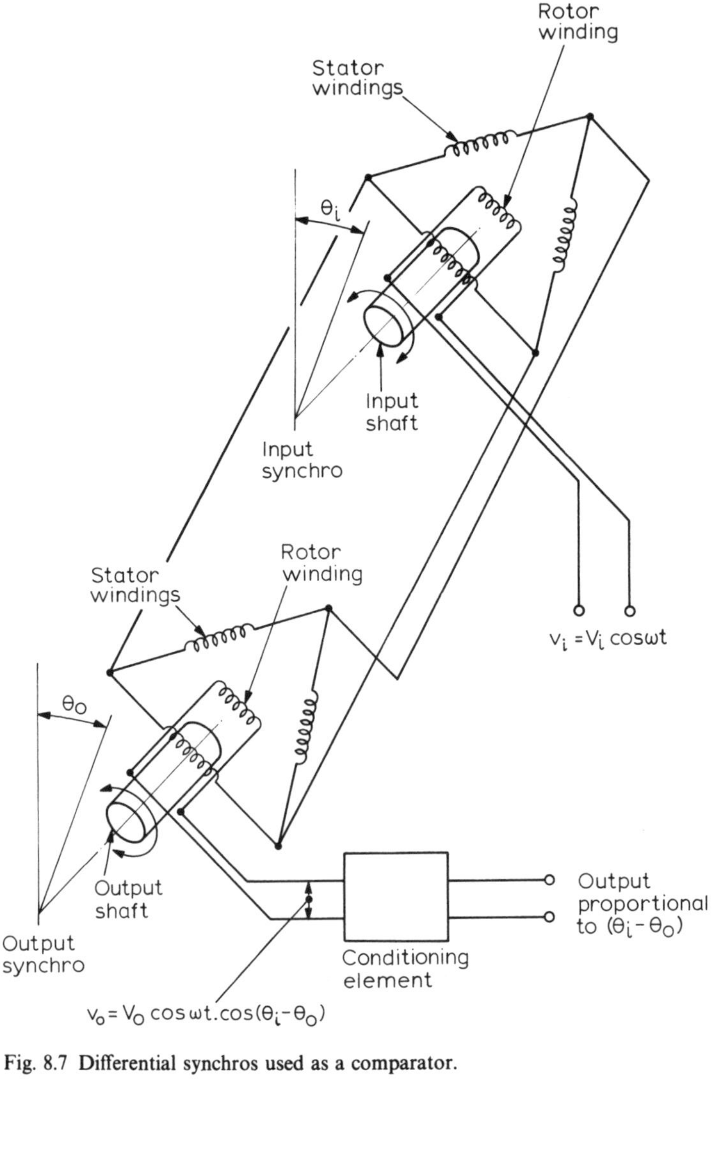

Fig. 8.7 Differential synchros used as a comparator.

forms a comparator, and its rotational equivalent may be obtained by using a rotary input potentiometer, and an angular-position transducer.

A further method of comparing rotations, found in control systems, uses *synchros*. A synchro is basically a rotary transformer, using the mutual inductance between rotor and stator coils. A laminated iron stator carries three windings 120° apart. The rotor consists of an H-shaped laminated iron core on which is wound a coil. Fig. 8.7 illustrates two synchros diagrammatically. One of these, the input synchro, is rotated to an input or demand angle θ_i. The second synchro is mounted on the output shaft of the system, and hence its angle is θ_o. The rotor of the input synchro is supplied with an alternating voltage $v_i = V_i \cos \omega t$. This induces e.m.f.'s in the stator windings, corresponding to the angular position of the input rotor. Currents flow along the three wire connection to the output synchro stator windings, and induce an e.m.f. in the rotor of the output synchro. This is $v_o = V_o \cos \omega t \cos(\theta_i - \theta_o)$, a function of the difference between the input and output angles. It has a maxima value when $(\theta_i - \theta_o)$ is 90°. In this type of synchro, the rotor and stator windings are of high impedance, to limit the current carried. The output is usually connected to a conditioning unit having a high input-impedance, this provides power to the regulating unit, to reduce the angle error. Reference 5 describes some synchro comparators.

In some systems the input and feedback voltages are connected to a differential *amplifier*, which may be regarded as carrying out the comparison or subtraction operation. The output from this amplifier is fed to a power amplifier, which in turn drives the regulating unit.

8.4 Servo-valve

Fig. 8.8(a) shows a hydraulic spool-valve controlling the flow of oil to and from a cylinder. When the spool is in the central position the lands cover the ports which lead to the cylinder, preventing flow. When the spool is displaced as shown, oil flows from the pressure supply to the right-hand side of the piston, and the left-hand side of the piston is connected to the return lines. The piston moves to the left at a constant velocity. If the ports are made rectangular, as shown in view z, and both ports and spool are precisely made, the volume flowrate may be made proportional to the spool displacement, as shown in Fig. 8.8(b).

Hence $\dot{V} = Kx$, where $\dot{V}$ is the volume flowrate (m^3/s)
and K is the flow constant for the valve parts and spool (m^3/s per metre displacement)

But also, $\dot{V} = vA$, where v is the piston velocity (m/s)
and A is the effective cross-section area of the piston (m^2)

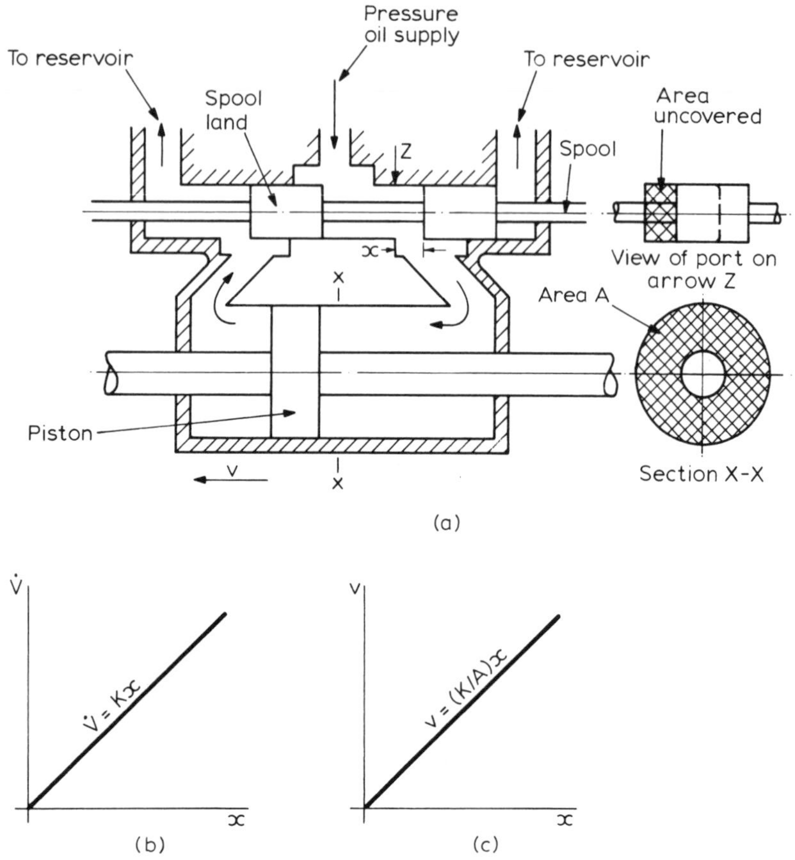

Fig. 8.8 Spool valve and piston characteristics.
(a) Spool valve and piston.
(b) Flowrate versus spool displacement.
(c) Velocity versus spool displacement.

Hence
$$vA = Kx$$
or
$$v = \left(\frac{K}{A}\right)x \tag{8.3}$$

i.e., velocity is proportional to the spool displacement, as shown in Fig. 8.8(c). The arrangement may be regarded as an open-loop system for the control of piston velocity, and as such is used in many engineering systems, such as controlling the velocity of cut on shaping or broaching machines, the rate of movement of a digger bucket on trench-diggers, and the rate of movement of a car-lift. The system diagram is shown in Fig. 8.9.

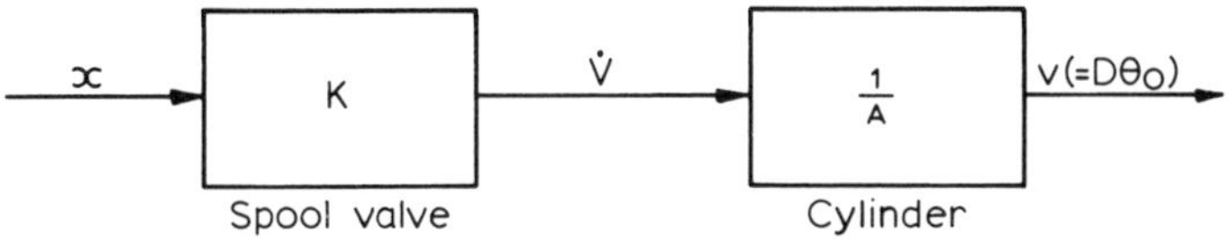

Fig. 8.9 System diagram for spool valve and piston.

The characteristics of the spool valve and piston may be completely altered by using proportional feedback. This is done by connecting a differential lever to the ends of the rods of the spool valve and the piston, as shown in Fig. 8.10. The lever pivots at points v and w, at the ends of the rods. Assume the lever is vertical as shown in (b)(i), the spool is in the central position and there is no flow. Note that the lever could take up angular positions, pivoting about a fixed point v, with the valve still centralised. The input or demand signal is a movement (θ_i) of the top point (u) of the lever. When a step input movement of θ_i is applied the piston offers a large resistance to motion, the spool valve a small resistance, hence the lever pivots about point w as in (b)(ii). Flow occurs due to the spool displacement having partly uncovered the ports, and the piston starts to move to the left. The top of the lever is now fixed, and the lever rotates about point u. In (b)(iii) the movement θ_o has caused x to reduce, partly closing the valve ports, and so the piston velocity reduces. In (b)(iv) the spool has returned to the central position, and $\theta_o = \theta_i$. The relationships may be shown mathematically:

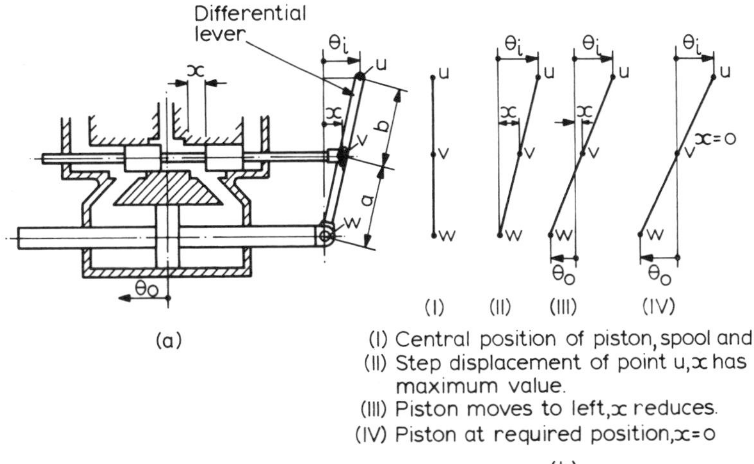

Fig. 8.10 (a) Hydraulic relay.
(b) Positions of differential lever.

If a = b, then from eqn. 8.2:

$$x = \tfrac{1}{2}(\theta_i - \theta_o)$$

Substituting this value of x in eqn. 8.3:

$$v = \left(\frac{K}{A}\right) \times \tfrac{1}{2}(\theta_i - \theta_o)$$

or

$$v = \frac{K}{2A}(\theta_i - \theta_o). \tag{8.4}$$

It is seen that the piston velocity is proportional to the difference between θ_i and θ_o, i.e., it is proportional to the error signal. It has a maximum value immediately after the input step θ_i is applied, and then reduces progressively, becoming zero when $\theta_o = \theta_i$. The system now operates as an automatic displacement control, and whatever step displacement θ_i makes, θ_o will follow, although not immediately.

The input step and response values against time are shown in Fig. 8.11 (a). The velocity of the piston at any point is $d\theta_o/dt$, and this may be denoted by $D\theta_o$, where D is the *operator D*, i.e. $D\theta_o = d\theta_o/dt$.The

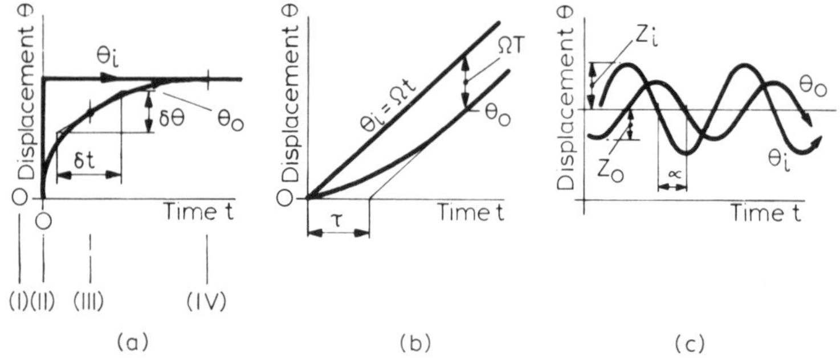

Fig. 8.11 Response of hydraulic relay to step, ramp and sinusoidal inputs.
(a) Response to a step input.
(b) Response to a ramp input.
(c) Response to a sinusoidal input.

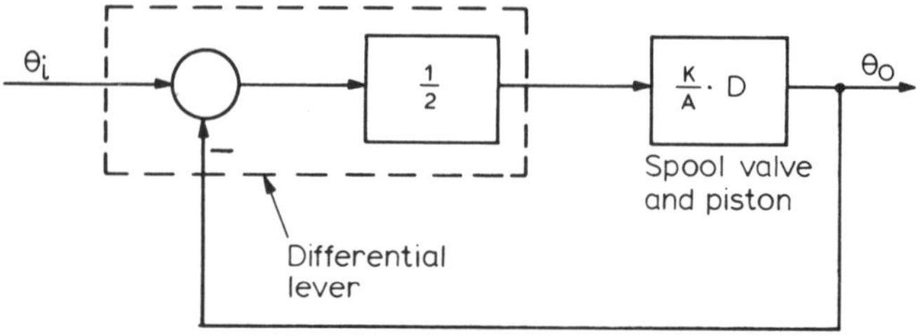

Fig. 8.12 Control system diagram for hydraulic relay.

operator D may be separated from the quantity on which it operates, θ_o in this case, as in the following analysis of the feedback servo-valve. Eqn. 8.4 may be restated thus:

$$D\theta_o = \frac{K}{2A}(\theta_i - \theta_o)$$

$$\therefore \quad \left(\frac{2A}{K}\right)D\theta_o = \theta_i - \theta_o$$

and

$$\theta_o + \left(\frac{2A}{K}\right)D\theta_o = \theta_i$$

$$\theta_o\left\{1 + \left(\frac{2A}{K}\right)D\right\} = \theta_i$$

$$\frac{\theta_o}{\theta_i} = \frac{1}{1 + \left(\frac{2A}{K}\right)D}$$

or

$$\frac{\theta_o}{\theta_i} = \frac{1}{1 + \tau D} \tag{8.5}$$

where $\tau = \dfrac{2A}{K}$ is the time-constant of the system.

The value of τ determines how fast the output θ_o of the system will move or respond after an input is applied. If θ_i is a step input, then θ_o will reach about 98 % of θ_i after a time equal to four time-constants. From eqn. 8.5 it may be seen that the response time increases as the piston area A increases, and reduces as the valve flow-constant K increases. The time-constant also determines how the system responds to ramp and sinusoidal types of input, as shown in Fig. 8.11(b) and (c). This servo-system is known as a *hydraulic relay*. Its system block diagram is shown in Fig. 8.12.

If point v on the lever is midway between points u and w, i.e., $a = b$, then a step input θ_i (of u) produces a displacement θ_o (of w) of the same magnitude, and the system has *unity gain*. If a is greater than b, then the final value of θ_o is a/b times greater than the input step θ_i, i.e., the gain is a/b. The response to ramp and sinusoidal inputs is also greater than the system with unity gain. The response times are also changed, since the time-constant (τ) of the hydraulic relay depends on the a/b ratio (see 8.8.5).

The hydraulic relay belongs to a type of a system known as *first-order* (i.e. its operation may be represented by a first-order differential equation), or exponential lag. A similar system using air is shown in 8.7.1. It must be appreciated that inertia effects must be negligible, i.e., the mass must be small compared with other effects, for the system to be *first-*

order. If the forces required to accelerate mass are not negligible, then the system becomes *second-order* or higher. Some temperature measurement and control systems are first-order, also electrical resistance-capacitance circuits. Each of these systems may be represented by eqn. 8.5, and its overall effect by the diagram of Fig. 8.13.

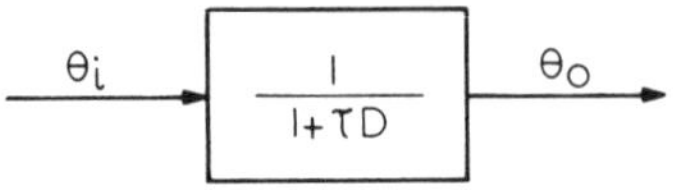

Fig. 8.13 Transfer operator of exponential lag.

If the input, θ_i to a first-order system is a step, then the output is given by:

$$\theta_o = \theta_i(1 - e^{-t/\tau}) \tag{8.6}$$

If the input is a *ramp*, i.e., $\theta_i = \Omega t$, then the output is given by:

$$\theta_o = \Omega t - \Omega\tau - \Omega\tau e^{-t/\tau} \tag{8.7}$$

If the input is sinusoidal, i.e. $\theta_i = Z_i \cos(2\pi f t)$, the output signal, after a time, settles down to a sinusoidal displacement at the same frequency as the input, but lagging behind the input, and having a smaller amplitude. Thus:

$$\theta_o = Z_o \cos(2\pi f t - \alpha) \tag{8.8}$$

The amplitude ratio is given by:

$$\frac{Z_o}{Z_i} = \frac{1}{\sqrt{\{1 + (2\pi f \tau)^2\}}} \tag{8.9}$$

and the lag angle is:

$$\alpha = \arctan\,(2\pi f \tau) \tag{8.10}$$

The use of these equations is shown in 8.7.1

8.5 Process-control valve

Fluid flowrate is one of the most commonly controlled process variables. In petroleum and chemical processing plant, and in steam plant for heating and for generating electricity etc., accurate control of the flowrate of liquids, gases or mixtures of gases and liquids is required.

The air-operated process-control valve illustrated in Fig. 8.14 is of a type commonly used for flowrate control, particularly where the use of electricity may be hazardous. Air at a controlled pressure is supplied to the *actuator* or *diaphragm motor* and controls the position of the valve stem in the following manner. The air pressure acting on the diaphragm causes a force proportional to the pressure to be applied to the helical

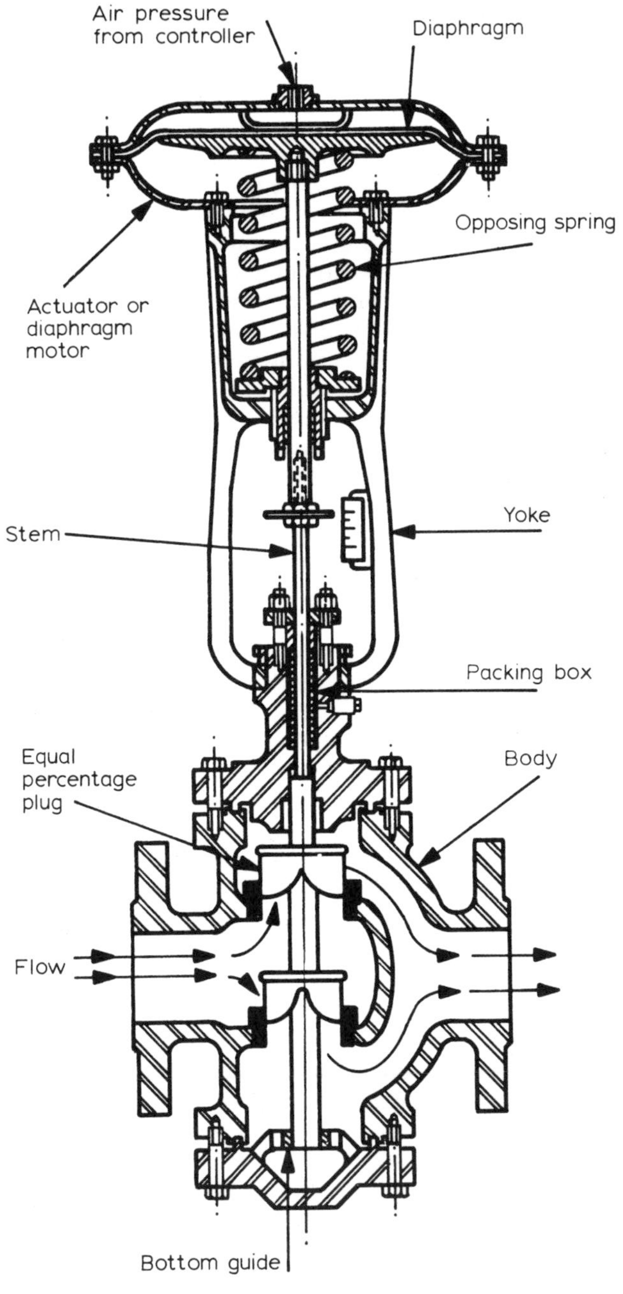

Fig. 8.14 Air-operated process-control valve.

compression spring. The spring has ideally a linear relationship between force and displacement, i.e., it has a constant rate, hence the displacement of the valve stem is proportional to the compression force in the spring. The flowrate is controlled directly by the *inner valve* or *plug*. This is illustrated in the control system block diagram Fig. 8.15 as giving a flowrate directly proportional to displacement of the valve. This leads to a linear overall relationship between flowrate and control pressure.

Three types of double-seated inner valve are illustrated in Fig. 8.16. The forces due to fluid pressure on a double-seated valve balance out, enabling a smaller actuator to be used than for a single-seated valve. The flowrate for a given valve position and given pressure difference across the valve depends on the shape of the plug. Although Fig. 8.15 illustrates a linear relationship between control air pressure and flowrate, this is not always the relationship required. The characteristics of the three types of plug illustrated in Fig. 8.16 are shown in Fig. 8.17. A plug is chosen to give the flow characteristics required for the particular process system involved. The system does not utilise feedback, and if the characteristic

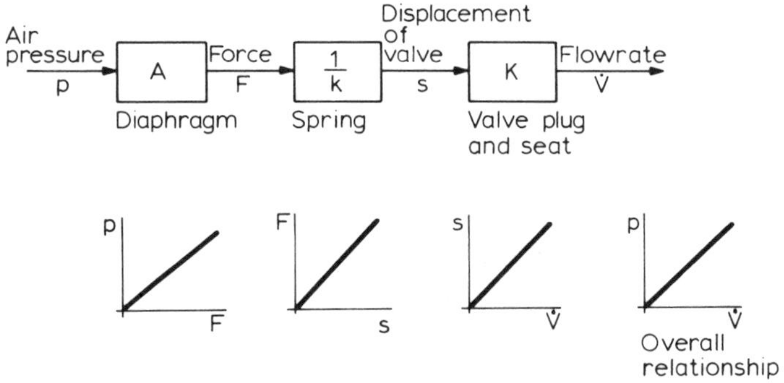

Fig. 8.15 Characteristics of process-control valve.

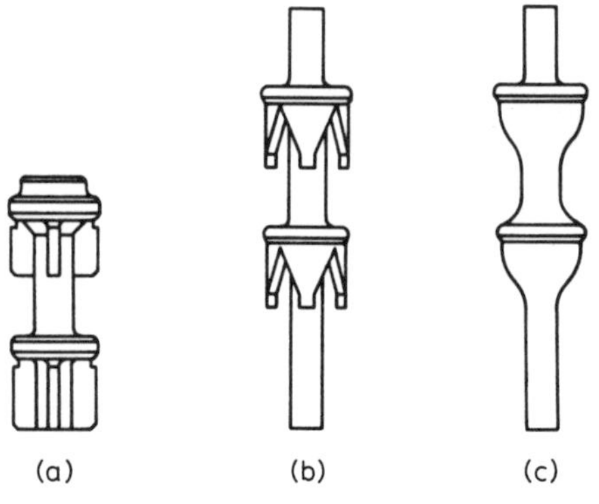

Fig. 8.16 Inner valves.

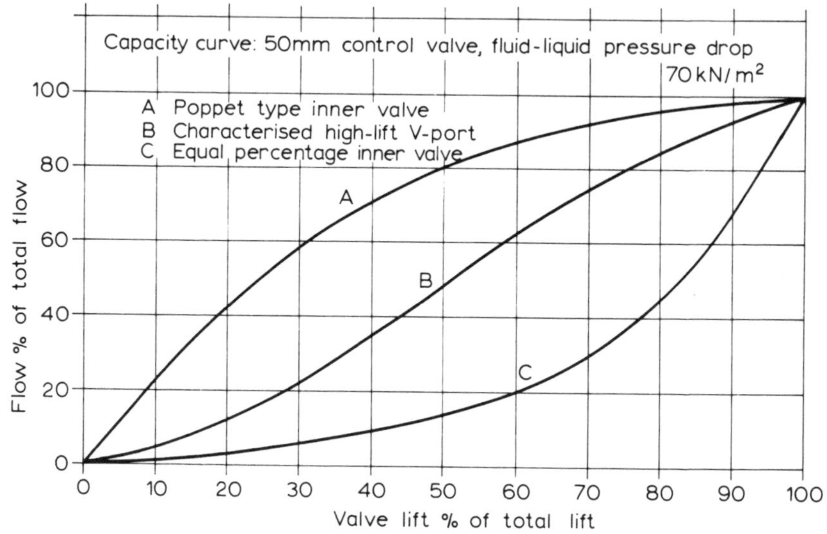

Fig. 8.17 Flow characteristics of control valves.

of the spring changes with time, or that of the plug changes due to erosion, or the friction force exerted by the guides changes, then, for a given control pressure and pressure difference across the valve, the flowrate will change.

Feedback may be introduced into the flowrate control system by using a flowmeter in addition to the valve, as shown in Fig. 8.18(a). The pressure difference $(p_1 - p_2)$ across the orifice plate of the orifice meter is a function of the flow rate $(\dot{V})$, as shown in (b). The demand signal, an air pressure, is fed to the comparator illustrated in (c) which consists of a lever pivoted at F. A force proportional to p_1 is applied at R, and a force proportional to p_2 is applied at S. If the flowrate is correct, then the back pressure (p_b), which operates the diaphragm motor of the valve, is at its correct value. If, say, the flowrate increases, the differential pressure $(p_1 - p_2)$ increses, and the lever moves away from the air-jet sensing head. The pressure to the diaphragm motor reduces, partly closing the valve, tending to correct the flowrate. The system gives a flowrate which is a function of the demand air pressure, although with a more complex and more expensive system. Fig. 8.19 shows the control system block diagram.

Fig. 8.20(a) shows a process-control valve which controls the flowrate of a fluid proportionally with a measured temperature. The temperature-sensing element is a vapour-pressure thermometer consisting of a metal 'bulb' immersed in the fluid whose temperature is to be controlled.The bulb is partially filled with a liquid, and the remainder is the vapour from the liquid. The bulb is connected through a capillary tube to a bellows in

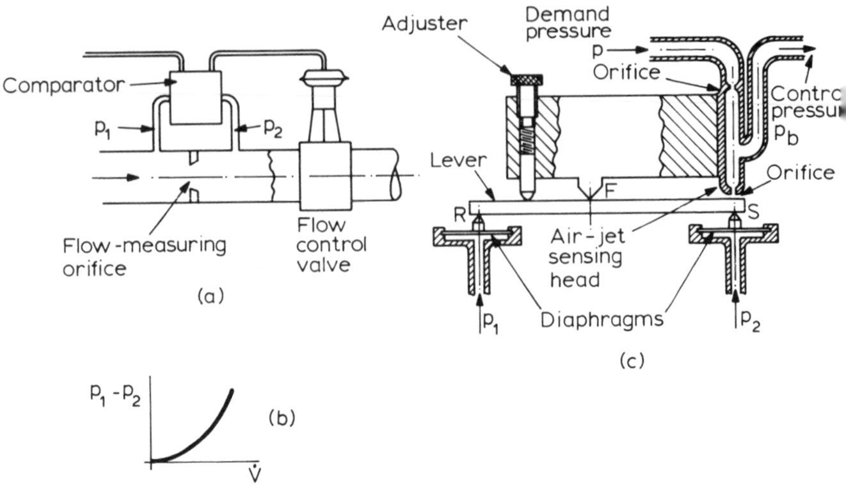

Fig. 8.18 (a) Feedback flowrate control system.
(b) Orifice characteristic.
(c) Pressure comparator.

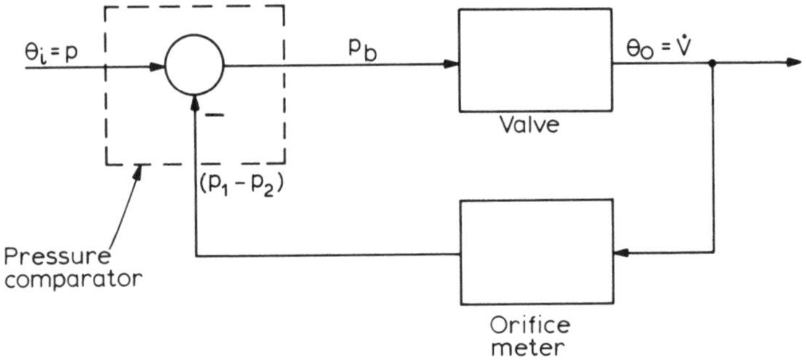

Fig. 8.19 Control system diagram for valve and orifice.

the valve body. When the temperature of the bulb increases, the vapour pressure rises, compressing the bellows and moving the valve towards the open position, against the force exerted by the belical spring. The operating point may be adjusted by rotating a selector knob, thus varying the force exerted by the spring. By careful design, the flowrate may increase in direct proportion to the bulb temperature, or by reversal of the valve disc and stem it may reduce in direct proportion.

Fig. 8.20(b) shows a valve of this type controlling the flow of cooling water through a heat exchanger. The valve opens as the temperature of the cooled fluid leaving the heat exchanger increases, thus increasing the

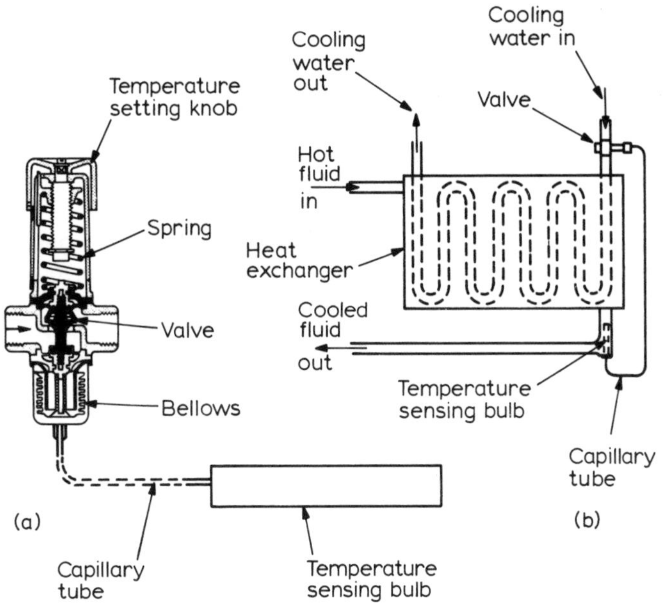

Fig. 8.20 (a) Temperature-controlled valve.
(b) Heat exchanger with temperature-controlled valve.

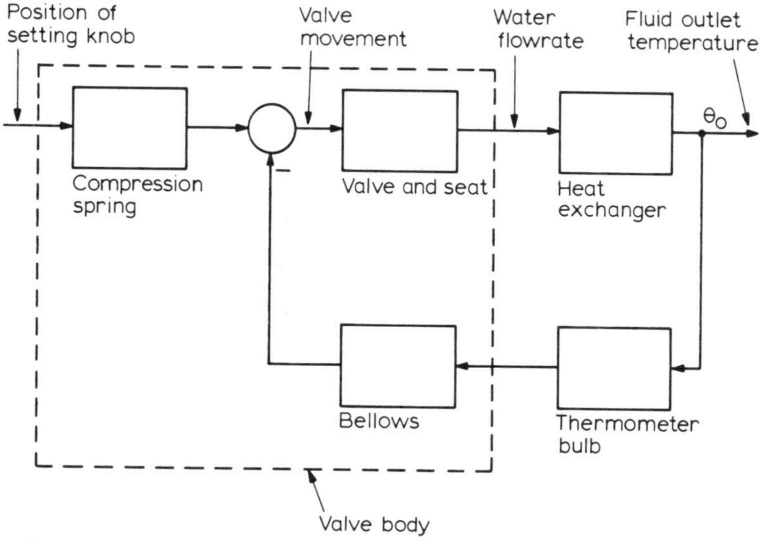

Fig. 8.21 Control system block diagram for heat exchanger temperature control.

cooling water flow, and tending to reduce the temperature to the desired value. The control system block diagram is shown in Fig. 8.21. It should be noted that the controlled variable is ultimately temperature, not flowrate.

8.6 Positive-feedback systems

Most control systems employ negative feedback, subtracting the output signal from the input signal to give an error signal. If through incorrect system design or operation the output signal becomes of opposite phase to the input signal, then the comparator subtracts a *negative* signal, and in effect *adds* the output to the input. The signal going through the forward loop alters the output in the wrong direction, i.e., it increases it when it should decrease it, and vice-versa. The feedback signal increases correspondingly and the forward-loop signal is increased further. The system output oscillates with increasing amplitude which can become dangerous and destructive. The condition is referred to as *instability*, and may occur when the system differential equation is of third order or higher type, which in mechanical systems is more likely to occur when mass is involved.

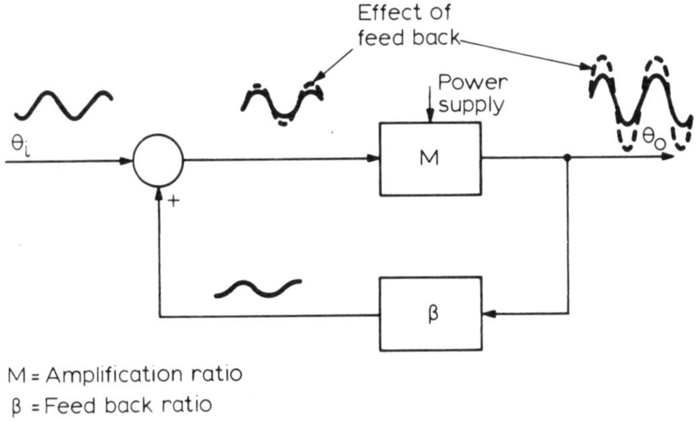

Fig. 8.22 Control system block diagram for amplifier with positive feedback.

In one type of system, positive feedback may be used by design. Fig. 8.22 shows an electrical amplifier system, where the forward loop transfer operator (or gain) is M. A fraction (β) of the output is fed back to the summing point and *added* to the incoming signal. The effect is as described in the preceding paragraph, i.e., the output signal has increasing amplitude. If the input signal θ_i is removed, the feedback signal may maintain the oscillation of the system indefinitely, and M or β

may be adjusted to keep the amplitude constant. The system may be used as an oscillator, but has the disadvantage of being potentially unstable.

8.7 Examples

8.7.1 Fig. 8.23 illustrates a pneumatic servo where θ_i, the input, is a displacement of point w on the differential lever, and θ_o is the displacement of the pneumatic ram. θ_o and θ_i are positive in the directions shown. The movement of the feedback link is $x = \frac{1}{2}(\theta_i - \theta_o)$. Movement of the blade, due to movement of the feedback link, alters its position relative to the air-jet nozzles A and B. A displacement $+x$ of the blade restricts air outlet from the nozzle B, increases its back pressure and also the pressure to the right of the piston. At the same time the pressure at A and to the left of the piston reduces. The pressure difference causes the piston to move to the left, at a steady speed. There is a range $\pm x$ where the velocity of the piston, $v = d\theta_o/dt$, is proportional to x, as shown in Fig. 8.24.
In an open-loop test, i.e., with the feedback link disconnected, the slope of the linear part of the v/x graph was found to be 5 mm/s per millimetre of displacement.

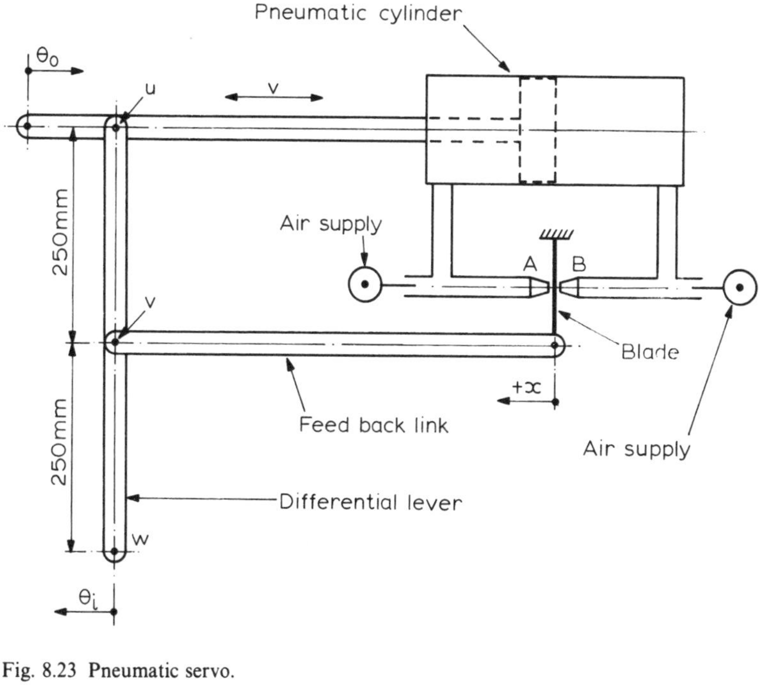

Fig. 8.23 Pneumatic servo.

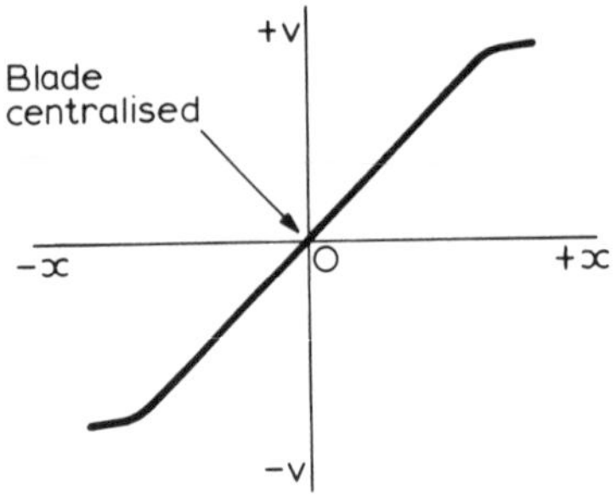

Fig. 8.24 Pneumatic servo open-loop characteristic.

(a) Sketch the system block diagram, and determine the differential equation representing the system.

(b) Calculate:

(i) the time-constant of the system for the given values

(ii) the initial piston velocity, and the time for θ_o to become 9.5 mm when the point w is moved sharply 10 mm to the left

(iii) the amount the value of θ_o lags behind θ_i when $\theta_i = 2t$ mm (i.e., point w moves steadily to the left at 2 mm/s).

(iv) the amplitude, frequency and phase lag when the input movement is $\theta_i = 20\cos(2\pi t)$ mm (i.e., $f = 1$ Hz).

(c) Show the input-output relationships on a base of time.

(a) In Fig. 8.25, the transfer operator for the nozzles and ram is shown in diagram (a) when the output is velocity $D\theta_o$. But the required output is displacement, θ_o, hence the transfer operator is that shown in (b), and incorporated in the control system diagram (c).

Considering the forward part of the loop:

$$\tfrac{1}{2}(\theta_i - \theta_o) \times \frac{5}{D} = \theta_o$$

$$\theta_i - \theta_o = \left(\frac{2}{5}\right) D\theta_o$$

and

$$\theta_i = \theta_o + \left(\frac{2}{5}\right) D\theta_o$$

$$= \theta_o \left\{1 + \left(\frac{2}{5}\right) D\right\}$$

$$\frac{\theta_o}{\theta_i} = \frac{1}{1 + \left(\frac{2}{5}\right) D}$$

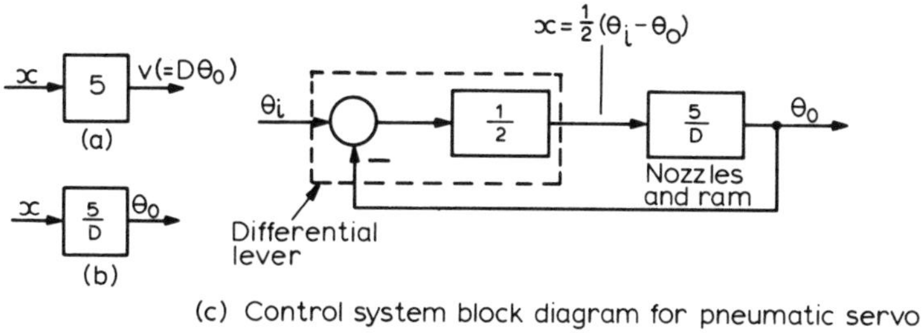

Fig. 8.25

(b) (i) From equation 8.5, the time-constant is $\tau = \frac{2}{5}$s.
(ii) Velocity immediately after step input is:

$$v = 5\left(\frac{\text{mm}}{\text{s}\,\cancel{\text{mm}}}\right) \times 10(\cancel{\text{mm}}) = 50\,\text{mm/s}$$

By eqn. 8.6, when θ_i is a step input:

$$\frac{\theta_o}{\theta_i} = 1 - e^{-t/\tau}$$

$$\therefore \quad \frac{9.5}{10} = 1 - e^{-t/\tau} \text{ and } t = 1.2\,\text{s}.$$

(iii) By eqn. 8.7, for a ramp input,

$$\theta_o = \Omega t - \Omega\tau - \Omega\tau e^{-t/\tau}$$

After a time equal to a few time-constants, the third term on the right-hand side is virtually zero. Hence, since $\Omega t = \theta_i$, then $\Omega\tau$ is the lag of θ_o relative to θ_i, thus

$$\text{lag} = \Omega\tau = 2 \times 0.4 = 0.8\,\text{mm}$$

(iv) By eqn. 8.8, for a sinusoidal input, the output has the same frequency as the input. By eqn. 8.9, the amplitude ratio is given by,

$$\frac{Z_o}{Z_i} = \frac{1}{\sqrt{\{1 + (2\pi f\tau)^2\}}}$$

$$\therefore \quad \frac{Z_o}{20} = \frac{1}{\sqrt{\{1 + (2\pi \times 0.4)^2\}}}$$

and

$$Z_o = 20(\pm 0.37)$$

$$= \pm 7.4\,\text{mm}.$$

i.e., the amplitude of the output oscillation is ± 7.4 mm.
By eqn. 8.9, the output waveform lags the input waveform by the

angle, $\alpha = \arctan(2\pi f\tau)$
$= \arctan(2\pi \times 0.4) = 68^\circ$

(c) These inputs and responses are illustrated in Fig. 8.11.

8.7.2 A speed control system is to be devised so that the speed of rotation of a pair of small rolls is proportional to the input voltage, i.e., the demand, to the control system. Sketch the configuration of the system, and the control system block diagram.

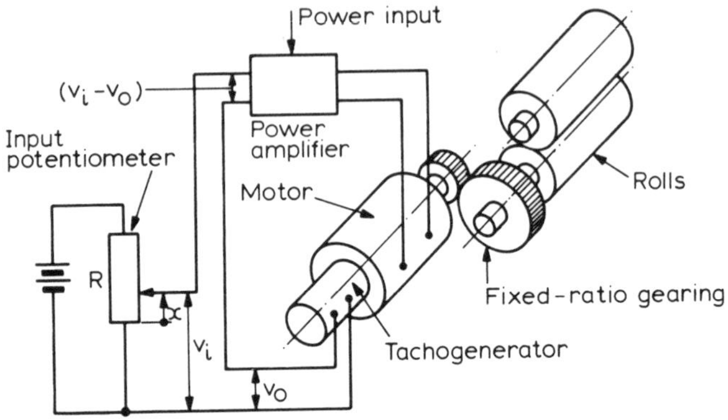

Fig. 8.26 Speed-control system for rolls.

The system is shown in Fig. 8.26. The required rotational speed is set by moving the slider of the input potentiometer a distance x, setting a demand voltage v_i. If the motor is stationary, then the output voltage from the d.c. tachogenerator is zero. Hence the input voltage to the power amplifier is v_i, and the output to the motor will be proportional to v_i. The motor accelerates, and the tachogenerator output v_o is proportional to the motor speed, and hence to the speed of the rolls. The input voltage to the power amplifier is now $(v_i - v_o)$. As the speed increases further, the value of $(v_i - v_o)$ reduces, reducing the input power to the motor. The motor speed will settle at a value depending on the demand value v_i. Any change of speed from this value during the rolling operation leads to an increase or decrease of power to the motor. The control system block diagram is shown in Fig. 8.27.

8.7.3 Devise a system to control the angular position of a directional aerial, the demand signal being the position of an input setting knob. Draw the control system block diagram.

The proposed system is shown in Fig. 8.28. Rotation of the input knob rotates the input synchro of a pair of differential synchros, the output synchro being connected to the aerial spindle. The output of the synchros is $v_o = V_o \cos(\omega t) \cos(\theta_i - \theta_o)$ where $V_i \cos(\omega t)$ is the supply signal. A conditioning unit gives out a d.c. signal proportional to $(\theta_i - \theta_o)$ to the motor, which drives the aerial shaft through reduction gears. The motor operating voltage is zero when $\theta_o = \theta_i$, and the aerial is then stationary. The control system block diagram is shown in Fig. 8.29.

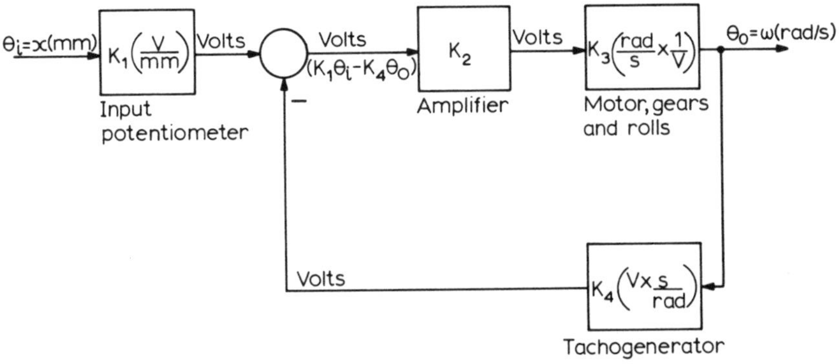

Fig. 8.27 Control system block diagram for speed control.

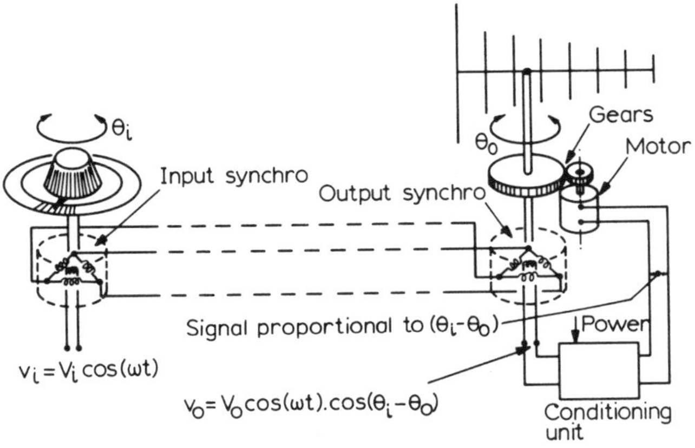

Fig. 8.28 Position-control system for aerial.

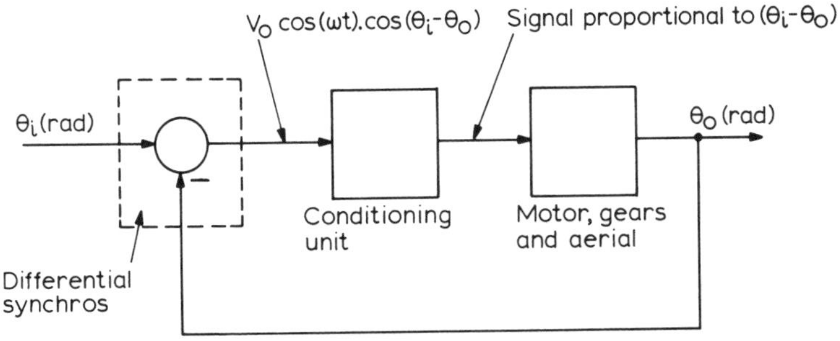

Fig. 8.29 Control system block diagram for aerial position control.

8.7.4 Explain how the control system shown in Fig. 8.30 maintains the electrical alternator shaft speed at a constant preset value, and draw the control-system block diagram.

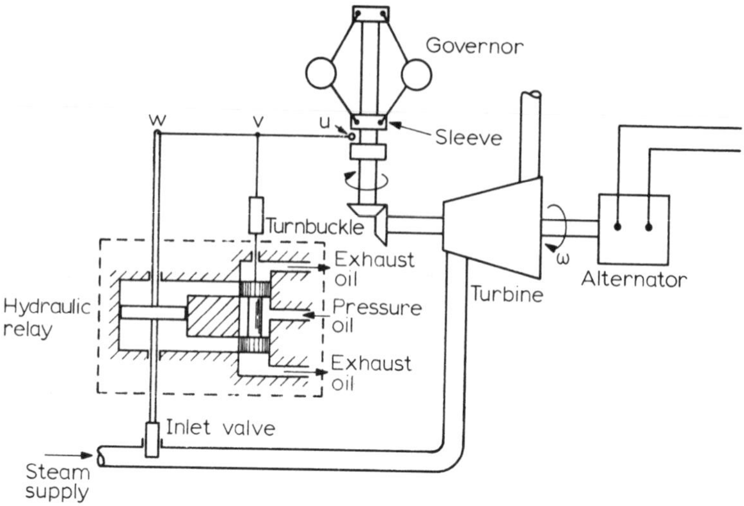

Fig. 8.30 Speed-control system for turbine/alternator.

The steam inlet valve spindle is stationary when the spool-valve of the hydraulic relay is in the central position as illustrated, at some particular speed value (ω). If the load on the alternator is increased, the output shaft speed falls as also does the speed of the mechanical governer, driven through the bevel gears. The rotating masses of the governer move to a smaller radius, moving the sleeve down. The movement of point u on the floating lever uvw is the input signal to the hydraulic relay. The corresponding movement of the piston opens the steam inlet valve and leads to an increased speed of the alternator shaft. When the speed is the set input speed (the demand), the spool-valve is in the central position, and the cylinder and steam-valve spindle are stationary.

The desired speed is set by rotating the turnbuckle to set the length between point v and the spool. The floating lever is the comparison element. Fig. 8.31 gives the control system block diagram. It should be noted that the hydraulic relay is a control system within a larger control system, i.e. it is a sub-system.

8.7.5 Devise a system to utilise the process-control valve of Fig. 8.14 in a steam turbine/alternator shaft speed control system.

A pressure signal which is a function of the error in the shaft speed is required. A possible way of obtaining this is from the small sleeve movement of a speed-sensing device such as that of Fig. 6.1, as shown in Fig. 8.32. The speed demand signal is a movement θ_i of point w on the differential lever uvw. The feedback signal, the movement (z) of the sleeve of the tachometer, moves point u on the lever. The movement of the midpoint (v) is $\frac{1}{2}(\theta_i - z)$. Movement of v causes more or less restriction of the outlet from the air-jet sensing head, increasing or reducing the back-

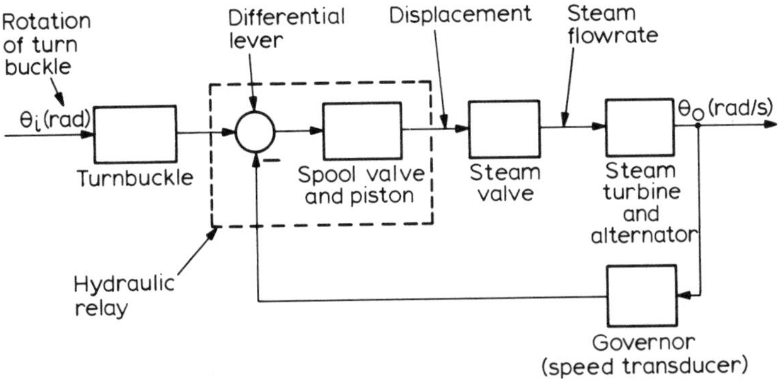

Fig. 8.31 Control system block diagram for turbine/alternator speed control.

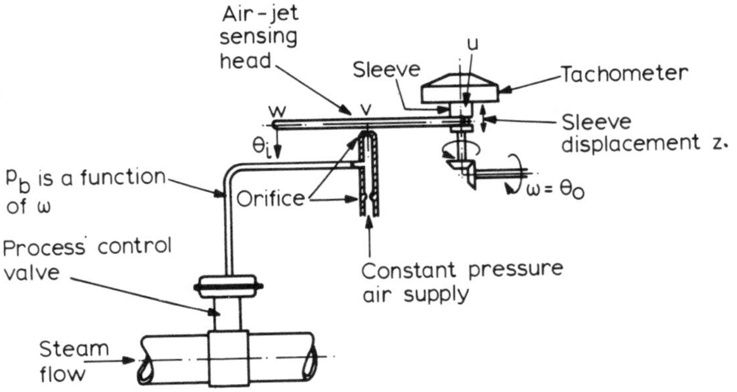

Fig. 8.32 Feedback control system using process-control valve.

pressure p_b, which in turn controls the opening of the process-control valve.

It may be seen that if the shaft speed increases, due say to a reduction of electrical load, the tachometer action raises the sleeve, reducing the air-jet restriction, reducing the back pressure, and hence closing the valve, reducing the steam flow and hence the speed of the alternator. The control system block diagram is shown in Fig. 8.33.

8.7.6 Devise a system to control the mass flow rate ($\dot{m}$) of granular material on a conveyor moving at a constant speed, the input being an electrical voltage from a remote point. The system is shown in Fig. 8.34.

The mass on a length of the conveyor belt is measured by the load cell, in conjunction with a Wheatstone bridge, giving an output voltage proportional to the mass on the weighing frame. Since the belt speed is constant, this voltage is proportional to the mass flowrate. This voltage is subtracted from the demand voltage using a differential amplifier, the

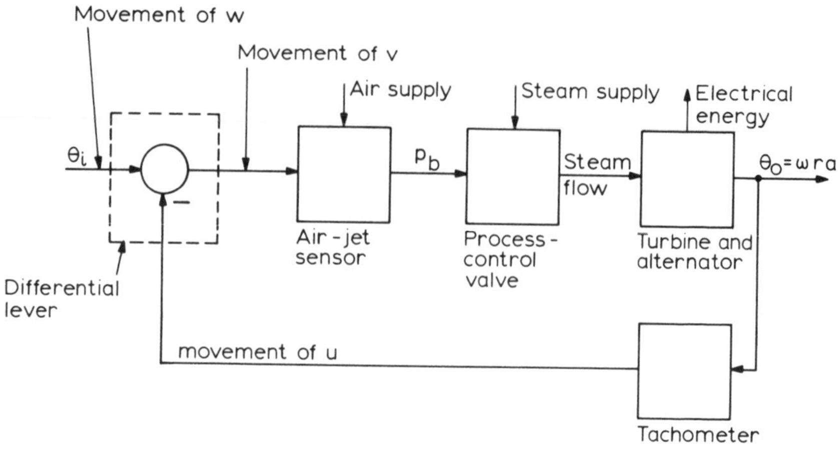

Fig. 8.33 Control system block diagram for speed-control system.

output of this being fed to a power amplifier. The power amplifier drives the motor (the regulating element) which raises or lowers the gate through a rack and pinion gear and hence alters the mass flowrate until the error voltage becomes zero. The control system block diagram is shown in Fig. 8.35.

8.8 Exercises

8.8.1 Devise a control system for the continuous control of liquid level in a vertical cylindrical tank, the desired level being set on a potentiometer, and the output being measured using a float and a d.c. l.v.d.t. Sketch the physical arrangement of the components and explain how the system works. Draw the control system block diagram.

8.8.2 Devise a control system for the powered operation of either a road vehicle's steering, or for a ship's rudder. Sketch the physical arrangement, explain how the system works, and draw the control system block diagram.

8.8.3 Devise an automatic *feedback* control system for the positioning of the valve stem in the process-control valve of Fig. 8.14. Explain any advantages it may have over the open-loop system. Draw the control system block diagram.

8.8.4 Lorries standing on a weighbridge are loaded with gravel from a hopper, the outlet from this being controlled by a flap valve. The flap valve is to be progressively closed as the mass of gravel added to the lorry approaches a preset value. The weighbridge utilises a load cell having strain gauges in a Wheatstone bridge. Outline a system using the output from the bridge to give the desired control, specifying a suitable

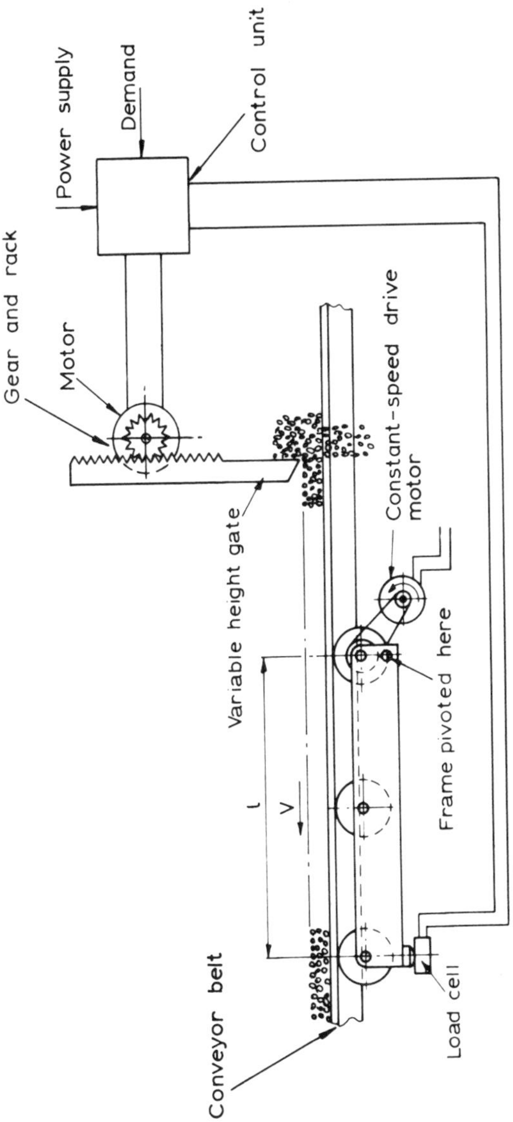

8.34 Mass-flowrate control system for conveyor.

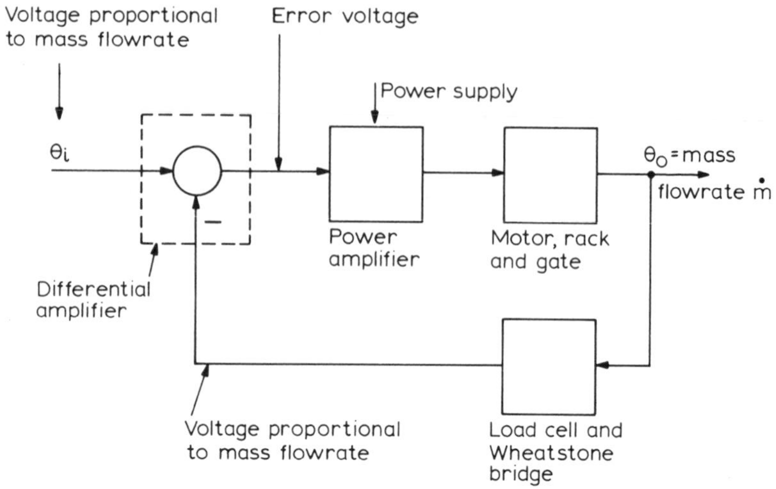

Fig. 8.35 Control system block diagram for mass-flowrate control system.

regulating element for the operation of the valve, and indicating how the required mass is set. Draw the system control diagram.

8.8.5 Show that for the hydraulic relay of Fig. 8.10, when a is not equal to b, the overall transfer operator is

$$\frac{\theta_o}{\theta_i} = \frac{a/b}{1 + \left\{\left(\frac{a+b}{a}\right)\frac{A}{K}\right\}D}.$$

8.8.6 A hydraulic relay has an effective piston area (A) of 800 mm^2, the flow constant for the spool-valve (K) is 0.005 l/s per mm of spool displacement, and for the floating lever $a = b$. Calculate:

(a) the time-constant of the system

(b) the initial piston velocity and the time for the output movement of the piston to reach 10 mm when the input is a step movement of 12 mm

(c) the amount the output lags the input when the latter is a steady movement (ramp input) of 2 mm/s

(d) the amplitude and phase lag of the output when the input is 6 cos 5t mm.

8.8.7 Devise a control system using the principle of the hydraulic relay for copy turning using a template. A stylus is to follow the contour of the template, and the piston and rod are to control the position of the tool. Draw the control-system block diagram, labelling each part. Discuss the accuracy of the movement of the tool relative to the template. If the hydraulic relay has the same A and K values as in 8.8.6, state what error would be likely to occur in machining the shape shown in Fig. 8.36.

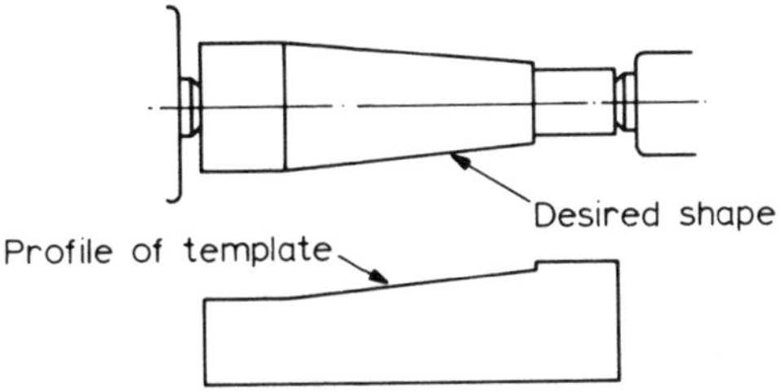

Fig. 8.36

8.8.8 Calculate the time-constant of the hydraulic relay of 8.8.6 if the A and K values are the same, but $a = 3b$.
8.8.9 A control system is required to maintain within close limits the thickness of soft plastic strip coming through a pair of rolls as shown in Fig. 8.37. Devise a suitable arrangement using an air-jet sensing head and a pneumatic cylinder, showing clearly how the desired thickness is set, and how the system controls it. Sketch the control system block diagram.

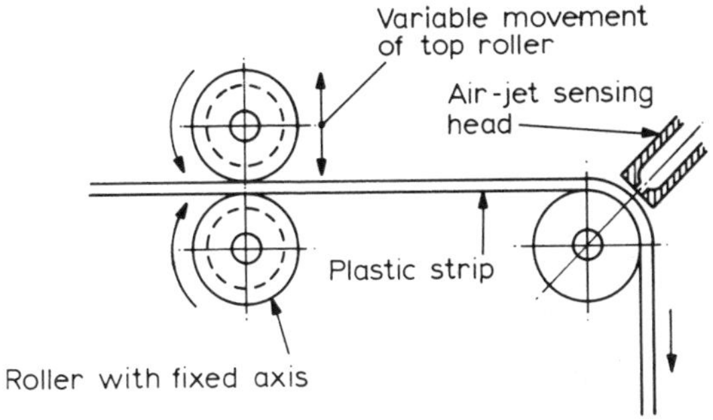

Fig. 8.37

8.8.10 For the plastic strip rolling operation of 8.8.9 the rollers are to be maintained at a constant temperature of 100°C by blowing into the hollow rollers air which has been heated by an electrical heater. The temperature of the air at outlet is to be measured by a thermistor which forms part of a Wheatstone bridge. The output from the bridge is to control the power to the heating element. Sketch a suitable system for this control and explain how it works, showing clearly how the input temperature is set. Sketch the control system block diagram.
8.8.11 For the plastic strip rolling operation of exercise 8.8.9 it is required to maintain the tension of the strip leaving the rolls to a predetermined value. Devise a control system to do this, explaining how it operates, and sketch the control system block diagram.
8.8.12 Water is supplied at mains pressure and is passed through the

cooling jacket of an internal combustion engine on a test bed. Devise a system to control the temperature of the water leaving the jacket by controlling the flowrate of water through it. Draw the control-system diagram showing clearly the function of the components of the system.

8.8.13 The rotational speed of a steam turbine and generator shaft is to be automatically controlled. A tacho-generator driven by the shaft provides a voltage, proportional to speed, to a summing amplifier. A second voltage, representing the required shaft speed, is fed to the same amplifier, whose output is fed to a power amplifier, which then controls the degree of opening of a steam flow valve.

Sketch the control-system block diagram, and clearly identify the parts of the system which comprise:

(a) the system input
(b) the system output
(c) the feedback signal
(d) the comparator
(e) the regulating unit.

8.8.14 A solar heating panel is connected in a closed circuit to a heating coil of tube inside a hot-water cylinder. The liquid in the solar panel circuit is to be circulated when the temperature at the top of the solar

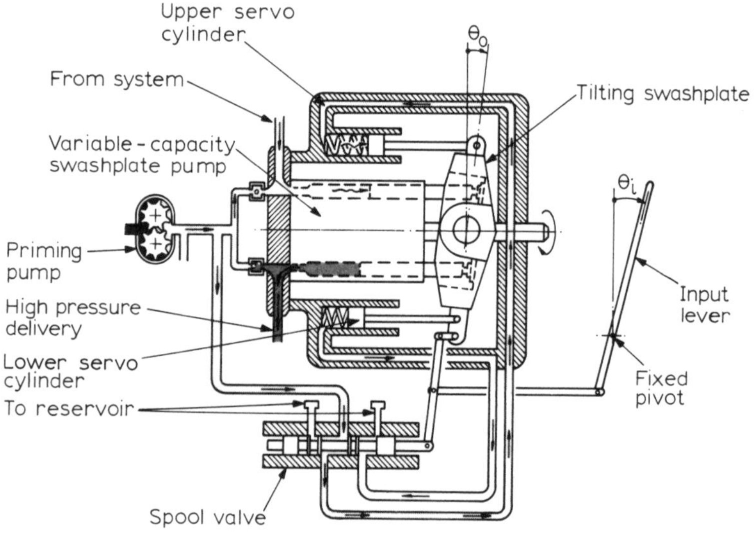

Fig. 8.38 Control system for power tilting of a swashplate.

panel exceeds the temperature of the water in the cylinder by T°, this value being set on a suitable control. Devise an automatic control system to do this, and draw (a) the circuit diagram (b) the control-system block diagram, clearly identifying the elements and signals.

8.8.15 Fig. 8.38 shows a variable-capacity hydraulic pump in which the flowrate is varied by tilting the swash-plate through an angle $\pm\theta^\circ$ from the mid position, giving flow in both directions. The servo system to tilt the swash-plate is necessary to provide the considerable force required. Explain how the system works, and draw the control-system block diagram, labelling the elements and signals.

8.8.16 Devise an automatic speed-control system for a petrol engine coupled to an electric generator, incorporating a speed-setting feature and an overspeed cut-out device for safety.

8.8.17 In a fuel-oil pre-heater similar to the heat-exchanger of Fig. 8.20 (b) the oil is heated to the required temperature by hot water flowing through the pipes in the heater casing. The oil flow is variable, according to demand.

Devise a control system to maintain the temperature of the oil leaving the heater to a preset value, and draw the control-system block diagram, labelling the elements and the signal throughout the system.

8.8.18 Devise a feedback control system so that the angular position of a valve spindle is maintained proportional to the pressure difference between two tanks containing inert gases. The total movement of the valve spindle is 330°, and the maximum pressure in each tank is 6 bar. Select suitable potentiometric transducers from those for which data are given in this chapter.

9 System response

9.1 Natural vibration of a spring, mass and damper system

Many engineering systems consist of components having springiness or *stiffness*. This combines with the mass of the system to give a particular frequency at which the system oscillates when it is disturbed, referred to as the *natural frequency*. In some of these systems, there are intentional energy dissipating elements, referred to as dampers, together with unavoidable friction effects which absorb energy. Where energy is absorbed, oscillations diminish more or less rapidly. We will first consider the oscillation of a spring and mass system which is assumed to be undamped and initially we will neglect friction effects.

9.1.1 Vibration of a spring and mass

Consider a mass (m) suspended on the end of a spring of negligible mass, the upper end of the spring being fixed. The arrangement is illustrated in Fig. 9.1. The spring has a stiffness value k, i.e., it requires a force of k newtons per metre of extension or compression. When the mass is pulled down from the equilibrium position by a distance X, and then released, it is found to oscillate vertically for an indefinite time. The strain energy in

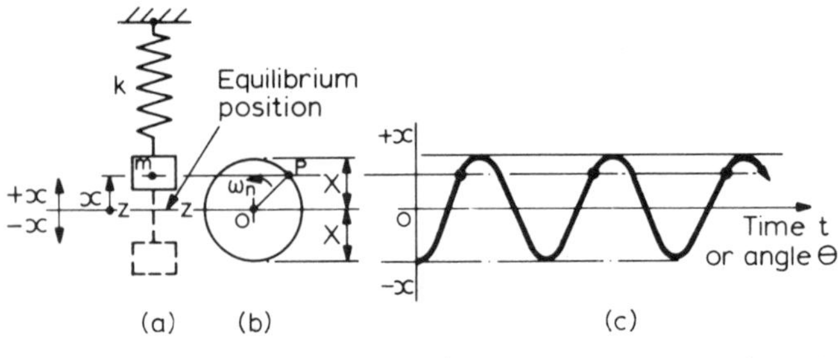

Fig. 9.1 Simple harmonic oscillation of a spring-mass system (undamped).

the spring due to the initial displacement is converted to kinetic energy as the mass accelerates. The kinetic energy is a maximum and the strain energy zero as the mass passes through the equilibrium position, after which the strain energy increases and the kinetic energy reduces. The process repeats until the energy of the initial displacement is dissipated in some way.

The force (F) exerted on the mass by the spring when the mass is at a displacement x (+ or −) from the equilibrium position ZZ is kx, i.e., F is proportional to x. Since this is the force accelerating the mass, the following equations apply:

$$F = kx \quad \text{and} \quad F = ma$$

hence

$$k = ma$$

and

$$x = \left(\frac{m}{k}\right)a \tag{9.1}$$

When the displacement (x) is positive, i.e. upward, in Fig. 9.1, then the acceleration (a) is downward, i.e. negative. Conversely, when x is negative, a is positive. Hence:

(a) the acceleration is proportional to the displacement, and

(b) the acceleration is always directed towards the equilibrium position.

When these two conditions apply, the oscillation is said to be simple harmonic motion (s.h.m.). Thus the vertical oscillation of the mass is of sinusoidal form, of amplitude equal to the initial displacement X. The frequency of the oscillation depends on the ratio k/m. The motion may be represented by a rotating *phasor* of length X (= OP) as shown in Fig. 9.1(b). The phasor rotates at an angular velocity ω_n rad/s, where:

$$\omega_n = \sqrt{(k/m)} \tag{9.2}$$

The angular velocity ω_n is referred to as the *undamped natural circular frequency* of the system.

The point P at the end of the phasor may be projected on to a horizontal axis of time or phasor angle to produce a sinusoidal curve as shown in Fig. 9.1(c). The frequency of the oscillation in hertz is geven by:

$$f_n = \frac{1}{2\pi}\sqrt{\left(\frac{k}{m}\right)} \quad \left(\text{since } f_n = \frac{\omega_n}{2\pi}\right). \tag{9.3}$$

The eqns. 9.1, 9.2 and 9.3 apply also when the spring and mass are horizontal, or in any other position, provided that there is no friction force retarding the motion of the mass. In practice, this can only be approached by mounting the mass on an air-support track or some similar device. The only effect of gravity is to change the equilibrium position of the mass, when the system is mounted in any position other than horizontally.

9.1.2 Vibration of a spring, mass and damper

In Fig. 9.2 a viscous damper is attached to the mass. A typical damper consists of a loose-fitting piston in an oil-filled cylinder. Holes may be drilled through the piston as shown. As the piston moves, oil transfers from one side of the piston to the other, either through the holes or past the circumference, exerting a drag force proportional to velocity, i.e.:

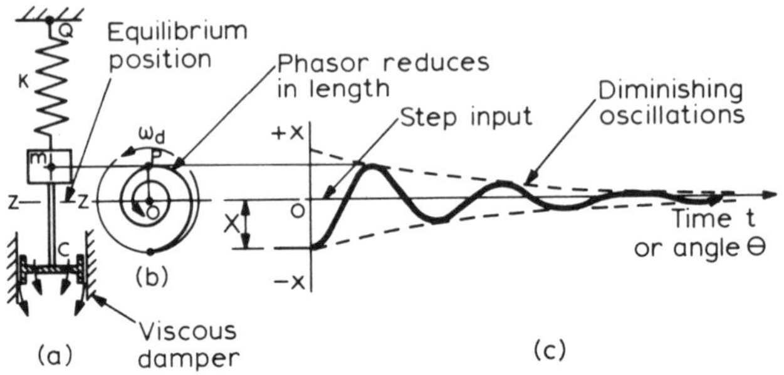

Fig. 9.2 Natural oscillation of a spring-mass-damper system.

$$F_D = cv \tag{9.4}$$

where	F_D	is the *viscous drag* force	(N)
	c	is the *damping constant*	(N s/m)
	v	is the piston velocity	(m/s)

When the mass is displaced by a distance X from the equilibrium position and released, the resulting oscillation diminishes as the damper dissipates energy from the system. If c is relatively small, i.e., the damping is light, the oscillation diminishes slowly. If c is relatively large, i.e. the damping is heavy, the oscillation diminishes more quickly. The rotating phasor representing the motion diminishes in length. Also, it rotates at an angular velocity ω_d which is less than ω_n for the undamped system. The angular velocity ω_d is the *damped natural circular frequency* of the system. If the damping is heavier still, the mass does not go past the equilibrium position ZZ, i.e., it does not *overshoot*, but approaches ZZ in a manner similar to that of the first-order systems described in Section 8.4. The displacement against time graphs for these conditions are illustrated in Fig. 9.3 and the following terms are used.

The *damping ratio* ζ (zeta) is a very convenient quantity to use. Its value for a system immediately gives some information about that system's response to a disturbance or input. Its value is given by:

$$\zeta = c/2\sqrt{(km)} \tag{9.5}$$

An undamped system has $c = 0$, and hence $\zeta = 0$.

If a system oscillates with diminishing amplitude, then the damping ratio is between 0 and 1, i.e. $0 < \zeta < 1$, and the system is said to be *underdamped*.

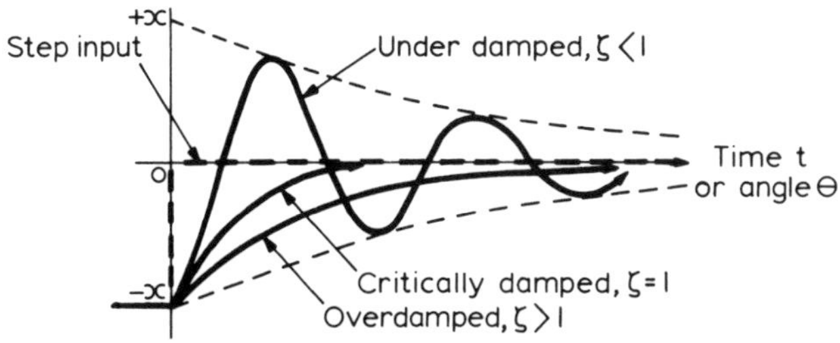

Fig. 9.3 Response to step input of spring-mass-damper system with different damping ratios.

If the damping ratio of a system is increased to unity, then the mass just fails to overshoot the equilibrium position, and the system is referred to as being *critically damped.*

If the damping ratio is greater than unity the response is slower than for the critically damped case, and the system is referred to as being *overdamped.*

The damping ratio value connects the undamped and damped natural frequency values thus:

$$\omega_d = \omega_n \sqrt{(1-\zeta^2)} \quad \text{and,} \tag{9.6}$$

$$f_d = f_n \sqrt{(1-\zeta^2)} \tag{9.7}$$

It should be noted that for a damped system, both the ω_d and ω_n values are of use.

In some systems, the spring, the mass and the damper are easily identified as separate items. For example, a motor vehicle body is a mass, mounted on suspension springs, and connected to the ground via the wheels. Dampers act between the body and the axles and hence the ground and without them the ride would be very undulating! The damping ratio in the case of passenger vehicles is in the region of 0.6, and this is checked by counting the overshoots after loading the car downwards and then releasing it suddenly. In the case of a crane suddenly picking up a mass, the 'spring' stiffness is that of the steel ropes supporting the mass, and also that of the structure of the crane. Natural damping may exist to a small extent in the material as it absorbs energy during its vibration, but there is not usually any way of adding damping to reduce this kind of oscillation.

A practical way of determining the approximate damping ratio of an underdamped system is to apply a sudden displacement, i.e., a step input. The sudden release of the mass in Fig. 9.2 from a displacement X is an example of a step input. Alternatively, the top of the spring, point Q, may be moved suddenly upward by a distance X, when the mass is at the equilibrium position. In either case, the input step and the response of the system to it may be represented as illustrated in Fig. 9.2(c), and again

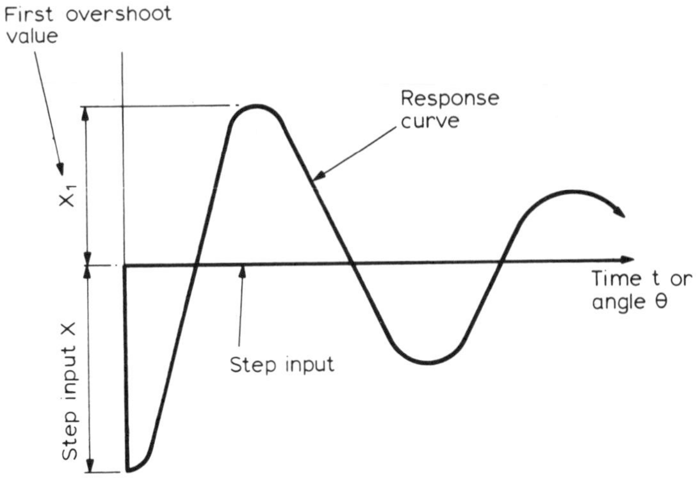

Fig. 9.4 First overshoot value.

in Fig. 9.4. The value of the first overshoot maxima X_1 is observed. The percentage first overshoot is calculated by:

$$\text{Percentage first overshoot} = \frac{X_1}{X} \times 100\% \qquad (9.8)$$

The damping ratio (ζ) is readily determined from the graph shown in Fig. 9.5. An example is shown in 9.5.3.

9.2 Forced vibration and resonance

Vibration of systems is usually undesirable, and is applied from a variety of sources. It may be caused by an oscillating movement, or an oscillating force. An oscillating force may arise from rotating or reciprocating machinery, e.g., the oscillating force due to the motion of each piston of a reciprocating engine or compressor or the component in one direction of the rotating centrifugal force due to rotation of an out of balance component, such as an out of centre mass on a lathe faceplate. An out of balance car wheel is illustrated in Fig. 9.6. The effective unbalance is equivalent to a mass m rotating at radius r. The centrifugal force due to this, on the wheel axle, is $F_r = mrp^2$, the suffix r indicating radial. The suspension spring system prevents horizontal movement of the axle relative to the vehicle body, which would occur due to F_n, the horizontal component of F_r. However, movement in the vertical direction may occur, due to F_v, the vertical component of F_r. Thus the vertical disturbing force is $F_v = F_r \sin pt$.

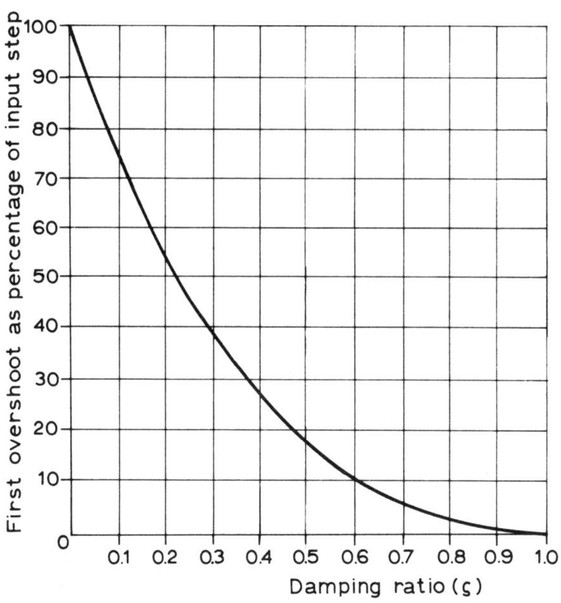

Fig. 9.5

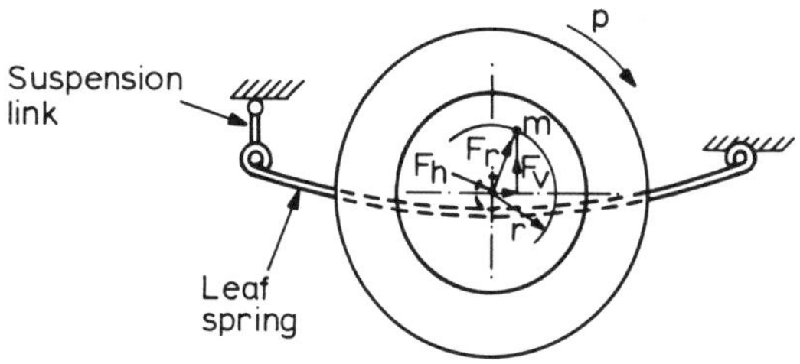

Fig. 9.6 Unbalance of a rotating wheel.

These oscillating forces cause oscillating displacements, and it is frequently more convenient to use displacements rather than forces in calculations of vibration. Fig. 9.7 illustrates some systems where the input is an oscillation, and the motion of the mass of the system may be regarded as the output oscillation. In (a) an instrument panel is illustrated, connected to a machine frame through springs and dampers. The frame oscillates due to the running of the machine. The object of the springs and dampers is to limit the oscillation of the instruments on the panel to a level which will not affect their operation. In (b) a passenger car is illustrated, whose mass is connected to the wheels and hence the road,

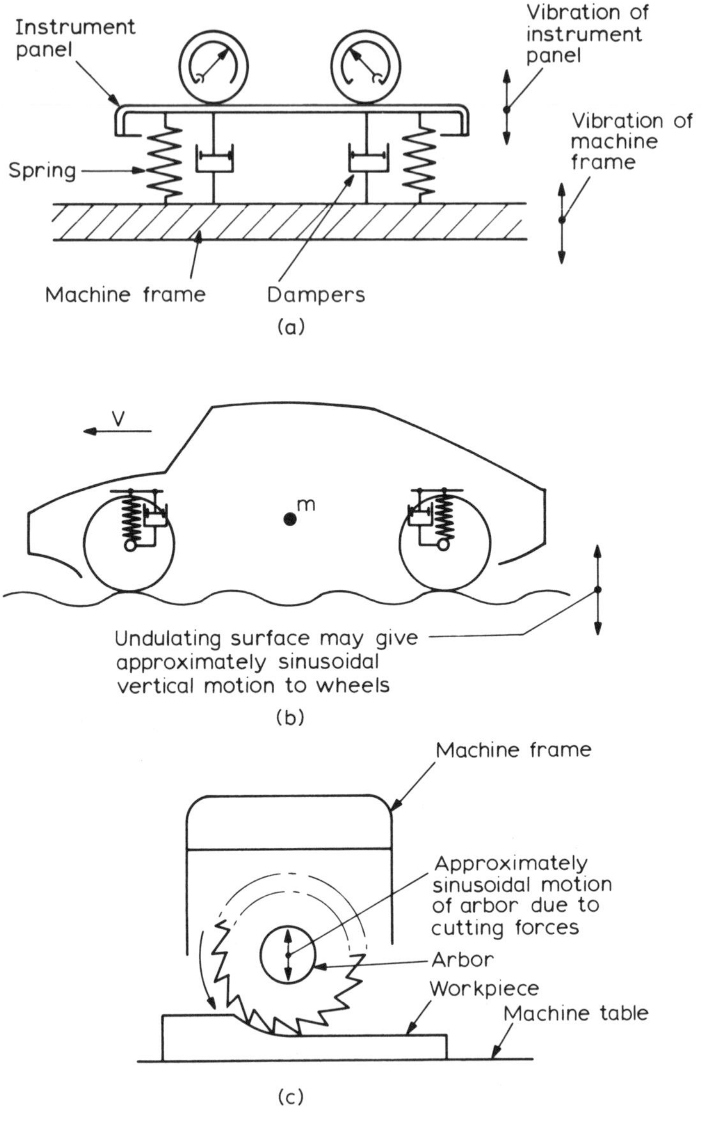

Fig. 9.7 Forced vibrations.
(a) Vibration of an instrument panel.
(b) Vibration of a vehicle on an undulating road.
(c) Vibration of a machine-tool frame.

by springs and dampers. Movement along an undulating road causes a vertical oscillation of the wheels. The object of the spring and damper system is to limit the oscillation of the car body to an acceptable level for passenger comfort. In (c) as each cutting tooth of the milling cutter bears on the workpiece, the cutter and the arbor on which it is mounted are forced upward against the 'spring' stiffness of the arbor and the machine structure. Some damping is present naturally due to energy absorbed by the vibrating metal, and by oil in the bearings. The resulting oscillation of the machine-tool structure depends on the values of the stiffness (k), the mass (m) and the damping constant (c) as it does in the preceding examples. The type of vibration discussed is referred to as *forced vibration*, since in general the system is forced to vibrate at a frequency other than its natural frequency the latter being either ω_n or ω_d (or f_n or f_d).

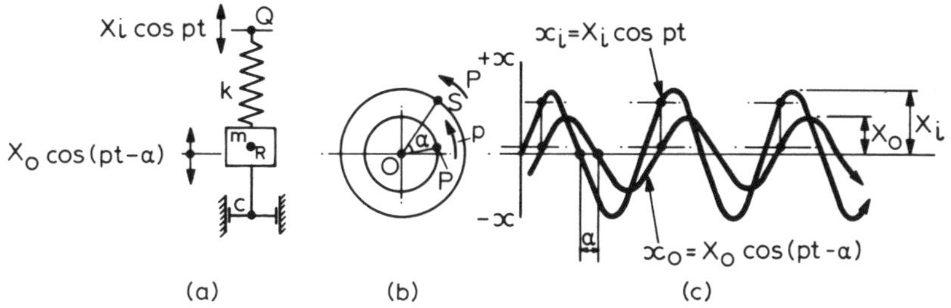

Fig. 9.8 Forced vibration of a spring-mass-damper system.
(a) Forced vibration.
(b) Phasor diagram.
(c) Displacement-time/angle relationships.

In the majority of cases, the applied force or displacement varies sinusoidally with time, or very nearly so. This causes a sinusoidal displacement of the mass of the system, at the same frequency. A vibrating system may be represented as in Fig. 9.8(a), where the point Q at one end of the spring is caused to move so that $x_i = X_i \cos(pt)$ where p is the circular frequency of the input oscillation in rad/s. It is found that the resulting oscillation of the mass is at this same frequency p, but the motion of R lags behind that of Q. The lag is usually expressed as an angle (α) in radians. The phasor diagram (b) shows this relationship. Thus the motion of the mass is $x_o = X_o \cos(pt - \alpha)$. The amplitude X_o of the output motion may be larger or smaller than the amplitude X_i of the input motion, and this is found to depend on the relationship between the value of the applied or *forcing* frequency (p) and the undamped natural frequency (ω_n) of the system. The following equations apply for the *steady-state* condition, that is, when the initial *transient* conditions in changing from rest have died out:

$$\textit{Amplitude ratio} \quad \frac{X_o}{X_i} = \frac{1}{\sqrt{\{(1-\mu^2)^2 + (2\zeta\mu)^2\}}} \qquad (9.9)$$

where the frequency ratio is $\mu = p/\omega_n$ (9.10)

The value of the lag angle (α) also depends on the frequency ratio (μ) and the damping ratio (ζ), and is given by:

$$\alpha = \arctan\{(2\zeta\mu)/(1-\mu^2)\} \tag{9.11}$$

Equation 9.9 indicates that the amplitude ratio (otherwise referred to as the *dynamic magnifier*, or in electrical work the *Q factor*) depends on the frequency ratio (μ) and the damping ratio (ζ). The curves of Fig. 9.8(c) show the output lagging the input by approximately 45°, and the oscillation of the mass is seen to be of smaller amplitude than the input oscillation of point Q. From examination of the sets of curves shown in Fig. 9.9, which are derived from eqns. 9.8 to 9.10, these conditions are met by the curves labelled $\zeta = 1$. From this it may be deduced that for this system, as the frequency of the forced oscillation of point Q is increased, with X_i constant, the oscillation of the mass becomes smaller.

When the damping ratio is less than about 0.6, the oscillation of the mass may have larger amplitude than the input, and reaches a maxima value when the frequency ratio is approximately one. This maxima represents the condition of *resonance*. If the damping ratio is low, the mass may have very large and potentially dangerous oscillations at this point. As the input frequency is increased past the resonance point the amplitude reduces rapidly. When the frequency ratio is three or more, the vibration of the mass has very small amplitude.

From Fig. 9.9 the following may be seen.

(a) For zero damping, the amplitude at resonance is theoretically infinite, as may be checked by putting $\mu = 1$ and $\zeta = 0$ in eqn. 9.8. (However, in practice there is almost always some damping in a system, and one of the lower curves apply).

(b) Where ζ is more than about 0.6, there is no resonance peak.

(c) For all values of ζ, the amplitude ratio X_o/X_i is very small when the frequency ratio is more than 3.

(d) When $\mu = 1$, for all values of ζ, the phase lag (α) is $\pi/2$ radians or 90°.

(e) For zero damping ($\zeta = 0$) the motion of the mass is in phase with the input oscillation when μ is less than 1. When μ is more than 1 the motion of the mass is exactly opposed to the input oscillation, i.e. $\alpha = \pi$ rad or 180°. This condition is illustrated in Fig. 9.10.

Two things are apparent from the curves of amplitude ratio Fig. 9.9(a). Firstly, if we wish an output oscillation to follow an input oscillation, very closely such as may be required in an automatic control system or in an instrument, then ζ should be 0.5 to 0.7, and the frequency ratio (μ) not more than about 0.5. Secondly, if we wish the output amplitude to be a minimum, we may either make the damping high, with a damping ratio of more than 2, and make the frequency ratio more than unity or, with light damping, make the frequency ratio more than 3.

Where a system has very high stiffness (k) and very small mass (m), then

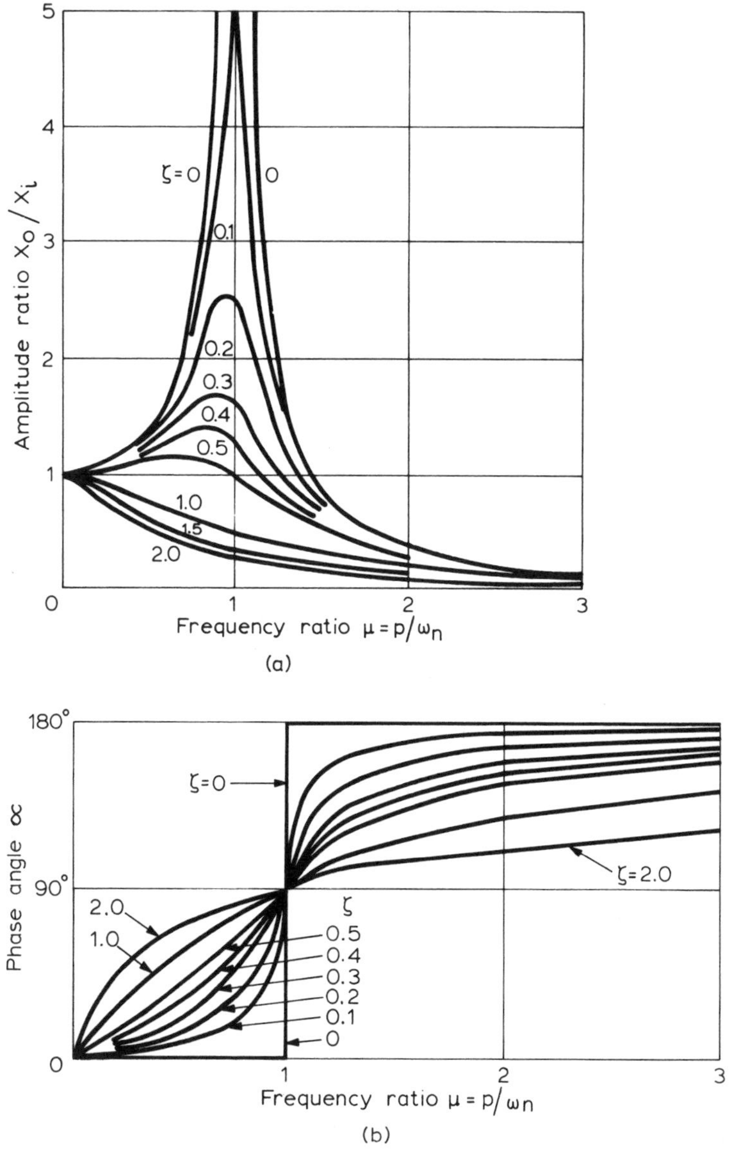

Fig. 9.9 Response curves for a spring-mass-damper system.

the undamped natural circular frequency (ω_n) is very high, and the first method may be used. A piezoeletric force or pressure transducer such as those discussed in Section 3.1 have very high natural frequencies and are used to measure forces or pressures at lower frequencies. (It should be

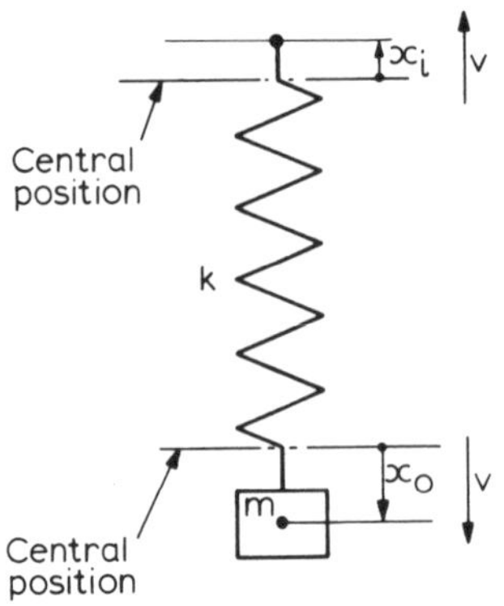

Fig. 9.10 Anti-phased oscillations.

noted that a transducer of this kind has low m, high k and low c values). An example of the second case is the motor vehicle engine, usually mounted on rubber blocks, of low stiffness (k). The applied force in the vertical direction from the reciprocating pistons is approximately sinusoidal. At low engine speeds, such as at tickover, the oscillation may be large, being near to resonance since the natural frequency of the mounting is low. As the throttle is opened and the engine speed increases, increasing the forcing frequency (p) past the resonance value, the engine oscillates very little on its mountings.

9.3 Oscillations in measurement and control systems

Many instruments, for example moving-coil voltmeters, ultra violet and pen recorders, are of second-order type having mass, stiffness and damping. Their responses to step and sinusoidal inputs are identical with those shown in Sections 9.1 and 9.2. However, if such a system has rotational rather than linear oscillation, then the moment of inertia (I) of the system is used instead of the mass (m), and the spring stiffness (k) must be given in rotational units (Nm/rad), as also must the damping constant (c), units (Nms/rad) otherwise all the equations apply.

The response of first-order control-systems to step, ramp and sinusoidal inputs was discussed in Section 8.4. Second-order control systems may be shown to have similar responses to those of the spring-mass-damper systems discussed in Sections 9.1 and 9.2. In a control system there may be a mass, or there may be electrical, fluid or thermodynamic elements which give the same effects as mass. Damping, as in the vibrating system, may be provided by a fixed- or variable-rate damper, or it may occur naturally in various elements. In a control system the 'spring' effect is due to the *loop gain*, i.e. the product of the K

values round the forward and feedback loop, which will include any actual elastic spring effects, and also the transfer operators of components such as transducers and amplifiers. Analysis of second- and higher-order control-system response is beyond the scope of this unit. It is sufficient if the student at this stage is aware of the similarity between the response of some control systems and of spring-mass-damper systems.

9.4 Vibration isolation

The curves of Fig. 9.9 give valuable information regarding the performance of vibrating systems, and should be referred to when considering vibration isolation, that is, the minimising of the effects of applied shocks or continuous oscillations. Two factors may be identified:

(a) the natural frequency of oscillation of the system should be well below the frequencies expected in the forcing oscillations,

(b) where there is no certainty that the frequencies of the natural and forcing oscillations are wide apart, then damping by some means or other must be applied to restrict the amplitude of the oscillation by continuously dissipating energy.

9.4.1 Anti-vibration mountings

Parts of machines and structures may be protected from excessive vibration by using anti-vibration mountings. Fig. 9.11 illustrates a panel connected to a vibrating machine-frame through helical coil springs. The application of a shock-load to the machine frame, such as by the mechanical operation of a punch or hammer, (either by the machine

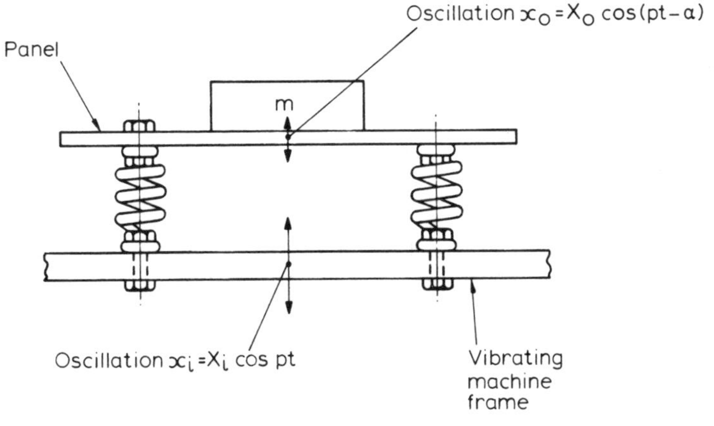

Fig. 9.11

discussed or an adjacent one), causes a sharp displacement of the frame. This is transmitted to the panel through the springs, and the panel will vibrate at its natural frequency (ω_n) until the shock energy is dissipated. Dissipation may occur due to hysteresis of the material of the springs, and through movement of air as the panel oscillates. If we assume zero damping, the eqns. 9.1 to 9.3 apply.

If the machine frame has a sustained oscillation, such as may occur due to rotating or reciprocating masses, then the panel will oscillate at the same frequency. If, again, we assume that the damping is zero, then the relative amplitudes of the frame and panel, and the phase lag between the two motions, are given by eqns. 9.9 to 9.11. The relationships are represented by the curves for $\zeta = 0$ in Fig. 9.9. From the amplitude-ratio curves, it may be seen (and verified using eqn. 9.8) that if the frequency ratio is 3 or more, then the amplitude of the oscillation of the panel will be generally less than 12 % of the amplitude of the frame oscillation. For frequency ratios less than this, however, the amplitude of the panel oscillation may be much larger, and theoretically infinite when the frequency ratio (μ) is unity, i.e., at resonance.

In practice, the vibration of a machine frame may have components of motion in the y and z directions, as well as in the x direction as shown in Fig. 9.11. To accommodate motion in all directions, spring mountings such as those illustrated in Fig. 9.12 are used. In this type a number of smaller springs are used, arranged in a double conical form. At the base of each cone form, the ends of the springs are secured to the baseplate. The other ends of the springs are secured to the central tubular member. The arrangement may be designed to give similar spring-stiffness (k) values in x, y and z directions. Each mounting is designed to support a given mass, and when that mass is attached, the resonant frequency of the spring-mass system is known. The attachment of other mass values will of course give different resonant frequencies. An example of the

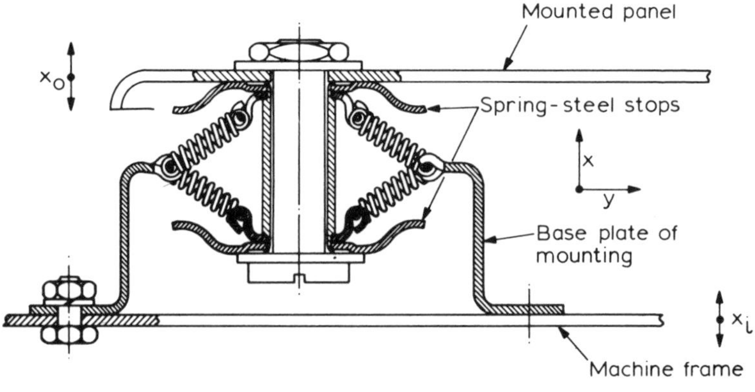

Fig. 9.12 Spring-type anti-vibration mounting for x-y-z directions.

application of this type of mounting is shown in example 9.5.7. A further feature are the dished end-plates at each end of the central tube. These are made of spring steel, and will absorb impact energy if the deflection of the mounting becomes excessive.

9.4.2. Anti-vibration mountings incorporating damping

In some applications it is desirable to limit the vibration amplitude of the mounted panel as the applied frequency approaches the resonant value. The mounting illustrated in Fig. 9.13 incorporates a friction damping device. This consists of two cup-shaped metal washers mounted on the centre tube, these being held apart, and in contact with the spring arrays, by a central coil spring. At resonance, the motion of the springs is restrained by the cups, the motion of the latter being restrained by friction with the centre column.

Where a greater degree of damping is desired, and damping in all directions of motion, the type of mounting illustrated in Fig. 9.14 may be used. In this device, a number of small 'buttons' are spring-loaded so that they bear against the inside of a cylinder which constitutes the body of the mounting. When oscillation in the x direction occurs, there are damping forces due to the friction of the buttons on the inside of the cylinder. When oscillations occur in the y and z directions, friction forces occur due to the motion of the stems of the buttons in their sleeves. The

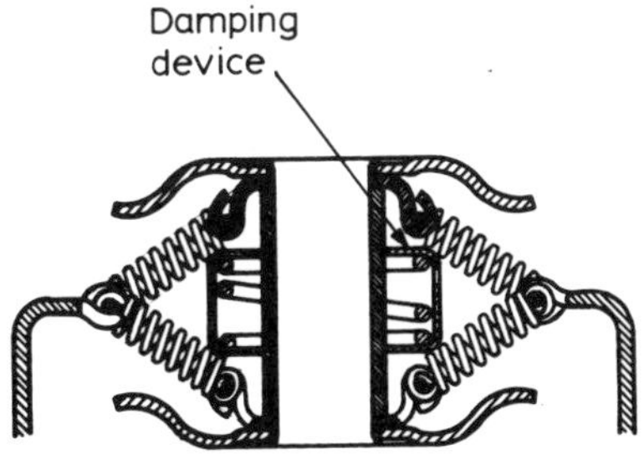

Fig. 9.13 Anti-vibration mounting with damper device.

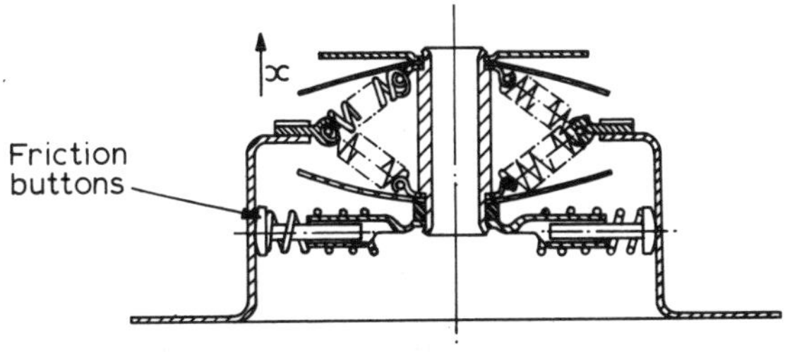

Fig. 9.14 Anti-vibration mounting with x-y-z damping.

buttons may be made of a suitable material to give the desired damping characteristics. It should be noted that the damping devices described in this section do not give a damping force proportional to velocity, hence they do not give 'viscous' damping. However, their response curves are of the same general form as those of Fig. 9.9 for viscous-damped systems.

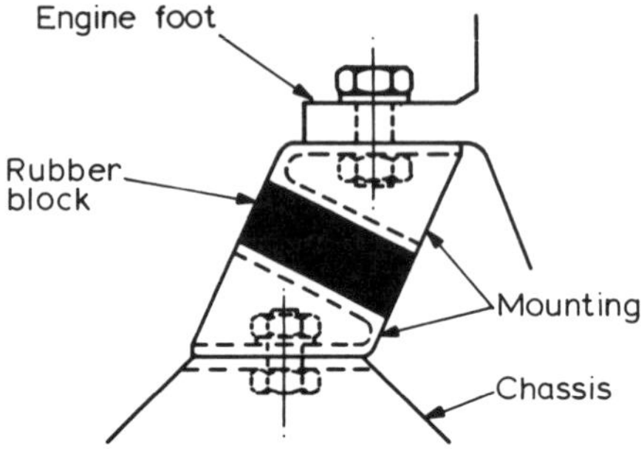

Fig. 9.15 Engine mounting.

Another common type of mounting is illustrated in Fig. 9.15. The spring element is a rubber block which is bonded between two metal end pieces. The device is commonly used for mounting engines on the chassis members of motor vehicles, and in the illustration an engine mounting foot is bolted to the top of the mounting, and the bottom half of the mounting is secured to the vehicle frame. Damping occurs due to the high hysteresis of the rubber material. This type of anti-vibration mounting may be designed to take heavy loads, and is frequently used for the mounting of heavy engines and machine tools in order to isolate their vibration from floors and structures, or vice-versa. Fig. 9.16 illustrates a heavy-duty mounting of this type.

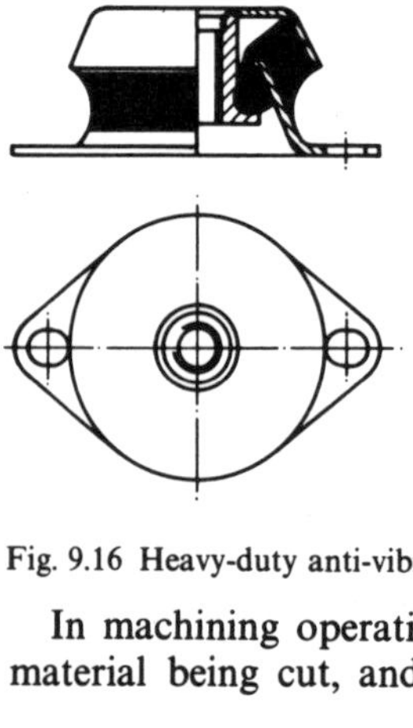

Fig. 9.16 Heavy-duty anti-vibration mounting.

In machining operations, interaction between the cutting tool, the material being cut, and the machine-tool structure causes vibration which results in oscillation of the cutting edge of the tool, referred to as 'chatter'. This type of vibration causes marking or irregularity of the machined surface, and is to be avoided. It is referred to as *self-induced*, since factors external to the machine are not involved. Prevention is by adjustment of cutting force and speed, and in some cases by applying additional damping, though this is not usually easy. It may be possible to stiffen the machine tool structure to improve the frequency ratio. Some of these ideas are illustrated by reference to the boring bar of Fig. 9.17. In (a) the bar is shown oscillating in the vertical plane. The boring bar is as large and stiff as it can be for the size of the hole being bored. Adjustments may be made to the speed and feed of the cut to minimise the vibration at its source. As a further resort, a bar having an oil-filled cavity containing a slug of metal as shown in (b) may be introduced as a damper (refs. 6 and 7).

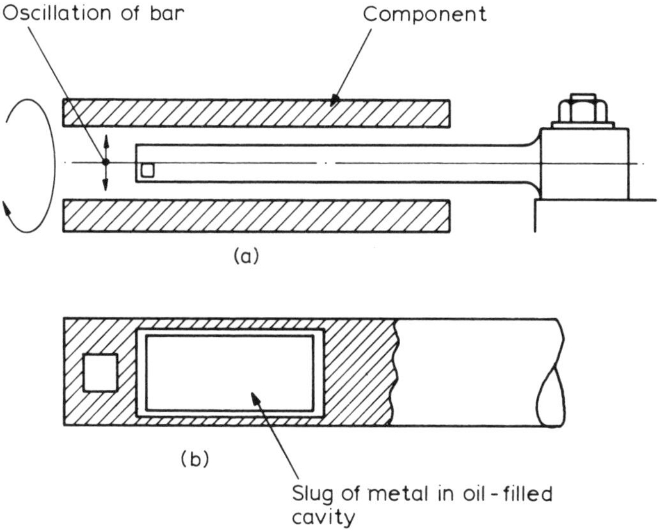

Fig. 9.17 (a) Vibration of boring bar.
(b) Boring bar with damping device.

9.4.3 Variation of disturbing force with rotational speed

Forcing vibrations frequently occur due to the rotation of shafts which are not perfectly balanced. If the imbalance gives the same effect as a mass m rotating at radius r from the axis of rotation, then the centrifugal force on the shaft is given by:

$$\text{centrifugal force} = mrp^2 \qquad (9.12)$$

where p is the rotational speed of the shaft in rad/s.

Fig. 9.18(a) plots the amplitude of the oscillating force applied in a given direction at different rotational speeds. The rotational speed is also the forcing frequency applied to the spring-mass-damper system. Fig. 9.18(b) plots the response of a system with light damping to a forcing oscillation from an out of balance rotor. The response curve starts from zero and after passing a resonant peak falls to a lower value. However, the increase of the out of balance force outweighs the

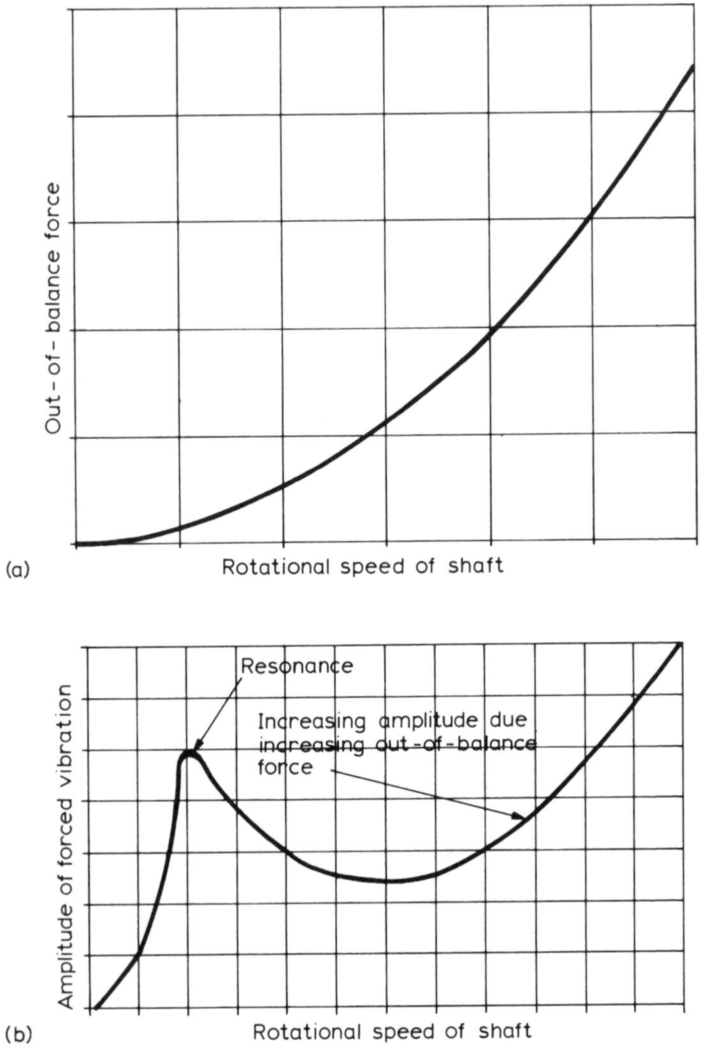

1 Fig. 9.18 Effect on vibration amplitude of out-of-balance force from a rotating shaft.

reduction in value of the dynamic magnification factor, and the amplitude of vibration increases. The curve should be compared with those of Fig. 9.9(a) for light damping.

9.5 Worked examples

9.5.1 A mass of 2 kg is mounted on a spring of stiffness 200 N/m as in Fig. 9.1. Calculate the natural frequency (f_n) and natural circular frequency (ω_n) values of the system.
Using eqn. 9.2

Natural circular frequency $\omega_n = \sqrt{(k/m)} = \sqrt{(200/2)}$
$= \sqrt{100} = \sqrt{10}$ rad/s

Natural frequency $f_n = \dfrac{\omega_n}{2\pi}$
$= 10/2\pi = 1.6$ Hz

9.5.2 A damped spring-mass system as shown in Fig. 9.2 was displaced by 20 mm from its equilibrium position and released from rest. Its first overshoot of the equilibrium position was 5 mm. Determine the damping ratio (ζ) of the system.
The percentage first overshoot is: (overshoot/step input) × 100%
i.e. (5/20) × 100% = 25%
From the graph Fig. 9.5, the damping ratio (ζ) is 0.43.
9.5.3 An instrument movement has a mass of 6.0 grams and a stiffness of 1.0 N/mm. Calculate the natural circular frequency (ω_n) and find the damping constant (c) necessary to just prevent overshoot when a step input is applied.

Natural circular frequency $\omega_n = \sqrt{(k/m)}$
$= \sqrt{\{(1.0 \times 10^3)/(6.0 \times 10^{-3})\}}$
$= 410$ rad/s

For just no overshoot, $\zeta = 1.0$
by eqn. 9.5: $\zeta = c/2\sqrt{(km)}$
$c = \zeta \times 2\sqrt{(km)}$
$= 1.0 \times 2\sqrt{(1.0 \times 10^3 \times 6.0 \times 10^{-3})}$
$= 4.9$ N s/m

9.5.4 A spring-mass-damper system is observed to have a first overshoot of 10%, and completes three oscillations in 9.6 seconds. Calculate the damped and undamped natural frequency and circular frequency values of the system.

$$\text{The natural damped frequency } f_{\text{d}} = \frac{n}{\text{time for } n \text{ oscillations}}$$

$$= \frac{3}{9.6} = 0.31 \text{ Hz}$$

From Fig. 9.5 the value of ζ is 0.6.

By eqn. 9.7:

$$f_{\text{d}} = f_{\text{n}}\sqrt{(1-\zeta^2)}$$

$$\therefore \quad f_{\text{n}} = f_{\text{d}}/\sqrt{(1-\zeta^2)}$$

$$= 0.31/\sqrt{(1-0.6^2)}$$

$$= 0.39 \text{ Hz}$$

By eqn. 9.3:

$$\omega_{\text{d}} = 2\pi f_{\text{d}} = 2\pi \times 0.31$$

$$= 1.9 \text{ rad/s}$$

By eqn. 9.6:

$$\omega_{\text{n}} = \omega_{\text{d}}/\sqrt{(1-\zeta^2)} = 1.9/\sqrt{(1-0.6^2)}$$

$$= 2.4 \text{ rad/s}$$

9.5.5 A spring-mass-damper system as in Fig. 9.2 has a mass of 1 kg and the spring stiffness is 500 N/m. Calculate:

(a) the value of the damping constant of the damper if the damping ratio of the system is 0.3

(b) the amplitude of the oscillation of the mass if point Q has the vertical motion 20 cos 16t mm.

(a) By eqn. 9.2, the undamped natural circular frequency of the system is:

$$\omega_{\text{n}} = \sqrt{(k/m)}$$

$$= \sqrt{(500/1)} = 22.4 \text{ rad/s.}$$

By eqn. 9.5:

$$c = \zeta \times 2\sqrt{(km)}$$

$$= 0.3 \times 2\sqrt{(500 \times 1)} = 13.4 \text{ N s/m}$$

(b) By eqn. 9.9, and 9.10 the amplitude ratio is:

$$\frac{X_{\text{o}}}{X_{\text{i}}} = \frac{1}{\sqrt{\{(1-\mu^2)^2 + (2\zeta\mu)^2\}}} \quad \text{and} \quad \mu = p/\omega_{\text{n}} \quad \text{where } p = 16 \text{ rad/s and } X_{\text{i}} = 20 \text{ mm}$$

$$\therefore \quad \mu = 16/22.4 = 0.71$$

$$\text{and} \quad X_{\text{o}} = 20 \times \frac{1}{\sqrt{\{(1-0.71^2)^2 + (2 \times 0.3 \times 0.71)^2\}}} = 31 \text{ mm}$$

9.5.6 In a closed-loop test of an automatic position-control system known to be of second-order type, a step change of the input signal caused a decaying oscillating output. The first overshoot was observed to be 27% of the input step, and four complete oscillations occured in 11 seconds.

(a) Determine the damping ratio (ζ) and undamped natural circular frequency (ω_n).

(b) If a sinusoidal signal 100 cos 5t mm is applied at the input calculate, for steady-state conditions,
(i) the amplitude of the output signal
(ii) the phase-lag angle of the output singnal relative to the input
(iii) the time-lag of the output wave relative to the input wave

(a) From the graph Fig. 9.5, a first overshoot of 27% of a step input corresponds to a damping ratio of 0.40.
The damped natural frequency is $f_d = 4/11 = 0.36$ Hz
The damped natural curcular frequency is

$$\omega_d = 2\pi \times f_d = 2\pi \times 0.36 = 2.28 \text{ rad/s.}$$

By eqn. 9.6, the undamped natural circular frequency is:

$$\omega_n = \omega_d / \sqrt{(1-\zeta^2)} = \frac{2.26}{\sqrt{(1-0.4^2)}} = 2.49 \text{ rad/s}$$

(b) (i) By eqn. 9.9 and 9.10,

$$X_o = X_i \times \frac{1}{\sqrt{\{(1-\mu^2)^2 + (2\zeta\mu)^2\}}} \quad \text{and} \quad \mu = \frac{p}{\omega_n} = \frac{5}{2.5} = 2$$

$$= 100 \times \frac{1}{\sqrt{\{(1-2^2)^2 + (2\times 0.4 \times 2)^2\}}}$$

$$= 100 \times \frac{1}{3.4} = 29 \text{ mm.}$$

(ii) By eqn. 9.11, the phase lag angle is given by:

$$\alpha = \arctan\{2\zeta\mu/(1-\mu^2)\} = \arctan\{2 \times 0.4 \times 2/(1-2^2)\} = \arctan\{1.6/(-3)\} = 152^\circ = 2.65 \text{ rad}$$

(iii) $2.65 \text{ rad} = 5\text{t rad}$

$\therefore$ $\text{t} = 0.53 \text{ s}$

This magnitude of output and lag would be intolerable in a position-control system and the natural frequency of the system needs to be raised so that it is operating with the frequency ratio (μ) less than 0.3 (see Fig. 9.9).

9.5.7 A machine tool has a mass of 800 kg and is to be mounted on four anti-vibration mountings. Calculate the required stiffness of each mounting if the machine is to be isolated from floor-transmitted vibrations greater than 100 Hz. Assume that no damping is provided by the mountings.

From Fig. 9.9(a), it is seen that when the frequency ratio ($\mu = p/\omega_n$) is greater than 3, the dynamic magnifier is very small. Hence if the frequency 100 Hz corresponds to $\mu = 3$, then the natural frequency (f_n) of the machine on its mountings must be $100/3 = 33.3$ Hz.
Hence the natural undamped circular frequency is $\omega_n = 33.3 \times 2\pi = 209.2$ rad/s

Since $\omega_n = \sqrt{(k/m)}$ then

$$\begin{aligned} k &= m\omega_n^2 \\ &= 800 \times 209^2 \\ &= 35.0 \text{ MN/m} \end{aligned}$$

This is stiffness of four mountings, hence the stiffness of each needs to be $35.0/4 = 8.75$ MN/m.

9.5.8 A two-wheeled trailer has a sprung mass of 100 kg, and it is found that each 10 kg mass added causes a vertical deflection of the springs of 4 mm. Calculate:

(a) the stiffness (k) of the suspension

(b) the natural undamped circular frequency of vertical vibration of the sprung mass on its springs

(c) the required damping constant (c) of the two dampers if the system is to have a damping ratio (ζ) of 0.8

(d) the amplitude of the vertical oscillation of the sprung mass about its mid position when travelling over an undulating road at (i) 36 km/h, (ii) 18 km/h. The undulations are of approximately sinusoidal form, the depth from hollow to crest being 50 mm, and the length between crests

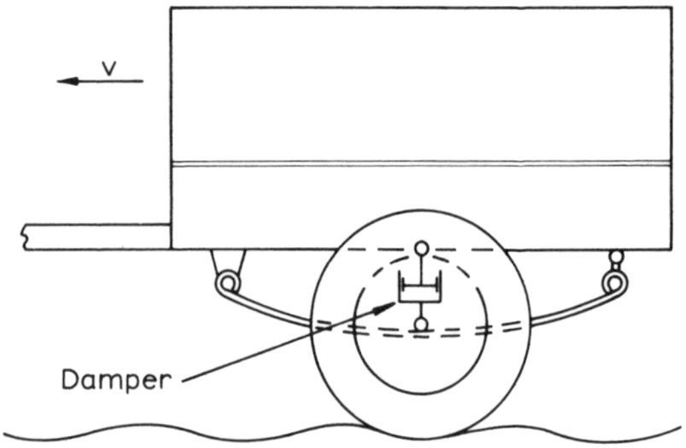

Fig. 9.19

1 m. Assume the tyres stay in contact with the road and neglect tyre deflection. The arrangement is illustrated in Fig. 9.19.

(a) The stiffness is given by $k = \delta F/\delta x$

$$= 10 \times 9.81/(4 \times 10^{-3})$$
$$= 24.5 \text{ kN/m}$$

(b) By eqn. 9.2, the natural undamped circular frequency is given by:

$$\omega_n = (k/m)$$
$$= (24500/100) = 15.7 \text{ rad/s}$$

(c) By eqn. 9.5, the damping constant is given by:

$$c = 2\sqrt{(km)} \times \zeta$$
$$= 2 \times \sqrt{(24500 \times 100)} \times 0.8$$
$$= 2.5 \text{ kN s/m}$$

(d) (i) Trailer velocity is:

$$v = \frac{36000}{3600} = 10 \text{ m/s}$$

$\therefore$ the periodic time of the forcing oscillation is 0.10 s.
and the forcing circular frequency is: $p = 20$ rad/s
The frequency ratio is: $\mu = 20\pi/15.65 = 4.0$

By eqn. 9.8 the amplitude ratio is: $\dfrac{X_o}{X_i} = \dfrac{1}{\sqrt{\{(1-\mu^2)^2 + (2\zeta\mu)^2\}}}$

$$\frac{X_o}{25} = \frac{1}{\sqrt{\{(1-4^2)^2 + (2 \times 0.8 \times 4)\}}}$$

and $$X_o = 25 \times \frac{1}{16.3}$$
$$= 1.5 \text{ mm}$$

(ii) Trailer velocity is 5 m/s.

$\therefore$ the periodic time of the forcing oscillation is 0.20 s
and the forcing circular frequency is $p = 10$ rad/s
The frequency ratio is: $\mu = 10\pi/15.65 = 2.0$

By eqn. 9.8, $\dfrac{X_o}{X_i}$ is found to be 0.23

Hence $$X_o = 25 \times 0.23$$
$$= 5.7 \text{ mm}$$

The oscillation is seen to be greater at the lower speed. This may be understood by referring to the graph Fig. 9.9(a).

9.6 Tutorial and practical work

9.6.1 From the literature available to you relating to transducers and measuring systems, find their natural frequency, frequency range and damping ratio, and compare their dynamic performances.
9.6.2 Determine the damping ratio and the damped natural frequency of the oscillation of liquid in a U-tube manometer by applying a step input of pressure. Determine the effects of (a) increasing the quantity of fluid, (b) using different fluids such as mercury, water, paraffin etc.
9.6.3 By applying a step input of voltage in each case, determine the damping ratio and if possible the damped natural frequency of voltage measuring instruments and recorders.
9.6.4 Distinguish between 'damping constant' and 'damping ratio'. Discuss the reasons for preferring to use the latter. Why do many instrument systems have a damping ratio of about of 0.65?
9.6.5 Distinguish between (a) 'frequency' and 'circular frequency', (b) 'undamped natural frequency', 'damped natural frequency' and 'resonant frequency', (c) 'applied frequency' and 'frequency ratio.'

9.7 Exercises

9.7.1 A machine of mass 100 kg is mounted on four springs, and the undamped natural frequency (f_n) of the system is to be 1.0 Hz. Calculate the required stiffness (k) of each spring.
9.7.2 When an input of 6 V was suddenly applied (step input) to a chart recorder the pen moved a maximum of 6.3 cm, and then after oscillating slightly, returned to 6.0 cm, the measurements being made from the 0V pen position. Determine the damping ratio (ζ) of the pen movement.
9.7.3 A mass of 6 kg is mounted on three helical springs whose total stiffness (k) is 15 kN/m. (a) Calculate the damping constant (c) to which the variable rate damper attached between the mass and the machine frame must be adjusted if the system is to have a damping ratio of 0.4. (b) Calculate the damped natural frequency of oscillation of the system.
9.7.4 In a test on the response of a galvanometer movement the following were observed:

(a) After zeroing, a step input of 1.0 V was applied, and it was observed that the maximum value the pointer reached was 1.54 V, and it completed three oscillations in 1.05 s.

(b) When a signal $1.0 + 0.1 \cos 2\pi ft$ volts was applied, the amplitude of the pointer movement in oscillating about the 1.0 V mark was a maximum at a frequency $f = 0.28$ Hz, its value being 0.25 V. Determine the damping ratio, and the damped and undamped natural frequencies of the meter movement from (a) and check that the results of test (b) are consistant with these values.

9.7.5 In the production-line weighing device illustrated in Fig. 9.20 masses having a minimum value of 0.9 kg and a maximum of 1.1 kg are to be weighed on a platform of mass 0.2 kg.

(a) If the scale deflection is to be ± 10 mm over the range, calculate the necessary spring stiffness (k).

(b) If the damping ratio is to be 0.7 when the nominal (1 kg) mass is on the table, calculate the damping constant (c) required in the dashpot.

(c) Calculate the damping ratio with (i) the minimum mass on the table and (ii) the maximum mass on the table.

(d) Determine the percentage overshoot with (i) the minimum, and (ii) the maximum masses when they are placed suddenly (not dropped) on the table.

(e) Determine the changed values in (a), (b), (c) and (d) if the springs are changed to give a deflection of ± 6 mm over the same range of mass.

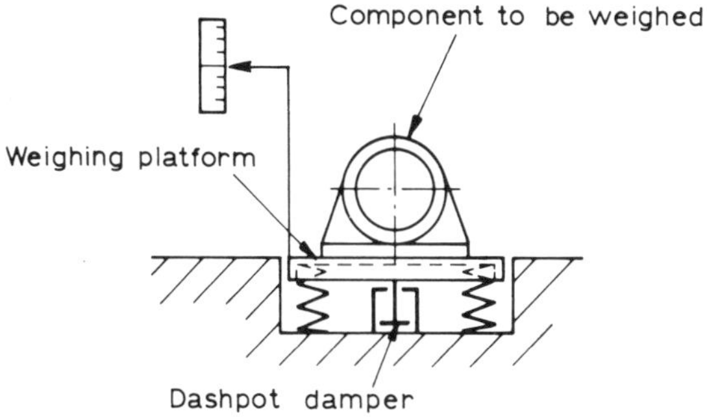

Fig. 9.20

9.7.6 In a pressure-measuring transducer consisting of a number of strain-gauges bonded to a diaphragm, the undamped natural frequency of the system was found to be 60 kHz, and the damping ratio 0.6. Calculate the amplitude of the output signal in terms of pressure if the input pressure to the transducer is fluctuating sinusoidally with an amplitude of 800 kPa at a frequency of 30 kHz. What is the percentage error in the output amplitude?

9.7.7 Fig. 9.21 illustrates a hydraulic spool valve connected to a cam follower through a helical spring. In tests, the spool mass (m) was found to be 100 gram, the spring stiffness (k) 30 N/m, and the damping ratio (ζ) 2.2. If the cam follower motion is $x_i = 4 \cos 5t$ mm calculate:

(a) the undamped natural circular frequency (ω_n) of the spool on its spring

(b) the amplitude of the steady-state oscillation of the spring

(c) the time lag between the motions of the cam follower and the spool valve.

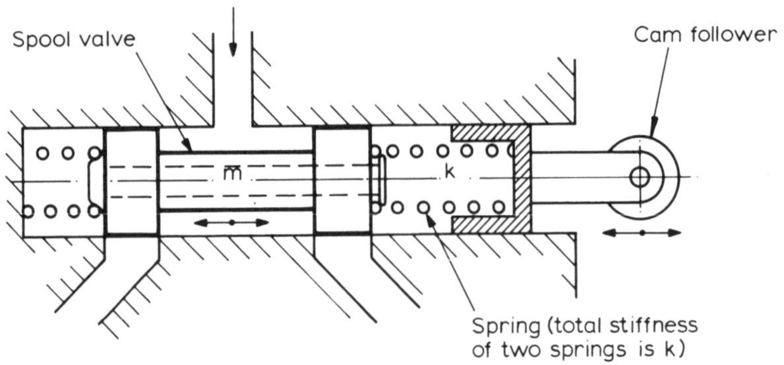

Fig. 9.21 Spool valve.

9.7.8 In a test on a sprung and damped two-wheeled trailer for an air-compressor the following values were determined:
deflection of springs: 15 mm for each 100 kg of added mass, mass of trailer with fully equipped compressor: 500 kg, the damping ratio $(\zeta) = 0.33$.

(a) Calculate the undamped and damped natural circular frequency values of the trailer on its suspension.

(b) When the fully-laden trailer is towed over a surface at a given speed a vertical motion $y_i = 15 \cos 30t$ mm is applied to the wheels and axles. Calculate the amplitude of the resulting vertical motion of the trailer.

(c) State the effect on the amplitude of vibration of:
(i) removing equipment (and hence mass) from the trailer,
(ii) driving faster over the same road surface,
giving reason(s) in each case.

9.7.9 Plot the amplitude ratio X_o/X_i for a second-order system for values of the frequency ratio (μ) from 0 to 1, for a damping ratio (ζ) equal to 0.6, taking values at suitable intervals. From the graph, determine the range of μ for which the output amplitude is within 3% of the input amplitude. If the system has an undamped natural frequency of 3 kHz, determine the frequency over which this applies.

10 Multiple-choice exercises

The following multiple-choice questions are intended for revision work. In each case, select either (a), (b), (c) or (d). The correct answers are given at the end of the section.
The second number of the reference denotes the relevant chapter.

10.2.1 The nearness of the value indicated by an instrument to the value being measured is its:
(a) accuracy
(b) precision
(c) sensitivity
(d) discrimination.

10.2.2 State which one of the following means 'the least change of the measured variable which can be detected at the output of the measuring system':
(a) sensitivity
(b) precision
(c) accuracy
(d) discrimination.

10.2.3 The following set of values are the deadweight pressures (p_d) applied to a pressure-gauge during calibration, and the corresponding indicated gauge pressure values (p). Select the one from (a) to (d) which has the maximum error expressed as a percentage of applied pressure:

		(a)	(b)	(c)	(d)
p (bar)	0	9.5	19.5	28.0	38.0
p_d (bar)	0	10.0	20.0	30.0	40.0

10.2.4 Errors which may occur either positive or negative, and which may be variable in magnitude, are classed as:
(a) observational errors
(b) systematic errors
(c) random errors
(d) hysteresis errors.

10.2.5 The characteristic of certain observers, in taking measurements to read systematically higher or lower than other observers is called:
(a) lack of precision
(b) operator bias
(c) lack of discrimination
(d) insensitivity.

10.2.6 State which one of the following in a Bourdan-tube type pressure gauge would lead to systematic errors:
(a) incorrect readings of the scale due to parallax
(b) variation of atmospheric pressure
(c) incorrect zero setting of the pointer
(d) friction in the pins and gears of the amplifying mechanism.

10.2.7 State which one of the following best describes transient error. The difference between:
(a) the output signal of a system and the input signal
(b) the output signal of a system and the input signal when the input signal is changing
(c) the output signal of a system and the input signal when both are changing at the same rate
(d) the output signal of a system and the input signal after a disturbance is applied, before the steady-state condition is reached.

10.2.8 With reference to measuring instruments, the fiducial value is:
(a) the value of full-scale deflection
(b) the most accurate point on the scale
(c) the mid-point on the scale
(d) the value of the standard used to calibrate the instrument.

10.3.1 In a load test on a motor the shaft angular velocity was 300 rad/s. The torque was found by using force transducers to measure F_1 and F_2 as shown in Fig. 10.1, the overall sensitivity of each channel being 0.1 V/N.

If the readings are $V_1 = 10$ volts and $V_2 = -10$ volts state which of the following values gives the shaft power in kilowatts:
(a) 0
(b) 0.12
(c) 6.0
(d) 12.

10.4.1 To determine the resistance of an individual strain gauge a Wheatstone bridge circuit was used as shown in Fig. 10.2. Using the values indicated in the diagram choose the actual resistance of the strain gauge:
(a) 2.0435 MΩ
(b) 20.435 Ω
(c) 204.35 Ω
(d) 2.0435 kΩ.

10.4.2 The potentiometer shown in Fig. 10.3 utilizes a standard cell of e.m.f. (E_s) 1.018 59 V at the temperature of the test. A 'null' is obtained on

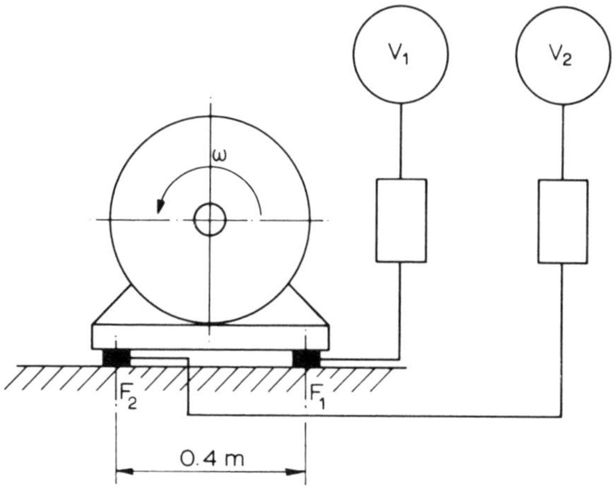

Fig. 10.1

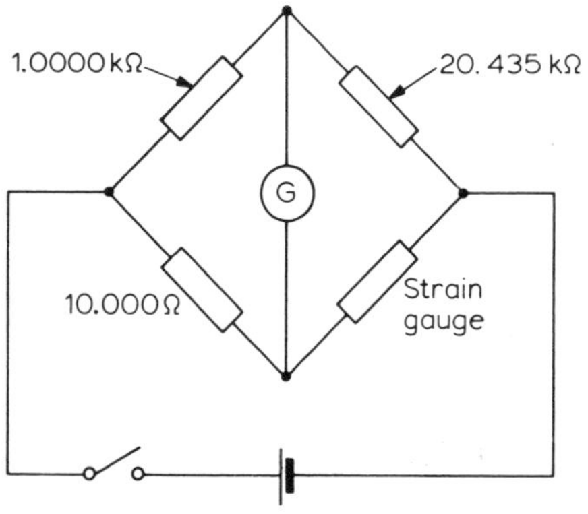

Fig. 10.2

the galvanometer when the length l_a is 25.4 cm, with the standard cell in circuit, i.e. the switch connected to 'a'. With the switch in position 'b', the null occurs when l_b is 50.8 cm. What is the value of the e.m.f. (E_x) of the cell being measured?

(a) 0.49
(b) 0.51
(c) 1.96
(d) 2.04.

10.4.3 The resolution of a wire-wound voltage-dividing displacement transducer can be improved by:

(a) increasing the applied voltage
(b) reducing the diameter of the resistance wire

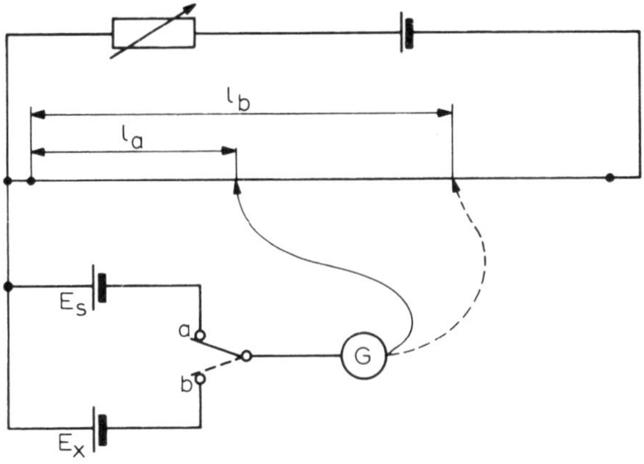

Fig. 10.3

(c) increasing the coil diameter
(d) reducing the applied voltage.

10.4.4 The maximum sensitivity of a null-type Wheatstone bridge is obtained when:
(a) all resistance arms have the same value
(b) R_1/R_2 is a maximum
(c) R_1/R_2 is a minimum
(d) $R_1/R_2 = 1$.

10.5.1 A pneumatic cylinder and ram are instrumented so that a force transducer provides a p.d. to the Y axis of an X-Y recorder, proportional to the ram force (F), whilst a displacement transducer supplies a p.d. to the X axis, proportional to the displacement (x) of the ram, and a graph is produced as shown in Fig. 10.4. State which one of the following is proportional to the mean power exerted by the ram during its stroke:

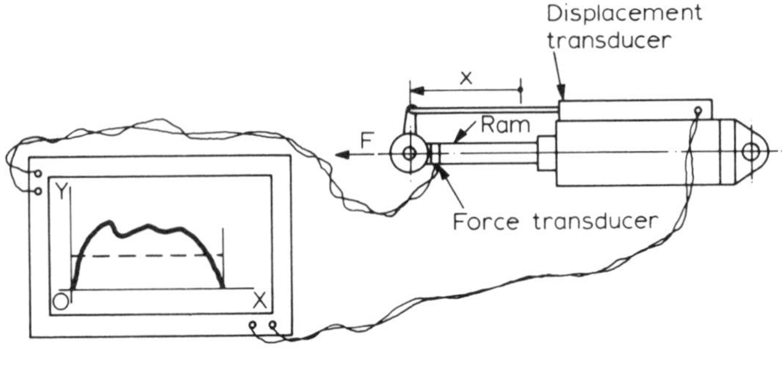

Fig. 10.4

(a) the area of the X-Y diagram
(b) the mean height of the diagram (shown as a broken line)
(c) the maximum slope (dY/dX) of the trace
(d) the area of the X-Y diagram, divided by the time taken for the stroke

10.6.1 A well-type manometer is used in preference to a simple U-tube to obtain:
(a) better accuracy
(b) better precision
(c) a constant zero
(d) higher sensitivity.

10.6.2 State which one of the following would give the least application error when measuring shaft speed:
(a) tachogenerator and voltmeter
(b) mechanical tachometer
(c) magnetic pick-up and timer-counter
(d) optical pick-up and timer-counter.

10.6.3 The graph Fig. 10.5 shows the errors in a dead-weight test on a pressure gauge. Assuming normal adjustment devices are available on the gauge, state which one of the following is true:

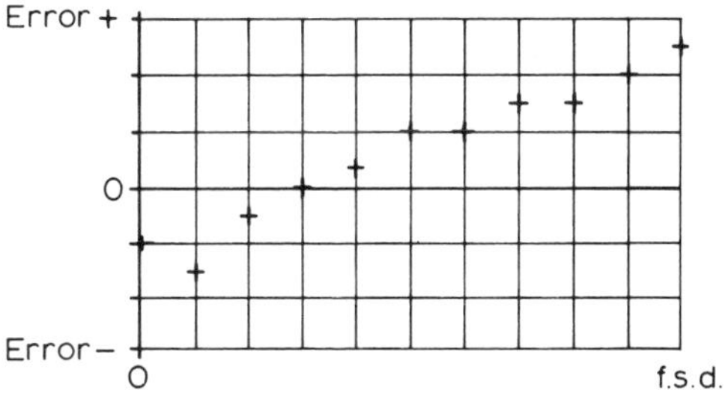

Fig. 10.5

(a) the accuracy of the gauge may not be improved by adjustment
(b) the best accuracy is obtainable by adjusting the magnification
(c) the best accuracy is obtainable by adjusting the zero only
(d) the best accuracy is obtainable by adjusting both the magnification and the zero.

10.9.1 A wheel suspended on a spring damper unit has a natural undamped frequency of 2.5 Hz and a damping ratio of 0.4. The frequency of damped natural vibrations is:
(a) 1.5
(b) 1.9
(c) 2.3
(d) 2.7.

10.9.2 In the systems terminology, state which one of the following best describes 'steady-state' response:

(a) the response to a step input
(b) the response to a sinusoidal input
(c) the response when the transient response has diminished to a negligible quantity
(d) the response when the input signal has not changed for a long time.

10.9.3 When a step of voltage is applied to a moving-coil voltmeter the pointer is seen to oscillate about the final value several times with diminishing amplitude until it finally comes to rest. Which one of the following is correct? The instrument system:
(a) is undamped
(b) is underdamped.
(c) is critically damped
(d) is overdamped.

10.9.4 A mass (m) is guided so that it may move vertically with negligible friction drag. It is connected through a spring of stiffness k to a point A which is caused to oscillate in a vertical direction with simple harmonic motion. State which one of the following correctly describes the sinusoidal motion of the system:

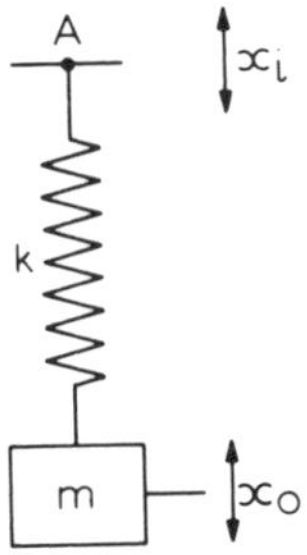

Fig. 10.6

	Amplitude relationship	Phase relationship
(a)	$X_o > X_i$	x_o in phase with x_i
(b)	$X_o > X_i$	x_o lags x_i
(c)	$X_o < X_i$	x_o lags x_i.
(d)	X_o/X_i depends on the frequency of x_i	x_o lags x_i.

10.9.5 Measuring instruments are designed to have a damping ratio of 0.7, when this is possible. This value is desirable because:
(a) no overshoot occurs when a step input signal is applied
(b) it gives the minimum possible settling time
(c) it is the minimum value at which no resonance will occur
(d) it gives the instrument the highest sensitivity.

Answers

Chapter 2

2.10.1 Sensitivity is 1 V/mm. Point accuracy is within $\pm 0.32\%$ Accuracy as percentage of f.s.d is within $\pm 0.08\%$
2.10.2 (a) $1, 3\pi$ mm/bar (b) -2% at 10 bar, $+0.6\%$ at 35 bar
2.10.3 -0.50%, $+0.26\%$, -0.06%

Chapter 3

3.8.1 (a) (i) $\pm 0.2\%$; $+0.2\%$, -0.1%; $+0.2\%$; $+0.2\%$, -0.1%; $+0.2\%$; $+0.2\%$; $+0.2\%$
(ii) $+2\%$ on all beams.
3.8.2 0.1 mV/N, $\pm 1.3\%$, $\pm 6.7\%$
3.8.3 0.5×10^{-3}, $+0.12\ \Omega$
3.8.4 $+0.24 \times 10^{-3}$, $+48$ MPa
3.8.5 Upper curve, 10 MΩ, -60 kΩ/°C

Chapter 4

4.7.1 20
4.7.2 (a) 2 mm (b) 25π
4.7.3 (a) n = 500 (b) n = 500 (c) n = 1125
4.7.4 31.6 mm
4.7.5 8.7 mm
4.7.6 (a) 1.6×10^{-3} (b) $+0.334\ \Omega$ (c) 5.02 mV (d) 17 μA
4.7.7 (a) 0.21×10^{-3} (b) 0.30×10^{-3} (c) 0.51×10^{-3}
4.7.8 (a) 133 V/m (b) 3.3 mA (c) 67 mW
4.7.9 0.678 A

Chapter 5

5.11.2 0.286 mm/bar, 86 mm
5.11.3 750 W
5.11.4 (a) 5.3 kN (b) 1900 J (c) 4.0 kN (d) 760 W
5.11.5 145 N m, 15.2 kW
5.11.7 130 Ω, 21 Ω, 230 Ω

Chapter 6

6.7.3 40
6.7.4 6.667 m, 24
6.7.5 (a) 1.62 (b) 1.62 rev/min.
6.7.6 104 pulse. Percentage error is less than 0.1 %. The error will reduce
6.7.7 0.87 V/MPa, 0.23 kPa, ± 3.3 % f.s.d.
6.7.8 15° 56′
6.7.9 732.5 mm
6.7.11 (b) (i) 0.4 % (ii) 2.0 % (iii) 0.2 mm or 2 in 1000

Chapter 7

7.7.1 1/180 mm/pulse, 180 Hz, 900 Hz/s. Discrimination is fifteen times better but there is gear backlash
7.7.2 19.7 s, 8.2 s

Chapter 8

8.8.6 (a) 0.32 s (b) 0.0375 m/s, 0.57 s (c) 0.64 mm (d) ± 3.2 mm, 58°
8.8.8 1.28 s

Chapter 9

9.7.1 990 N/m
9.7.2 0.7
9.7.3 (a) 240 N s/m (b) 7.3 Hz
9.7.4 (a) 0.29 Hz, 0.28 H_3 (b) Consistent
9.7.5 (a) 98 N/m (b) 15.2 N s/m (c) (i) 0.73 (ii) 0.67 (d) (i) 6 % (ii) 8 % (e) 164 N/m, 19.6 N s/m, 0.73, 0.67, 6 %, 8 %
9.7.6 833 kPa, + 4 %
9.7.7 (a) 17.32 rad/s (b) 2.5 mm (c) 0.44 s
9.7.8 (a) 11.4, 10.8 rad/s (b) 2.4 mm (c) Reduce in each case
9.7.9 3 % accuracy is maintained up to 2 kHz input

Solutions of multiple-choice questions.

10.2.1	(a)	**10.3.1**	(d)	**10.6.3**	(d)
10.2.2	(d)	**10.4.1**	(c)	**10.9.1**	(c)
10.2.3	(c)	**10.4.2**	(d)	**10.9.2**	(c)
10.2.4	(c)	**10.4.3**	(b)	**10.9.3**	(b)
10.2.5	(b)	**10.4.4**	(b)	**10.9.4**	(d)
10.2.6	(c)	**10.5.1**	(d)	**10.9.5**	(c)
10.2.7	(d)	**10.6.1**	(c)		
10.2.8	(a)	**10.6.2**	(d)		

References

(1) BS 5233: 1975 Glossary of terms used in metrology.
(2) Hayward, A. J. T., Repeatability and Accuracy (ME Publications 1977).
(3) Herceg, Edward E., Handbook of Measurement and Control (Schaevitz Engineering).
(4) Adams, L. F., Engineering Measurements and Instrumentation. (English Universities Press 1975 – now Hodder and Stoughton).
(5) Oliver, Frank J., Practical Instrumentation Transducers (Pitman 1972).
(6) Hahn, R. S., Design of Lanchester Damper for Elimination of Metal-Cutting Chatter. *Trans.* A.S.M.E. Vol 73 (1951).
(7) Sweeney, G., Vibration of Machine Tools (The Machinery Publishing Co. 1971).

Appendix 1

Unit Systems and Conversions

The International System of metric units (SI) has provided a coherent and elegant framework which has removed many of the artificial divisions between quantities in, for example, mechanics, electrics, and heat. Consequently, it has found wide acceptance by engineers and scientists throughout the world, and will undoubtedly be universally adopted. The system is based on seven base units and two supplementary units, from which the host of derived units is obtained. The system is described in the British Standards publication PD5686: 1972, 'The use of SI units', from which the following definitions are taken.

Definitions of the SI base units

metre

The metre is the length equal to 1 650 763·73 wavelengths in vacuum of the radiation corresponding to the transition between the levels $2p_{10}$ and $5d_5$ of the krypton-86 atom.
[11th CGPM (1960), resolution 6]

kilogram

The kilogram is the unit of mass; it is equal to the mass of the international prototype of the kilogram.
[1st CGPM (1889) and 3rd CGPM (1901)]

second

The second is the duration of 9 192 631 770 periods of the radiation corresponding to the transition between the two hyperfine levels of the ground state of the caesium-133 atom.
[13th CGPM (1967), resolution 1]

ampere

The ampere is that constant current which, if maintained in two straight parallel conductors of infinite length, of negligible circular cross-section, and placed 1 metre apart in vacuum, would produce between these conductors a force equal to 2×10^{-7} newtons per metre of length. [CIPM (1946), resolution 2 approved by the 9th CGPM (1948)]

kelvin

The kelvin, unit of themodynamic temperature, is the fraction 1/273·16 of the thermodynamic temperature of the triple point of water. [13th CGPM (1967), resolution 4]

Note 1. The 13th CGPM (1967, resolution 3) also decided that the unit kelvin and its symbol K should be used to express an interval or a difference of temperature.

Note 2. In addition to the thermodynamic temperature (symbol T) expressed in kelvins, use is also made of Celsius temperature (symbol θ) defined by the equation $\theta = T - T_0$, where $T_0 = 273{\cdot}15$ K by definition.

The Celsius temperature is in general expressed in degrees Celsius (symbol °C). The unit 'degree Celsius' is thus equal to the unit 'kelvin', and an interval or a difference of Celsius temperature may also be expressed in degrees Celsius.

candela

The candela is the luminous intensity, in the perpendicular direction, of a surface of 1/600 000 square metre of a black body at the temperature of freezing platinum under a pressure of 101 325 newtowns per square metre.
[13th CGPM (1967), resolution 5]

mole

The mole is the amount of substance of a system which contains as many elementary entities as there are atoms in 0·012 kilogram of carbon 12.

Note. When the mole is used, the elementary entities must be specified, and may be atoms, molecules, ions, electrons, other particles, or specified groups of such particles.
[14th CGPM (1971), resolution 3]

The supplementary units, the *radian* (plane angle) and *steradian* (solid angle), may be regarded either as base units or as derived units, and may be defined thus:

radian – the plane angle subtended at the centre by an arc of unit length at unit radius;

steradian – the solid angle subtended at the centre by unit area of a spherical surface at unit radius.

The base- and supplementary-unit symbols are as follows.

	Quantity	*Name of unit*	*Symbol*
Base units	length	metre	m
	mass	kilogram	kg
	time	second	s
	electric current	ampere	A
	thermodynamic temperature	kelvin	K
	luminous intensity	candela	cd
	amount of substance	mole	mol
Supplementary units	plane angle	radian	rad
	solid angle	steradian	sr

Derived units may be expressed in the units of the base or supplementary units; for example, the unit of force may be expressed in terms of mass and acceleration, in accordance with Newton's laws, as kg m/s^2, but in the SI it is given the name '*newton*'.

Other units having special names are listed below.

Quantity	*Name of SI derived*	*Symbol*	*Expressed in terms of SI base or supplementary units or in terms of other derived units*
frequency	hertz	Hz	$1\ \text{Hz} = 1\ \text{s}^{-1}$
force	newton	N	$1\ \text{N} = 1\ \text{kgm/s}^2$
pressure and stress	pascal	Pa	$1\ \text{Pa} = 1\ \text{N/m}^2$
work, energy, quantity of heat	joule	J	1 J = 1 Nm
power	watt	W	1 W = 1 J/s
quantity of electricity	coulomb	C	1 C = 1 As
electrical potential, potential difference, electromotive force	volt	V	1 V = 1 W/A
electric capacitance	farad	F	1 F = 1 As/V
electric resistance	ohm	Ω	$1\ \Omega = 1\ \text{V/A}$
electric conductance	siemens	S	$1\ \text{S} = 1\ \Omega^{-1}$
magnetic flux, flux of magnetic induction	weber	Wb	1 Wb = 1 Vs
magnetic flux density, magnetic induction	tesla	T	$1\ \text{T} = 1\ \text{Wb/m}^2$
inductance	henry	H	1 H = 1 Vs/A
luminous flux	lumen	lm	1 l = 1 cd sr
illuminance	lux	lx	$1\ \text{lx} = 1\ \text{lm/m}^2$

Other units, not part of the SI, are recognised by the International Committee for weights and measures (CIPM), and are listed below.

Quantity	*Name of unit*	*Unit symbol*	*Definition*
time	minute	min	1 min = 60 s
	hour	h	1 h = 60 min
	day	d	1 d = 24 h
plane angle	degree	°	$1° = (\pi/180)$ rad
	minute	′	$1' = (1/60)°$
	second	″	$1'' = (1/60)'$
volume	litre	l	1 l = 1 dm^3
mass	tonne	t	1 t = 10^3 kg
fluid pressure	bar	bar	1 bar = 10^5 Pa

The following prefixes are used to give decimal multiples and sub-multiples of quantities.

Factor by which unit is to be multiplied	*Prefix*	
	Name	*Symbol*
10^{12}	tera	T
10^9	giga	G
10^6	mega	M
10^3	kilo	k
10^2	hecto	h
10	deca	da
10^{-1}	deci	d
10^{-2}	centi	c
10^{-3}	milli	m
10^{-6}	micro	μ
10^{-9}	nano	n
10^{-12}	pico	p
10^{-15}	femto	f
10^{-18}	atto	a

Many existing instruments are calibrated in units of the foot–pound–force–second (f.p.s) system, or in non-SI metric units such as kilogram-force (kgf), or kgf/cm^2 for pressure or stress. Much data is available, for example from North American sources, in f.p.s. units. For these reasons it may be necessary to convert quantities expressed in these units into SI units. The use of *Newton unity brackets* for this purpose is recommended. The equation

$$1 \text{ in} = 25{\cdot}4 \text{ mm}$$

may be written as

$$1 = \left[\frac{25{\cdot}4 \text{ mm}}{1 \text{ in}}\right]$$

where [ ] is the Newton unity bracket.

Any expression may be multiplied by an unlimited number of unity brackets. A few examples are listed below.

Quantity	*Exact unity bracket*	*Approximate unity bracket*
mass	$1 = \left[\frac{1 \text{ lb}}{0{\cdot}453\,592\,37 \text{ kg}}\right]$	
length	$1 = \left[\frac{1 \text{ microinch}}{0{\cdot}0254\ \mu\text{m}}\right]$	
volume		$1 = \left[\frac{1000 \text{ cm}^3}{1 \text{ litre}}\right]$
force	$1 = \left[\frac{1 \text{ kgf}}{9{\cdot}806\,65 \text{ N}}\right]$	$1 = \left[\frac{1 \text{ lbf}}{4{\cdot}448\,22 \text{ N}}\right]$
pressure	$1 = \left[\frac{10^5 \text{ Pa}}{1 \text{ bar}}\right]$	
power		$1 = \left[\frac{1 \text{ h.p.}}{745{\cdot}7 \text{ W}}\right]$
temperature	$1 = \left[\frac{1{\cdot}8\,^\circ\text{F}}{1\,^\circ\text{C}}\right]$	

The use of unity brackets for converting an instrument setting is shown in example 2.8.4. Examples of data conversion are shown below.

Example A1 The force required for cutting in a lathe is given by $F = KA$, where F is the tangential force (lbf), K is a constant for the material used, and A is the area of the cut (in^2). Derive an expression for a constant K_{SI} in SI units in terms of K_{fps} in f.p.s. units so that if A is expressed in mm^2 then F will be given in newton units.

Rearranging the given equation to obtain the units of K_{fps},

$$K_{fps} = \frac{F}{A}\left(\frac{\text{lbf}}{\text{in}^2}\right)$$

$$K_{SI} = K_{fps}\left(\frac{\text{lbf}}{\text{in}^2}\right) \times \left[\frac{4{\cdot}448\ \text{N}}{\text{lbf}}\right] \times \left[\frac{\text{in}^2}{25{\cdot}4^2\ \text{mm}^2}\right]$$

$$= \frac{4{\cdot}448}{25{\cdot}4^2} \times K_{fps}\left(\frac{\text{N}}{\text{mm}^2}\right)$$

i.e.

$$K_{SI} = 0{\cdot}0069\ K_{fps}\ \text{N/mm}^2$$

Example A2 Dynamic viscosity (η) is given by (shear stress)/(velocity gradient), expressed in units of lbf s/ft^2 or N s/m^2. Derive an expression for η_{SI} in terms of SI units, given values of η_{fps} in f.p.s. units.

$$\eta_{SI} = \eta_{fps}\left(\frac{\text{lbf s}}{\text{ft}^2}\right) \times \left[\frac{4{\cdot}448\ \text{N}}{\text{lbf}}\right] \times \left[\frac{\text{ft}^2}{0{\cdot}3048^2\ \text{m}^2}\right]$$

$$= 47{\cdot}9\ \eta_{fps}(\text{Ns/m}^2)$$

Appendix 2: Syllabus

Engineering Instrumentation and Control IV (TEC U77/422)

Aims of the unit:

To give students a basic instrumentation and control background appropriate to both mechanical and production engineering technicians and out of which more specialised studies can develop.
To extend the students' knowledge of and ability to use instrumentation systems.
To introduce the concept of feedback so that students can appreciate the operation of control systems.

Specific objectives of the unit

The part of the text covering each objective is indicated in the right-hand column.
All objectives should be understood to be prefixed by the words: The expected learning outcome is that the student:

A. Basic instrumentation	Section
1. Appreciates the use of a block diagram to represent a measuring system and knows the terms.	
1.1 States that a measuring system can be represented by a block diagram consisting of a transducer, a signal conditioner and a display unit.	1.3
1.2 Identifies the elements in simple measurement systems, e.g. a temperature measurement system, a pressure measurement system.	1.2
1.3 States that a transducer changes information from one form to another, e.g. flow to pressure, speed to voltage.	1.4

1.4 States that a signal conditioner is a device to convert the transducer signal into a form suitable for display.	1.2
1.5 States that a display/recorder is a device for recording the measured variable.	1.2
1.6 Explains the following terms when applied to a measuring system and interprets specification of systems using such terms.	
(a) Accuracy, tolerance.	2.2
(b) Reproducability, repeatability, stability, constancy.	2.4
(c) Calibration, primary and secondary standards.	2.3
(d) Response times.	2.7
(e) Sensitivity.	2.6
(f) Range, capacity.	2.6
2. Describes the principle of operation of some common transducers.	
2.1 Describes a spring as a transducer converting force to displacement.	3.1.1
2.2 Describes the principle of operation of a resistance transducer, i.e. a strain gauge.	3.2
2.3 Defines gauge factor.	3.2
2.4 Calculates uniaxial strains from resistance data.	3.6.3
2.5 Describes bonding techniques.	3.2
2.6 Describes the principle of operation of a resistance transducer, i.e. a thermistor.	3.3
2.7 Uses a calibration graph for a thermistor.	3.6.5
2.8 Describes the principle of operation of a piezo-electric transducer.	3.1.2
2.9 Identifies the input and output of a piezo-electric transducer.	3.1.2
2.10 Describes the principle of operation of a linear variable differential transformer.	3.4
2.11 Describes a typical input-output graph of a linear differential transformer.	3.4
2.12 Describes the principles of operation of photo-conductive and photo-electric transducers.	3.5
3 Describes the principle of operation of common signal conditioners.	
3.1 States that an amplifier is a signal conditioner giving a mechanical or electrical output larger than the input.	4.2
3.2 Explains the mechanical amplifier system of: (a) single lever (b) compound levers.	4.2.1
3.3 Explains the principle of the lever system in an extensometer such as a Huggenberger.	4.2.1

3.4 Calculates the amplification of a lever system such as 3.3.	4.5.3
3.5 Explains the mechanical amplifier system of: (a) simple gear train (b) compound gear train.	4.2.1
3.6 Explains the principle of the gear systems in a dial test indicator	4.2.1
3.7 Calculates the amplification of a gear system such as 3.6.	4.5.4
3.8 Explains the principle of the Wheatstone bridge	4.3
3.9 States the balance condition and uses in simple calculations.	4.5.8, 4.5.9,
3.10 Explains how the bridge can be used:	4.5.10
(a) in the null condition	4.3.1
(b) as a direct indicating instrument	4.3.2, 4.3.3
3.11 Uses a Wheatstone bridge.	
3.12 Describes methods of and reasons for compensation eg. dummy strain gauge.	4.3.5, 4.3.6
3.13 Explains the principle of the potentiometer.	4.4.1, 4.4.2
3.14 States the balance condition and uses in simple calculations.	4.5.12, 4.5.13
3.15 Explains how the potentiometer can be used:	
(a) in the null condition	4.4.1, 4.4.2
(b) as a direct indicating instrument.	
3.16 Identifies the input and output signals of a charge amplifier.	4.2.4
4 Knows the different forms of different display units.	
4.1 States that a mechanically operated pointer on a scale is a display unit.	5.1
4.2 Describes the principle of operation of an ultra violet recorder.	5.3, 5.4
4.3 Describes the principle of operation of an *X*-*Y* plotter.	5.5, 5.6
4.4 States that a c.r.o. is an *X*-*Y* display unit.	5.7
4.5 Compares typical response times of (a) moving coil instruments (b) ultra-violet recorders (c) *X*-*Y* plotter (d) c.r.o. (e) mechanically operated pointers.	5.8
5 Explains frequency, displacement, force and pressure measuring systems.	
5.1 Explains and compares the frequency measuring devices: tachometer, stroboscope and pulse counter.	6.1
5.2 Explains and compares the displacement measuring devices: dial test indicator, linear variable differential transformer and floats.	6.2
5.3 Explains and compares the force measuring devices: spring/lever system, proving ring, strain gauge load cell and piezo-electric system.	6.3

5.4 Explains and compares the pressure measuring devices: Bourdon tube, vertical and inclined manometers and piezo-electric system.	6.4
5.5 Describes calibrations methods for the systems in 5.1, 5.2, 5.3 and 5.4.	6.1.3 6.2.3 6.3.2 6.4.3

B) A complete measurement system

6 Selects, tests and evaluates a measurement system given a variable to be measured consistent with the programme being followed, e.g. strain measurement using a strain gauge system, level measurement using a float activated lever system.	6.8
6.1 Analyses the system requirements.	
6.2 Specifies a suitable system and makes a critical evaluation of the choice of components.	
6.3 Tests the system and analyses the results.	
6.4 Writes a report.	

Control

7 Knows definitions associated with automatic control systems.	
7.1 Differentiates between 'open-loop' and 'closed-loop' systems	7.1
7.2 Explain the terms:	
(a) demand or reference signal	7.2
(b) positive and negative feedback signal	7.2, 8.6
(c) error or deviation signal	7.2
(d) power amplification.	7.2
7.3 Distinguishes between 'process' and 'servo' type systems.	8, 8.4, 8.5
7.4 Distinguishes between 'continuous', 'on-off' and 'sequence' types of control systems.	7.3, 7.4, 8.1 to 8.7
8 Appreciates the elements of a basic control system incorporating feedback.	
8.1 Identifies the elements in a block diagram of a simple control system, e.g. a thermostat, thickness of plate in a rolling mill, a cistern.	7.8
8.2 Describes the effect of feedback on a system.	7.1
8.3 Describes the concept of instability.	8.6
9 Describes common elements in a control system.	
9.1 Describes the principle of operation of the following comparison elements:	
(a) differential lever	8.3
(b) potentiometer	8.3
(c) synchro	8.3

9.2 Describes the principle of operation of the following control elements:	
(a) servo-valve	8.4
(b) process-control valve	8.5
10 Analyses and proposes simple control systems.	
10.1 Analyses a given system into its components and identifies the function of each, eg. a mechanical handling system involving the control of movement of material from a hopper along a conveyor belt.	7.6.1, 7.6.2, 7.6.5, 8.7.1, 8.7.4.
10.2 Proposes a control system, specifying the functions of the components, eg. in control of level in a hopper.	7.6.3, 7.6.4, 8.7.2, 8.7.3, 8.7.5, 8.7.6.

System response

11 Understands the concept of system response.	
11.1 States that all systems have natural frequencies.	9.1, 9.1.1.
11.2 Describes the behaviour of over-damped, under-damped and critically-damped systems when subject to (a) a step input (b) a sinusoidal input.	9.1.2, 9.2
11.3 States that the resonance condition is when the applied frequency equals the frequency of the system and there is positive feedback.	9.2
11.4 Explains how damping is used to obviate such things as machine tool chatter.	9.4
11.5 Describes	
(a) dash pot damping system	9.1.2,
(b) spring damping systems.	9.4.1
11.6 Describes the factors that determine the damping in spring damping systems.	9.2

Index